Element	Symbol	Atomic number	Atomic weight†	Element	Symbol	Atomic number	Atomic weight
Actinium........	Ac	89	227	Molybdenum....	Mo	42	95.95
Aluminum.......	Al	13	26.98	Neodymium.....	Nd	60	144.27
Americium.......	Am	95	[243]	Neptunium......	Np	93	[237]
Antimony........	Sb	51	121.76	Neon...........	Ne	10	20.183
Argon...........	A	18	39.944	Nickel..........	Ni	28	58.69
Arsenic..........	As	33	74.91	Niobium			
Astatine.........	At	85	[210]	(Columbium)...	Nb	41	92.91
Barium..........	Ba	56	137.36	Nitrogen.........	N	7	14.008
Berkelium.......	Bk	97	[245]	Osmium.........	Os	76	190.2
Beryllium........	Be	4	9.013	Oxygen.........	O	8	16
Bismuth.........	Bi	83	209.00	Palladium.......	Pd	46	106.7
Boron..........	B	5	10.82	Phosphorus.....	P	15	30.975
Bromine.........	Br	35	79.916	Platinum........	Pt	78	195.23
Cadmium........	Cd	48	112.41	Plutonium.......	Pu	94	[242]
Calcium.........	Ca	20	40.08	Polonium........	Po	84	210
Californium......	Cf	98	[248]	Potassium.......	K	19	39.100
Carbon..........	C	6	12.011	Praseodymium...	Pr	59	140.92
Cerium..........	Ce	58	140.13	Promethium.....	Pm	61	[145]
Cesium..........	Cs	55	132.91	Protactinium....	Pa	91	231
Chlorine.........	Cl	17	35.457	Radium.........	Ra	88	226.05
Chromium.......	Cr	24	52.01	Radon..........	Rn	86	222
Cobalt..........	Co	27	58.94	Rhenium........	Re	75	186.31
Columbium				Rhodium.......	Rh	45	102.91
(see Niobium)				Rubidium.......	Rb	37	85.48
Copper..........	Cu	29	63.54	Ruthenium......	Ru	44	101.1
Curium..........	Cm	96	[245]	Samarium......	Sm	62	150.43
Dysprosium.....	Dy	66	162.46	Scandium........	Sc	21	44.96
Erbium..........	Er	68	167.2	Selenium........	Se	34	78.96
Europium.......	Eu	63	152.0	Silicon.........	Si	14	28.09
Fluorine.........	F	9	19.00	Silver..........	Ag	47	107.880
Francium........	Fr	87	[223]	Sodium.........	Na	11	22.991
Gadolinium......	Gd	64	156.9	Strontium.......	Sr	38	87.63
Gallium.........	Ga	31	69.72	Sulfur..........	S	16	32.066‡
Germanium......	Ge	32	72.60	Tantalum.......	Ta	73	180.95
Gold............	Au	79	197.0	Technetium.....	Tc	43	[99]
Hafnium.........	Hf	72	178.6	Tellurium.......	Te	52	127.61
Helium..........	He	2	4.003	Terbium........	Tb	65	158.93
Holmium........	Ho	67	164.94	Thallium........	Tl	81	204.39
Hydrogen.......	H	1	1.0080	Thorium........	Th	90	232.05
Indium.........	In	49	114.76	Thulium........	Tm	69	168.94
Iodine..........	I	53	126.91	Tin............	Sn	50	118.70
Iridium..........	Ir	77	192.2	Titanium........	Ti	22	47.90
Iron............	Fe	26	55.85	Tungsten........	W	74	183.92
Krypton.........	Kr	36	83.80	Uranium........	U	92	238.07
Lanthanum......	La	57	138.92	Vanadium.......	V	23	50.95
Lead............	Pb	82	207.21	Xenon..........	Xe	54	131.3
Lithium.........	Li	3	6.940	Ytterbium......	Yb	70	173.04
Lutetium........	Lu	71	174.99	Yttrium........	Y	39	88.92
Magnesium......	Mg	12	24.32	Zinc...........	Zn	30	65.38
Manganese......	Mn	25	54.94	Zirconium......	Zr	40	91.22
Mercury.........	Hg	80	200.61				

* From *The Journal of the American Chemical Society.*

† A value in brackets denotes the mass number of the isotope of longest known half life.

‡ Because of natural variations in the relative abundance of the isotopes of sulfur, its atomic weight has a range of ± 0.003.

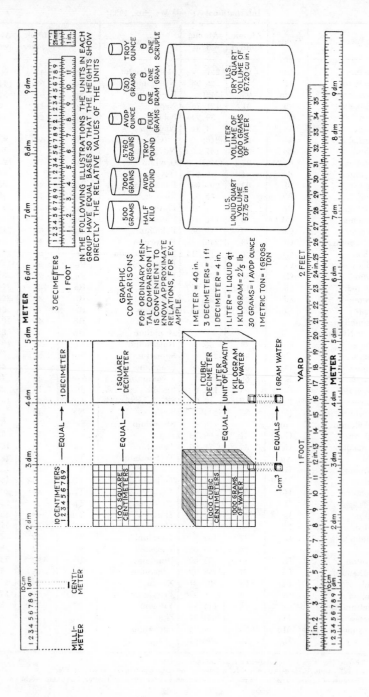

IN THE FOLLOWING ILLUSTRATIONS THE UNITS IN EACH GROUP HAVE EQUAL BASES SO THAT THE HEIGHTS SHOW DIRECTLY THE RELATIVE VALUES OF THE UNITS

GRAPHIC COMPARISONS

FOR ORDINARY MENTAL COMPARISON IT IS CONVENIENT TO KNOW APPROXIMATE RELATIONS, FOR EXAMPLE

1 METER = 40 in.
3 DECIMETERS = 1 ft
1 DECIMETER = 4 in.
1 LITER = 1 LIQUID qt
1 KILOGRAM = 2⅕ lb
30 GRAMS = 1 AVDP OUNCE
1 METRIC TON = 1 GROSS TON

3 DECIMETERS
1 FOOT

1 DECIMETER

1 SQUARE DECIMETER

1 CUBIC DECIMETER
LITER
UNIT OF CAPACITY
1 KILOGRAM OF WATER

1 GRAM WATER

10 CENTIMETERS
1 2 3 4 5 6 7 8 9

100 SQUARE CENTIMETERS

1000 CUBIC CENTIMETERS
1000 GRAMS OF WATER

1 cm³

MILLIMETER
1 2 3 4 5 6 7 8 9

CENTIMETER

—EQUAL→
—EQUAL→
—EQUAL→
—EQUALS→
EQUALS

500 GRAMS
HALF KILO

7000 GRAINS
AVDP POUND

5760 GRAINS
TROY POUND

AVDP OUNCE
FOUR GRAMS

(30) GRAMS
ONE DRAM

ONE GRAM

TROY OUNCE
ONE SCRUPLE

U.S. LIQUID QUART VOLUME 57.75 cu in.

LITER VOLUME OF 1000 GRAMS OF WATER

U.S. DRY QUART VOLUME OF 67.20 cu in.

MILLIMETER
25 mm
1 in.

METER
3 DECIMETERS 1 FOOT

YARD

1 FOOT

METER

FEET

CHEMICAL CALCULATIONS

Chemical Calculations

H. V. ANDERSON

Professor of Chemistry
Lehigh University

New York   Toronto   London

McGRAW-HILL BOOK COMPANY, INC.

CHEMICAL CALCULATIONS

Library of Congress Catalog Card Number 54-8797

8 9 0 MPC 75 74 73 72 71 70 69 68 67

PREFACE

The verification of the fundamental principles of general chemistry is unquestionably best understood by the solving of illustrative problems. Practically all the books in elementary or general chemistry include some problems to illustrate a principle or concept. However, the presentation of this material is of necessity very brief and left largely to the instructor for further elucidation. This text is designed primarily to be used in conjunction with or to supplement those portions of any general chemistry book dealing with chemical arithmetic.

Emphasis is definitely placed on the "common-sense" approach in solving problems. The strict use of dimensional units is advocated and exemplified throughout the text. At times, certain statements of fact may be formulated and used only after a thorough understanding of the principle involved.

The use of the slide rule by the student to expedite the performing of arithmetical computations is to be encouraged.

This text is a revision of previous editions of Long and Anderson's "Chemical Calculations." The writer wishes to acknowledge gratefully the original coauthorship of Dr. J. S. Long whose contributions at the outset were largely responsible for the publication of the early editions of the book. The writer is also indebted to Herman E. Collier, Jr., for suggestions, criticism, and the reading of the manuscript.

H. V. ANDERSON

CONTENTS

CHAPTER I

MEASURES AND WEIGHTS

OUTLINE

Measures and Weights.
    Metric system.
    Conversion of English system to metric system. and vice versa.
    Significant figures.   Exponents.
    The use of dimensional units.

In the scientific world a uniform method of expressing measures and weights has been established. This organization for measures and weights is the **metric system** or **centimeter-gram-second (cgs)** system of units, in which the units are not only interrelated but definite and fixed.

Length. The fundamental unit of length is the **meter (m)** which is divided into 100 equal parts, called **centimeters (cm)**. A centimeter is further subdivided into **millimeters (mm)** such that 1 cm equals 10 mm, or 1 mm is 0.1 cm.

TABLE I. LENGTH

Unit length	Abbreviation	Expressed in centimeters
1 kilometer..............	km	100,000 cm (1,000 m)
1 meter.................	m	100 cm
1 decimeter..............	dm	10 cm
1 centimeter.............	cm	1 cm
1 millimeter.............	mm	0.1 cm
1 micron................	μ	0.0001 cm (10^{-4} cm)
1 millimicron............	mμ	0.0000001 cm (10^{-7} cm)
1 angstrom..............	A	0.00000001 cm (10^{-8} cm)
1 x unit................	XU	0.00000000001 cm (10^{-11} cm)

For purposes of measuring still smaller unit lengths, various submultiples of the meter are used. For convenience in expressing small entities such as the dimensions of colloidal particles, wavelength of light (visible, ultraviolet, X rays, γ rays, cosmic rays), or atomic or ionic distances, the following units of length are employed: the **micron**

(μ), **millimicron**[1] (**mμ**), **angstrom** (**A**), and the **x unit** (**XU**). These units are included in Table I to show concisely the actual relationship between each unit and the centimeter.

Volume. The unit of volume is the **cubic centimeter** (**cu cm**), which is the volume of a cube of inside edge 1 cm in length. A still larger unit of volume is the **liter** (**l**).

At the outset it was intended that the mass of 1 kg of water should be equal to the mass of 1 cu dm or 1,000 cu cm of water at 4°C, or more accurately at 3.98°C (the temperature at which water has its maximum density).   However, precise measurements have shown that 1 kg of water at 4°C measures actually 1,000.027 cu cm instead of exactly 1,000 cu cm.   Since the milliliter is the unit of capacity in the centimeter-gram-second system, then 1 ml = 1.000027 cu cm, or 1 l = 1,000 ml = 1,000.027 cu cm.   For practical purposes the **cubic centimeter** and the **milliliter** can be considered the same and thus used interchangeably in chemical calculations.

Weight. The unit of weight is the **gram** (**g**), which is the weight of 1 ml of water at 4°C (the temperature at which water has its maximum density is 4°C, more precisely 3.98°C).   Above and below 4°C the density of water is less than 1 g/cu cm.   Water at this temperature is the standard selected in the determination of the density of liquids and solids.   The subject of density will be considered in greater detail in Chap. II.   A larger unit of weight is the **kilogram** (**kg**), equal to 1,000 g.   Thus 1,000 ml, or 1 l, of water weighs 1 kg.   A unit smaller than the gram is known as the **milligram** (**mg**) and is one one-thousandth part of a gram (1 mg = 0.001 g), or 1,000 mg corresponds to 1 g, or 0.2 g is 200 mg.

On the ordinary analytical balance weighings are carried out to a lower limit of 0.1 mg, or 0.0001 g.   In microanalysis weighings can be carried out to 1 microgram, now termed 1 gamma (γ), or 0.000001 g, or 0.001 mg.

The legal system of measures and weights in common use in everyday life in the United States and Great Britain and generally referred to as the "English system" is made up of units that are definitely not interrelated.   The result of this nonconformity in the system leads to distinct confusion; in many instances it is not conveniently applicable; and at best it is cumbersome to deal with.   This is especially true in

---

[1] The prefix *micro-* denotes "millionth"; the prefix *milli-* denotes "thousandth." Thus, 1 micron (μ) = 1 millionth meter = $\frac{1}{1,000,000}$ m = 10^{-6} m = 10^{-4} cm = 10^{-3} mm (0.001 mm).   Also, 1 millimicron (mμ) = 1 one-thousandth micron = $1/10^3 \times 10^{-4}$ cm = 10^{-7} cm = 10 A.

the measurement of wavelengths of light or sound and the weighing of extremely minute quantities which workers in the sciences are compelled to make in the laboratory at all times.

TABLE II. SOME COMMON UNIT MEASURES AND WEIGHTS
(A) Conversion of English System to Metric System

Length	Cubic
1 inch (in.) = 2.54 cm = 25.4 mm 1 foot (ft) = 0.3048 m = 30.48 cm 1 mile (mi) = 1.609 km	1 cu in. = 16.3868 ml 1 cu ft = 28.316 liters (l) = 0.028 cu m 1 cu yd = 0.7645 cu m
Capacity	Weight
1 fluid dram = 3.70 ml 1 fluid ounce (fl oz) = 29.57 ml 1 fluid quart (fl qt) = 0.9463 l 1 gallon (U. S.) = 3.7853 l	1 grain (gr) = 64.7989 mg 1 oz* (avdp) = 28.35 g 1 lb* (avdp) = 453.59 g 1 oz (Troy) = 31.1034 g

(B) Conversion of Metric System to English System

Length	Cubic
1 meter (m) = 39.370 in. = 3.2808 ft = 1.0936 yd 1 kilometer (km) = 0.62137 mile (mi)	1 milliliter (ml) = 0.0610 cu in. 1 cubic meter (cu m) = 35.314 cu ft = 1.308 cu yd
Capacity	Weight
1 liter (1,000 ml) = 1.0567 qt 1 decaliter (10 l) = 2.6418 gal	1 milligram (mg) = 0.0154 grain 1 kilogram (1,000 g) = 2.2046 lb (avdp)

* The symbol for pounds is lb, originating from the Latin *libra*. The symbol for ounce is oz, unquestionably from the Spanish *onza*, which is one sixteenth part of the *libra*.

TABLE III. CONVENIENT WEIGHT CONVERSIONS

Weight (mass)...............	Grams	Ounces (avdp)	Pounds (avdp)	Kilograms
Abbreviation.................	g	oz	lb	kg
Grams........................	1.0	0.03527	0.00220	0.001
Ounces (avdp)...............	28.3495	1.0	0.0625	0.028349
Pounds (avdp)...............	453.59	16.0	1.0	0.45359
Kilograms...................	1,000.0	35.274	2.2046	1.0

It is frequently necessary to make conversions from the English system of units to the metric system, and vice versa. Some of the common units and their conversions are given in Table II.

TABLE IV. CONVENIENT CAPACITY CONVERSIONS

Capacity.........	Fluid ounces	Pints	Quarts	Gallons	Milliliters	Liters
Abbreviation......	fl oz	pt	qt	gal	ml	l
Fluid ounces......	1.0	0.0625	0.03125	0.0078125	29.5729	0.029573
Pints.............	16.0	1.0	0.5	0.125	473.167	0.47317
Quarts...........	32.0	2.0	1.0	0.25	946.333	0.9463
Gallons..........	128.0	8.0	4.0	1.0	3785.3	3.7853
Milliliters........	0.033815	0.002113	0.001056	0.000264	1.0	0.001
Liters...........	33.8147	2.1134	1.0567	0.2642	1000.0	1.0

Prefix	Abbreviation	Meaning	
mega-	M	one million	10^6
kilo-	k	one thousand	10^3
hecto-	h	one hundred	10^2
deka-	dk	ten	10
deci-	d	one-tenth	10^{-1}
centi-	c	one-hundredth	10^{-2}
milli-	m	one-thousandth	10^{-3}
micro-	μ	one-millionth	10^{-6}
millimicro-	mμ	one thousand-millionth $\frac{1}{10^3} \times \frac{1}{10^6} = 10^{-9}$	

SIGNIFICANT FIGURES

In chemical calculations it is important to know how many *significant figures* should be retained in an answer. This is determined by the accuracy of the data from which the answer is derived, and this result is no more accurate than the least accurate of the given data. The following paragraphs deal with significant figures.

Suppose that a sample of powder is weighed on a trip scale or platform balance and is balanced when a total weight of 5.6 g is noted. This indicates that this weight is correct or reliable to the nearest tenth of a gram, or is conveniently expressed as 5.6 ± 0.1 g. If the powder is weighed on a more accurate analytical balance and a weight of 5.6155 g is obtained, this result is reliable to the nearest ten-thousandth part of a gram (the nearest tenth of a milligram), or expressed as 5.6155 ± 0.0001 g.

Now the first weighing of the powder, namely, 5.6 g, contains only two digits, whereas the more accurate weighing of 5.6155 g contains five digits. The first weighing is said to be correct to two significant figures, and the last weighing is reliable to five significant figures.

In the examples just cited, significant figures then are the digits in a measured result which indicate the degree of precision of the measurement. It is obvious that the last weighing of the powder is more precise than the first weighing, owing to the more precise instrument used in the weighing process.

In general, a significant figure is any one of the digits 1, 2, 3, . . . , 9. Zero is significant, depending upon the position it occupies in the number. Thus, when zero is used only to locate the decimal point, it is *not* considered a significant figure. However, zero *is* significant when used to express a definite quantity. For example:

1. In the measured result 0.0045 there are *two* significant figures, since the zeros locate the decimal point only and are therefore not significant.

2. In the number 3.500 there are *four* significant figures, since the zeros are here used to express a definite quantity. Likewise the number 3.505 contains *four* significant figures.

3. A number like 56,200, to indicate that the zeros are significant figures, can be expressed as the first digit in units place (as a factor) multiplied by an integral power of 10. Thus, 5.62×10^4, or 5.620×10^4, or 5.6200×10^4. Then the significant numbers are given by the factor at the left.

4. In the number 0.0030 there are *two* significant figures. The zero after the 3 is significant, whereas the zeros before the 3 locate the decimal point and are therefore not significant. That is, zeros are significant if they occur within a number or at the end of a number.

It should also be noted that in determining the number of significant figures no consideration is given to the decimal point. This can be seen from the foregoing examples.

In making chemical calculations the procedure of "rounding off," or "rounding," a number should be followed. This consists of dropping from a given number one or more digits at the right. When the digit dropped is greater than 5, the last retained digit is increased by 1; if it is less than 5, the last retained digit is left unchanged. When the discarded digit is 5, the procedure is to round off the last retained digit to an *even* number. Thus, to round off the number 1.29275 to five, four, or three significant figures, respectively, one will obtain: 1.2928; 1.293; 1.29. The number 0.089 would be rounded off once to 0.09. The number 71.55 would be rounded to 71.6.

Attention should be called to the important fact that in the case of a decimal number which is less than 1, the zero should always be placed before the decimal point; *e.g.*, .18 should always be written 0.18. This is done to avoid confusion and possible error in calculation by misplacing the decimal point and at the same time to emphasize that the number is not the whole number 18.

Further examples of the application of the foregoing principles in rounding off numbers follow:

47.6|53 = 47.7	0.675|43 = 0.675	0.08|987 = 0.09
7.56|5 = 7.56	0.075|5 = 0.076	0.075|6 = 0.076
257|500 = 258,000	0.00|985 = 0.01	38.0|5 = 38.0

In the addition or subtraction of a number of quantities, the values to be added or subtracted should be converted to the smallest number of decimal places of any given quantity. The following are examples of this procedure.

Example 1.   Add the following quantities:

```
18.2154 should be rounded off to...........  18.22
 2.563 should be rounded off to............   2.56
 4.55 remains the same....................    4.55
 1.008 should be rounded off to............   1.01
                                             ------
                                             26.34
```

Example 2.   Subtract 497.3 from 878.08:

```
878.08 should be rounded off to............  878.1
497.3 remains the same....................   497.3
                                             ------
                                             380.8
```

In multiplication or division the rule is to retain as many significant figures in each factor and in the answer as are contained in the factor having the largest percentage deviation. Generally, as many significant figures may be retained in each factor and in the answer as are contained in the factor having the least number of significant figures.

Thus, in the multiplication 0.112×21.76, all figures in each quantity are significant. If the last figure in each term is uncertain and if the first quantity is assumed to have an uncertainty of 1 in the last place, or a deviation of 1 unit in every 112 units, then $1/112 \times 100 = 0.9$ per cent deviation. Likewise, in the second quantity, $1/2,176 \times 100 = 0.045$ per cent possible deviation. The first quantity 0.112 with three significant figures, having the largest per cent possible deviation, governs the number of significant figures which should be retained in the answer, and the last figure is doubtful.

In the multiplication $0.112 \times 21.76 \times 1.0765$, the final answer should be expressed to three significant figures. However, in carry-

ing out intermediate computations, one more significant figu
be retained than in the final answer in order to eliminate accu
errors in rounding off numbers. Thus

$$0.112 \times 21.8 \times 1.08 = 0.2442 \times 1.08 = 0.2637 = 0.264$$

Likewise when 56.2 is divided by 48.76, the quotient is 1.15, not
1.152, since the answer is no more accurate than the least accurate of
the given data, and in this case the answer is expressed to three significant figures.

The use of the slide rule to perform multiplication or division
computations is to be encouraged whenever three significant figures
are sufficient. Also, a four-place table of logarithms will suffice to
give four significant figures.

EXPONENTS

Problems in chemical arithmetic, particularly those concerned with
the application of the mass-action principle, involve the use of exponential terms. It seems then that a brief review of the fundamental
laws of exponents is warranted.

A. By definition $a^n = a \times a \times a \cdots a$ (to n factors), where n is
a positive integer, a can be any number called the **base,** and n is called
the **exponent,** or the **power** of a. Thus

$$10^4 = 10 \times 10 \times 10 \times 10 = 10{,}000 = 1.0 \times 10^4$$
$$10^3 = 10 \times 10 \times 10 \qquad = 1{,}000 = 1.0 \times 10^3$$
$$10^2 = 10 \times 10 \qquad = 100 = 1.0 \times 10^2$$
$$10^1 = 10 \qquad = 10 = 1.0 \times 10^1$$

When n is a negative integer,

$$a^{-n} = \frac{1}{a^n} \qquad \text{and conversely} \qquad \frac{1}{a^n} = a^{-n}$$

Thus

$$10^{-4} = \frac{1}{10^4} = \frac{1}{10{,}000} = 0.0001 = 1.0 \times 10^{-4}$$
$$10^{-3} = \frac{1}{10^3} = \frac{1}{1{,}000} = 0.001 = 1.0 \times 10^{-3}$$
$$10^{-2} = \frac{1}{10^2} = \frac{1}{100} = 0.01 = 1.0 \times 10^{-2}$$
$$10^{-1} = \frac{1}{10^1} = \frac{1}{10} = 0.1 = 1.0 \times 10^{-1}$$

When n is zero and $a \neq 0$,

$$a^0 = 1$$

Then
$$10^0 = 1 = 1 \times 10^0$$

B. The product of a^n and a^m, where a is the same base in each term and n and m are integers either positive or negative, follows:
$$a^n \times a^m = a^{n+m}$$
It can be seen from this rule that in multiplying powers of 10, the *exponents are added*. Thus
$$2^2 \times 2^3 = 2^{2+3} = 2^5$$
$$10^2 \times 10^3 = 10^{2+3} = 10^5 = 1.0 \times 10^5$$
$$10^7 \times 10^{-4} = 10^{7+(-4)} = 10^3 = 1.0 \times 10^3$$
$$10^{-5} \times 10^{-7} = 10^{-5+(-7)} = 10^{-12} = 1.0 \times 10^{-12}$$
$$(2 \times 10^4) \times (3 \times 10^3) = 6 \times 10^{4+3} = 6 \times 10^7$$
$$(1.8 \times 10^{-4}) \times (2 \times 10^{-3}) = 3.6 \times 10^{-4+(-3)} = 3.6 \times 10^{-7}$$
$$(4 \times 10^{-10}) \times (3 \times 10^3) = 12 \times 10^{-10+3} = 12 \times 10^{-7} = 1.2 \times 10^{-6}$$
In multiplying two exponential numbers possessing different bases and different exponents, *i.e.*, $a^n \times b^m$, the result is not equal to $(a \times b)^{n+m}$, but is the product of a raised to the nth power times b raised to the mth power. This is illustrated by the product of $3^2 \times 4^3 = 9 \times 64 = 576$.

C. The quotient $a^n/a^m = a^{n-m}$, where n and m are integers either positive or negative.

From this rule it should be noted that in *dividing* powers of 10, the *exponent of the denominator is subtracted from the exponent of the numerator*. Thus
$$\frac{10^6}{10^3} = 10^{6-3} = 10^3$$

$$\frac{1.0 \times 10^{14}}{1.0 \times 10^{11}} = 1.0 \times 10^{14-11} = 1.0 \times 10^3$$

$$\frac{6 \times 10^8}{2 \times 10^{-2}} = 3 \times 10^{8-(-2)} = 3 \times 10^{10}$$

$$\frac{5.0 \times 10^{-10}}{2.5 \times 10^2} = 2 \times 10^{-10-(2)} = 2 \times 10^{-12}$$

$$\frac{1.5 \times 10^{-5}}{0.3 \times 10^{-3}} = 5 \times 10^{-5-(-3)} = 5 \times 10^{-2}$$

Other rules that are concerned with exponents but do not have as much application in chemical calculations as those just exemplified are
$$(a^n)^m = a^{nm}$$
$$(a \times b)^n = a^n \times b^n$$
$$(a/b)^n = a^n/b^n$$
$$a^{1/n} = \sqrt[n]{a}$$

where n is a positive integer;

$$a^{m/n} = (\sqrt[n]{a})^m \qquad \text{and} \qquad a^{-m/n} = \frac{1}{a^{m/n}}$$

where n and m are positive integers.

It is also helpful to be able to express a number as the product of a number between 1 and 10 and an integer power of 10.

Thus, the number 7,300.0 expressed in terms of the power of 10 is 7.3×10^3. It could also be expressed as follows: 730×10, 73×10^2, 0.73×10^4, or 0.073×10^5, but it is the custom to express the first digit in units place and then multiply it by the integral power of 10. The number 0.00018 would be expressed as 1.8×10^{-4}. Note that in the example $7,300.0 = 7.3 \times 10^3$ the decimal point was shifted *three* (the power of 10) places to the *left* of the decimal in the original number. This is always true when the power of 10 is a *positive* integer. Also, in the example $0.00018 = 1.8 \times 10^{-4}$, the decimal point was shifted *four* (the power of 10) places to the *right* of the decimal in the original number. This, also, is always true when the power of 10 is a negative integer.

Other examples that follow will assist in making these rules clear.

Example 1. The velocity of light is 30 billion cm/sec. Expressed as an exponential number it would be $30,000,000,000$ cm/sec $= 30 \times 10^9$ cm/sec, or 3.0×10^{10} cm/sec.

1 faraday $= 96,500$ coulombs $= 9.65 \times 10^4$ coulombs

1 g $= 1,000$ mg $= 1.0 \times 10^3$ mg

3 miles $= 480,000$ cm $= 4.8 \times 10^5$ cm

1 μ = one-millionth of a meter $= \dfrac{1}{1,000,000}$ m $= \dfrac{1}{10^6}$ m $= 1 \times 10^{-6}$ m

1 μg = one-millionth of a gram $= \dfrac{1}{1,000,000}$ g $= \dfrac{1}{10^6}$ g $= 1 \times 10^{-6}$ g

1 A $= 0.00000001$ cm $= 1 \times 10^{-8}$ cm

Example 2. Illustrate the method of expressing the number 0.00055 in terms of the various powers of 10.

$$0.00055 = 5.5 \times 10^{-4}$$
$$0.0055 = 5.5 \times 10^{-3}$$
$$0.055 = 5.5 \times 10^{-2}$$
$$0.55 = 5.5 \times 10^{-1}$$
$$5.5 = 5.5 \times 10^{0}$$
$$55.0 = 5.5 \times 10^{1}$$
$$550.0 = 5.5 \times 10^{2}$$
$$5500.0 = 5.5 \times 10^{3}$$
$$55000.0 = 5.5 \times 10^{4}$$

In this illustrative example it should again be noted that when the decimal point is shifted to the right the exponent is positive, and when the decimal point is shifted to the left, the exponent is negative. Also, the number of places involved in the shift is numerically the same as the exponent.

The Use of Dimensional Units. The student should recognize the distinct necessity and importance of attaching the proper dimensional units to respective numbers in making various conversions, or, for that matter, in the solution of any problem involving dimensions. From the following examples it will be observed that dimensional units are carried along and made to perform the same mathematical operations of multiplication, division, and cancellation as the numbers themselves, *e.g.*, $1 \times ml/l = ml$; $cm \times \mu/cm = \mu$; $in. \times cm/in. = cm$; $mm \div mm/cm = cm$; $lb/gal \times gal/cu\ in. = lb/cu\ in.$ (read "pounds per cubic inch"). It should be borne in mind that in operations of addition or subtraction only quantities of like dimension may be employed.

Throughout this text emphasis will be placed on the definite use of dimensional units in the solution of problems.

Example 1. Convert 0.1 ft to (*a*) centimeters and (*b*) microns.

(*a*) Since 1 ft = 12 in., or 12 in. per 1 ft, and 1 in. = 2.54 cm, or 2.54 cm per 1 in., the *conversion factors*, *i.e.*, the number of inches per *one* foot, and the number of centimeters per *one* inch, are 12 in./ft, and 2.54 cm/in.

$$0.1\ ft = 0.1\ ft \times \frac{12\ in.}{1\ ft} \times \frac{2.54}{1\ in.}\ cm = 3.048\ cm$$

NOTE. In this multiplication process the dimensional units feet (ft) and inches (in.) cancel out and the final answer is in centimeters (cm), which in turn is a check on the solution of the problem.

(*b*) Since 1 micron = 1 μ = 10^{-4} cm, or 1 cm = 1 $\mu/10^{-4}$ = 10^4 μ, then 10^4 μ/cm is a *conversion factor*. From part (*a*) since 0.1 ft = 3.048 cm, then

$$0.1\ ft = 3.048\ cm \times \frac{10^4\ \mu}{1\ cm} = 30,480\ \mu$$

Example 2. A thin metal foil has a thickness of 2.54 microinches ($\mu in.$). Express this thickness in (*a*) inches and (*b*) millimeters.

(*a*) Since 1 microinch = 1 $\mu in.$ = 1/1,000,000 in. = $1/10^6$ in. = 10^{-6} in., then 10^{-6} in./$\mu in.$ is a *conversion factor*, and

$$2.54\ \mu in. = 2.54\ \mu in. \times \frac{10^{-6}\ in.}{1\ \mu in.} = 2.54 \times 10^{-6}\ in.$$

(*b*) Since 1 in. = 25.4 mm, then 25.4 mm/in. is a *conversion factor*.

From part (a) since 2.54 μin. = 2.54 × 10⁻⁶ in., then

$$2.54 \text{ μin.} = 2.54 \times 10^{-6} \text{ in.} \times \frac{25.4 \text{ mm}}{1 \text{ in.}} = 64.5 \times 10^{-6} \text{ mm}$$

$$= 6.45 \times 10^{-5} \text{ mm}$$

Example 3. Express a volume of 358.4 cu ft of a gas in the following units: (a) liters; (b) cubic meters.

(a) Since 1 cu ft = 28.3 l, then 28.3 l/cu ft is a *conversion factor*

$$358.4 \text{ cu ft} \times \frac{28.3 \text{ l}}{1 \text{ cu ft}} = 10{,}142.7 \text{ l}$$

(b) Since 35.314 cu ft = 1 cu m, or 1 cu ft = 1/35.314 cu m = 0.0283 cu m, then the *conversion factor* is 0.0283 cu m/cu ft, and

$$358.4 \text{ cu ft} = 358.4 \text{ cu ft} \times \frac{0.0283 \text{ cu m}}{1 \text{ cu ft}} = 10.14 \text{ cu m}$$

Alternate Solution. Since 1,000 l = 1 cu m, or 1 l = 1/1,000 cu m = 10⁻³ cu m, then 10⁻³ cu m/l is a *conversion factor*. From part (a) 358.4 cu ft = 10,142.7 l, and

$$358.4 \text{ cu ft} = 10{,}142.7 \text{ l} \times \frac{10^{-3} \text{ cu m}}{1 \text{ l}} = 10.14 \text{ cu m}$$

Example 4. The weight of 1 gal of water is 8.34 lb. Express this unit in (a) pounds per cubic foot, and (b) kilograms per cubic meter.

(a) Since 1 cu ft liquid = 7.481 gal liquid, then the *conversion factor* is 7.481 gal water/cu ft water.

$$\frac{8.34 \text{ lb water}}{1 \text{ gal water}} = \frac{8.34 \text{ lb water}}{1 \text{ gal water}} \times \frac{7.481 \text{ gal water}}{1 \text{ cu ft water}}$$

$$= \frac{62.36 \text{ lb water}}{1 \text{ cu ft water}}$$

or 62.36 lb of water per cubic foot of water.

(b) Since 1 cu ft liquid = 7.481 gal liquid, 1 cu m = 35.314 cu ft, and 1 lb = 453.6 g = 0.4536 kg, the various *conversion factors* are $\frac{7.481 \text{ gal water}}{1 \text{ cu ft water}}$, $\frac{35.314 \text{ cu ft water}}{1 \text{ cu m water}}$, $\frac{0.4536 \text{ kg water}}{1 \text{ lb water}}$; then

$$\frac{8.34 \text{ lb water}}{1 \text{ gal water}} = \frac{8.34 \text{ lb water}}{1 \text{ gal water}} \times \frac{7.481 \text{ gal water}}{1 \text{ cu ft water}}$$

$$\times \frac{35.314 \text{ cu ft water}}{1 \text{ cu m water}} \times \frac{0.4536 \text{ kg water}}{1 \text{ lb water}}$$

$$= \frac{(8.34 \times 7.481 \times 35.314 \times 0.4536) \text{ kg water}}{1 \text{ cu m water}}$$

$$= \frac{998.9 \text{ kg water}}{1 \text{ cu m water}}$$

or 1 cu m of water weighs approximately 1,000 kg.

Example 5. The speed of light is 186,000 miles/sec. Sound travels at the rate of about 1,090 ft/sec at 32°F. Approximately, what is the ratio of the speed of light to the speed of sound at 32°F?

Since 5,280 ft = 1 mile, the *conversion factor* is 5,280 ft/mile, and

$$\frac{186,000 \text{ miles}}{1 \text{ sec}} = \frac{186,000 \text{ miles}}{1 \text{ sec}} \times \frac{5,280 \text{ ft}}{1 \text{ mile}} = \frac{982,080,000 \text{ ft}}{1 \text{ sec}}$$

$$= 9.82 \times 10^8 \text{ ft/sec}$$

$$1,090 \text{ ft/sec} = 1.09 \times 10^3 \text{ ft/sec}$$

$$\text{Ratio} = \frac{9.82 \times 10^8 \text{ ft/sec}}{1.09 \times 10^3 \text{ ft/sec}} = \frac{9.0 \times 10^5}{1} = \frac{900,000}{1}$$

or light travels about 900,000 times as fast as sound at 32°F.

Problems

1-1. Make each of the following weight conversions:

(a) 35.2 kg to grams
(b) 0.25 g to milligrams
(c) 334.6 mg to grams
(d) 6.7 μg to milligrams
(e) 5550.0 g to kilograms

1-2. Make each of the following weight conversions:

(a) 225.20 mg to grams
(b) 0.00055 g to milligrams
(c) 55.5 kg to grams
(d) 50.0 μg to milligrams
(e) 575.0 g to kilograms

1-3. Complete each of the following conversions:

(a) 0.2 m to millimeters
(b) 25.4 cm to meters
(c) 224.0 ml to liters
(d) 1.5 l to milliliters
(e) 5.0 cu m to liters

1-4. Complete each of the following conversions:

(a) 76.0 cm to millimeters
(b) 750.0 mm to meters
(c) 11.2 l to milliliters
(d) 358.0 ml to liters
(e) 0.5 cu m to liters

1-5. Complete each of the following conversions:

(a) 1.5 ft to centimeters
(b) 358.4 cu ft to liters

    (c) 22.4 l to cubic feet

    (d) 224.0 cu ft to cubic meters

1-6. Complete each of the following conversions:

    (a) 39.37 mm to inches

    (b) 1.5 μin. to inches

    (c) 16.0 lb to grams

    (d) 32.8 g to ounces (avdp)

1-7. Make each of the following conversions:

    (a) 7.054 oz (avdp) to grams

    (b) 5.5 qt to fluid ounces

    (c) 16.0 fluid ounces to milliliters

    (d) 50.0 lb (avdp) to kilograms

1-8. It has been stated that 1/100,000 μg of DDT (dichlorodiphenyltrichlorethane) will kill a common housefly. What part of a gram does this weight represent?   *Ans.* 10^{-11} g.

1-9. A standard biotin solution contains 5 mg of biotin (vitamin) in 50 ml of solution. How many micrograms (μg) of biotin is contained in 1 ml of this solution?   *Ans.* 100 μg.

1-10. It is possible by means of a newly designed chemical analytical balance to make weighings with an accuracy of $\frac{2}{100}$ of 1 mg. Express this accuracy in weighing in terms of (a) grams, and (b) micrograms (gammas).

1-11. To aid in the search for improved metals, an "electronic sleuth" can detect metal impurities weighing of the order of 3×10^{-9} g. Express this weight in (a) milligrams, and (b) micrograms (gammas).

1-12. It was determined by a special thickness gauge that 0.00365 cm of zinc was plated on an iron sheet. What was the plate thickness in angstrom units?

1-13. A plating of rhodium on a piece of glass measures 254 A thick. How many microinches does this thickness represent?

1-14. An ultraviolet lamp emits 95 per cent of its radiation at a wavelength of 2,537 A. Express this wavelength in terms of (a) centimeters, (b) millimicrons, and (c) microns.

1-15. The shortest visible waves and the longest visible waves of the electromagnetic spectrum are 3.7×10^{-5} and 6.7×10^{-5} cm in length, respectively. Express these wavelengths in (a) microns, (b) millimicrons, and (c) angstrom units.

CHAPTER II

DENSITY

OUTLINE

Density.
Specific gravity.
    Specific gravity of solids: Solid heavier than water, and insoluble in water.
Solid heavier than water, but soluble in water. Pycnometer method for powders
insoluble in water.
    Specific gravity of liquids.
    Percentage concentration.

DENSITY

The **density** of a substance, at a given temperature, is the number
of units of mass[1] of the substance contained in one unit of volume, or
its mass per unit volume.

$$\text{Density} = \frac{\text{mass}}{\text{volume}} \quad \text{or} \quad D = \frac{M}{V}$$

Density is expressed in dimensional units such as (*a*) grams per
milliliter (g/ml), (*b*) grams per liter (g/l), (*c*) pounds per cubic foot
(lb/cu ft), and (*d*) pounds per gallon (lb/gal).

Matter may exist in three states, namely, solid, liquid, and gas.
It is a familiar fact that many substances can exist in all three states
under proper conditions. The density of a substance will vary with a
given state; thus water (liquid) at 4°C has a maximum density of
1 g/ml; ice (solid) at 0°C has a density of 0.917 g/ml; the density of
water vapor at 100°C is 0.590 g/l.

---

[1] Frequently, the terms mass and weight are used interchangeably. It should
be borne in mind that the mass of a body refers to the quantity of matter in that
body and is a constant; the weight of a body refers to the pull of gravity on that
body and varies slightly with location.

The mass of a body is proportional to its weight in the same locality. One
may, therefore, compare the mass (or quantity of matter) of a body with the
quantity of matter in a given standard weight, such as a gram or kilogram weight.
This comparison may be made on a balance, by applying the principle of the lever,
in which the object to be weighed is placed on a pan suspended from the left end
of a beam and the weights are placed on a pan suspended from the right end of
the beam until equilibrium is established, the beam acting as a lever.

The density of a substance also varies with temperature, since the volume of a body varies with temperature, while the mass of the body remains the same. As previously stated, water has a maximum density of 1 g/ml at 4°C; above and below 4°C the density of water is less than 1 g/ml. Thus, at 1°C the density of water is 0.99993 g/ml, and at 21°C its density is 0.99802 g/ml. In the case of mercury, the density varies inversely with temperature, that is, the lower the temperature of the mercury, the greater the density, or the higher the temperature of the mercury, the smaller the density. Thus, at 0°C the density of Hg is 13.5955 g/ml, at 15°C it is 13.5585 g/ml, and at 100°C it becomes 13.3522 g/ml.

Likewise, the density of gases (g/l) varies inversely with temperature. This, together with other facts, will be given further consideration in a following chapter.

SPECIFIC GRAVITY

The **specific gravity** (**sp gr**) of a solid (or liquid) may be' defined as the ratio of the weight of a given volume of solid (or liquid) to the weight of an equal volume of water at 4°C, or some other designated temperature. [The temperature of 4°C (more accurately 3.98°C) is usually specified for water, for the obvious reason of simplification in making the comparison, since at 4°C 1 ml of water weighs 1 g—its maximum density.]

Specific gravity is also the ratio of the density of the solid (or liquid) to the density of water at 4°C, or specific gravity of solid (or liquid) = density of solid (or liquid)/density of water at 4°C. It follows then that density of solid (or liquid) = specific gravity of solid (or liquid) × density of water at 4°C.

Example. If 1 ml of mercury weighs 13.5856 g at 4°C and 1 ml of water weighs 1 g at the same temperature, then sp gr of Hg = $\dfrac{13.5856 \text{ g/ml}}{1.0000 \text{ g/ml}}$ = 13.5856, or mercury is 13.5856 times as heavy as water, both substances at 4°C. It follows that since 1 gal of water weighs 8.34 lb at 4°C, the weight of 1 gal of mercury at 4°C would be 13.5856 × 8.34 lb/gal = 113.3039 lb/gal, which should be rounded off to 113 lb/gal. (Why?)

In handbooks of chemistry and physics one finds the specific gravity of substances measured at, say, 20°C and referred to water at 4°C, expressed as follows: sp gr $\left(\dfrac{20°}{4°} \text{ C}\right)$. Thus

$$\text{sp gr} \left(\frac{20°}{4°} \text{ C}\right) \text{ of Hg} = \frac{13.5461 \text{ g/ml}}{1.0000 \text{ g/ml}} = 13.5461$$

It should be noted that when a comparison is made between the weights of 1 ml of a solid (or liquid) at any temperature and 1 ml of water at 4°C, the *specific gravity* of the substance and its *density* (in common metric units) are *numerically the same*. However, it should be emphasized that *specific gravity* is *without* dimensional units, being a *pure number*, whereas *density* possesses the dimensional unit *grams per milliliter, pounds per cubic foot*, and so on.

SPECIFIC GRAVITY OF SOLIDS

A. Consider first the case of a solid heavier than water and insoluble in water. By definition

$$\text{sp gr of a solid} = \frac{\text{weight of a definite volume of the solid}}{\text{weight of an equal volume of water}}$$

To obtain the volume of a known weight of a solid, which may be, and usually is, of irregular shape, or in powdered form, one measures the increase in volume of a liquid when the solid is immersed in the liquid.

Example 1. A quantity of quartz sand weighs 33.8 g in air. It is transferred to a 100-ml graduate containing 40 ml of water. The final reading of the volume was 53.0 ml. Determine the specific gravity of the sand.

The volume increase was 13.0 ml (the volume of water displaced by the sand), which equals the volume of the quartz sand. Since 13.0 ml of water weighs 13.0 g, then

$$\text{sp gr of quartz sand} = \frac{33.8 \text{ g}/13.0 \text{ ml}}{13.0 \text{ g}/13.0 \text{ ml}} = 2.6$$

The volume of the solid may also be obtained by application of the well-known **principle of Archimedes: When an object is immersed in water, it appears to lose weight. This loss in weight is equal to the weight of water displaced by the object.** The volume of a body wholly immersed in water is exactly equal to the volume of water it displaces. Then

$$\text{sp gr of a solid (heavier than water)} = \frac{\text{weight of solid in air}}{\text{loss of weight in water}}$$

or

$$\text{sp gr} = \frac{W_a}{W_a - W_w}$$

where W_a = weight of solid in air
W_w = weight of solid in water
$W_a - W_w$ = loss of weight in water of the body heavier than water, *i.e.*, the body is entirely immersed in water

Example 2. A piece of galena (impure lead sulfide) weighs 5.50 g in air and 4.76 g in water. What is the specific gravity of the galena?

$$W_a = 5.50 \text{ g} \qquad W_w = 4.76 \text{ g}$$

$$\text{sp gr} = \frac{W_a}{W_a - W_w} = \frac{5.50 \text{ g}}{5.50 \text{ g} - 4.76 \text{ g}} = \frac{5.50 \text{ g}}{0.74 \text{ g}} = 7.4$$

Example 3. A piece of metal weighs 7.0 g in air, 3.5 g in water, and 4.2 g in an oil. Calculate (a) the specific gravity of the metal, and (b) the specific gravity of the oil.

(a) $\qquad$ sp gr of metal $= \dfrac{W_a}{W_a - W_w} = \dfrac{7.0 \text{ g}}{7.0 \text{ g} - 3.5 \text{ g}} = 2.0$

(b) $\qquad$ sp gr of oil $= \dfrac{\text{loss of weight in oil}}{\text{loss of weight in water}} = \dfrac{W_a - W_o}{W_a - W_w}$

$$= \frac{7.0 \text{ g} - 4.2 \text{ g}}{7.0 \text{ g} - 3.5 \text{ g}} = \frac{2.8 \text{ g}}{3.5 \text{ g}} = 0.80$$

Example 4. What is the weight in ounces of 1 cu in. of gold (sp gr = 19.3)? One cubic foot of water weighs about 62.5 lb, or about 1,000 oz.

$$\text{sp gr} = \frac{\text{density of solid}}{\text{density of water at 4°C}}$$

or density of solid = sp gr × density of water at 4°C.

Let x = density of solid

$$= 19.3 \times \frac{1,000 \text{ oz}}{1 \text{ cu ft}} \times \frac{1 \text{ cu ft}}{1,728 \text{ cu in.}} = 11.2 \text{ oz/cu in.}$$

or 11.2 oz = weight of 1 cu in. of gold.

B. To obtain the specific gravity of a solid heavier than water, but soluble in it, one must use some liquid in which the substance is insoluble, *e.g.*, petroleum ether. The density of the liquid in which the solid is immersed must, of course, be known. The procedure is first to weigh the substance in air, and then its weight immersed in the liquid is obtained. The difference between these two weights is the weight of the displaced liquid. Next, one finds the volume of the substance from the relation

$$\text{Volume of substance} = \frac{\text{weight of displaced liquid}}{\text{density of displaced liquid}}$$

followed by the determination of the density of the substance and then its specific gravity.

Example 5. A lump of sugar weighs 4.00 g in air, and 2.375 g when immersed in petroleum ether. The density of petroleum ether is 0.65 g/ml. Determine the specific gravity of sugar.

$$\text{Volume of sugar} = \frac{\text{weight of displaced liquid}}{\text{density of displaced liquid}}$$

$$= \frac{4.00 \text{ g} - 2.375 \text{ g}}{0.65 \text{ g/ml}}$$

$$= \frac{1.625 \text{ g}}{0.65 \text{ g/ml}} = 2.5 \text{ ml}$$

$$\text{Density of sugar} = \frac{\text{weight of sugar}}{\text{volume of sugar}} = \frac{4.00 \text{ g}}{2.5 \text{ ml}} = 1.6 \text{ g/ml}$$

The weight of a volume of water equal to the volume of sugar = 2.5 g. Then

$$\text{sp gr of sugar} = \frac{4.0 \text{ g}}{2.5 \text{ g}} = 1.6$$

C. It is frequently necessary to obtain the specific gravity of powders that are insoluble in water. In this instance a small flask or pycnometer (Fig. 1), carefully dried, is weighed empty; then the flask and capillary stopper are filled with water and weighed. The flask is next emptied and dried, using alcohol and finally an ether or acetone rinse to facilitate the drying operation. A convenient quantity of powder is now carefully introduced into the dry flask, the stopper replaced, and the weight of flask plus powder sample is obtained. The weight of powder can thus be noted. The bottle with powder in it is then filled with water, and stopper replaced, observing that water overflows the capillary. The outside of the flask is wiped dry and the weight of flask, powder, and sufficient water to fill the flask is obtained. The following example will serve to illustrate the method.

Fig. 1

Example 6. Determine the specific gravity of a powder from the following:

Weight of sample in air...............................	3.556 g
Weight of pycnometer filled with water.................	20.004 g
Weight of pycnometer + sample + enough water to fill it.	21.782 g

Solution

Weight of pycnometer filled with water.................	20.004 g
Weight of sample in air...............................	3.556 g
	23.560 g
Weight of pycnometer + sample + enough water to fill it.	21.782 g
Weight of water displaced or loss of weight in water.....	1.778 g

$$\text{sp gr} = \frac{\text{weight of solid}}{\text{loss of weight in water}} = \frac{3.556 \text{ g}}{1.778 \text{ g}} = 2.00$$

NOTE. To avoid confusion in performing operations of addition and subtraction, it will be found convenient to use the straight line under the column of numbers to be added and to indicate subtraction by the wavy line below the subtrahend.

Problems

Density of water expressed in various units:

1 kg/l	8.3 lb/gal
1 g/ml	62.5 lb/cu ft
1 g/cu cm	1,000 oz/cu ft

2-1. (a) White cast iron has a density of 482 lb/cu ft. (b) Cast aluminum has a density of 168.5 lb/cu ft. Determine the specific gravity of each of the foregoing materials. *Ans.* (a) 7.71; (b) 2.70.

2-2. (a) The element osmium (Os) is the heaviest of all metals, and has a density of 1,405 lb/cu ft. (b) The lightest of the metallic elements is lithium (Li); it has a density of 33.3 lb/cu ft. What are the respective specific gravities of these two metals? *Ans.* (a) 22.5; (b) 0.533.

2-3. (a) The specific gravity of a steel is 7.87. (b) The specific gravity of magnesium is 1.74. Determine the density of each of these materials in pounds per cubic foot. *Ans.* (a) 492 lb/cu ft; (b) 109 lb/cu ft.

2-4. What is the weight in pounds of a block of sandstone measuring 1 by 1½ by 4 ft? The specific gravity of sandstone is 2.5. *Ans.* 938 lb/cu ft.

2-5. What is the weight in ounces of a cube of lead of 1 in. edge length? The specific gravity of lead is 11.3. *Ans.* 6.54 oz.

2-6. What is the calculated weight in tons of a mound of sulfur 200 by 50 by 1,000 ft? The specific gravity of sulfur is 2.04. *Ans.* 637,500 tons.

2-7. A cube of brass measured 1.5 cm on an edge. It was plated with gold (sp gr 19.33) to a thickness of 0.78 μ. What was the weight in grams of gold plating? *Ans.* 0.02 g.

2-8. What weight, in ounces, of tin plating covers a surface of sheet steel of surface area 400 sq ft and a thickness of 30 μin.? Specific gravity of tin is 7.3. *Ans.* 7.3 oz.

2-9. The specific gravity of platinum is 21.37. A piece of platinum wire has a diameter of 0.92 mm. What length of this wire will weigh 1.1 g? *Ans.* 77 mm.

2-10. A piece of hard-drawn copper wire 12 in. long weighs 0.0078 lb. The specific gravity of the copper is 8.9. Calculate the diameter of the wire. *Ans.* 0.05 in.

2-11. Cast gold has a specific gravity of 19.3. Calculate the weight of a piece of gold that displaces 1.14 ml of water. *Ans.* 22.0 g.

2-12. Sulfur has a specific gravity of 2.04. What is the weight of sulfur that displaces 2.5 ml of water? *Ans.* 5.1 g.

2-13. A piece of granite weighs 2.36 g in air and 1.56 g in water at 4°C. Calculate the specific gravity of this specimen of granite. *Ans.* 2.95.

2-14. A piece of metal weighs 13.2418 g in air and 11.6840 g in water. Determine the specific gravity of the metal. *Ans.* 8.50.

2-15. Determine the specific gravity of an insoluble powder from the following data:

Weight of sample in air.. 2.7 g
Weight of pycnometer filled with water......................... 26.5 g
Weight of pycnometer + sample + water to fill it................ 28.3 g

Ans. 3.0.

2-16. Determine the specific gravity of a powdered mineral from the following data:

Weight of sample in air..................................... 3.1255 g
Weight of pycnometer filled with water..................... 37.9153 g
Weight of pycnometer + sample + water to fill it............. 39.8458 g

Ans. 2.61.

2-17. A solid weighs 7.3400 g in air and 5.8295 g in water. (*a*) What is the specific gravity of the body? (*b*) What is the density of the body in pounds per cubic foot?

2-18. A piece of mineral weighs 36.6 g in air and 29.6 g in water. (*a*) What is the specific gravity of the mineral? (*b*) What is the density of the mineral in pounds per cubic foot?

2-19. A steel casting of a machine part weighs 1,250 lb. Determine the weight of this machine part if the alloy magnalium was used in making the casting. The specific gravity of steel is 7.83. The specific gravity of magnalium is 2.5.

2-20. A piece of metal weighs 8.42 g in air, 7.42 g when suspended in water, and 7.56 g when suspended in kerosene. What is the specific gravity of the metal and of the kerosene?

2-21. A body weighs 9.2 g in air, 7.5 g in water, and 8.5 g in oil. Calculate the specific gravity of the body and of the oil.

2-22. A glass ball weighs 9.25 g in air, 8.2 g in water, and 8.36 g in gasoline. What is the specific gravity of the gasoline?

2-23. A small piece of ore weighs 8.5 g in air, 4.6 g when suspended in water, and 5.5 g when suspended in oil. Determine the specific gravity of the ore and of the oil. How much does 1 cu ft of ore weigh?

2-24. A lead sinker weighs 10 oz in air. The density of lead is 11.3 g/ml. What will the sinker weigh in pure water? How much will it weigh in salt water of specific gravity 1.25?

2-25. A 100-ml graduated cylinder contains water up to the 75-ml mark; 25 g of rhombic sulfur is put into this graduate. The specific gravity of rhombic sulfur is 2.04. What will be the final reading of the water level in the cylinder?

SPECIFIC GRAVITY OF LIQUIDS

The specific gravity of liquids may be determined by means of a (*a*) pycnometer, (*b*) hydrometer, or (*c*) Westphal balance.

In the determination of the specific gravity of liquids by the pycnometer method, one compares the weight of a given volume of the liquid in question with the weight of an equal volume of water at 4°C or some other specified temperature.

As previously stated, water at 4°C has a density (maximum) of 1 g/ml. If the comparison of the density of the liquid is made with the density of water at 4°C, the specific gravity of the liquid and its density are numerically the same, noting, of course, that specific gravity is a pure number, whereas density possesses a unit of dimension, *e.g.*, g/ml.

Now, suppose the comparison is made of the density of a liquid at 25°C with the density of water at 4°C. The specific gravity of the liquid would be expressed as follows:

$$\text{sp gr}\left(\frac{25°}{4°}\,\text{C}\right) = \frac{\text{density of liquid at 25°C (g/ml)}}{\text{density of water at 4°C (1 g/ml)}}$$

If the density of a liquid measured at 25°C is 1.098 g/ml and is compared with the density of water at 4°C (1 g/ml), then

$$\text{sp gr}\left(\frac{25°}{4°}\,\text{C}\right) = \frac{1.098 \text{ g/ml}}{1.000 \text{ g/ml}} = 1.098$$

This states that the liquid is 1.098 times as heavy as water, or 1 ml of liquid weighs 1.098 times as much as 1 ml of water, or that 1 gal of liquid weighs 1.098 times as much as 1 gal of water.

If the density of a liquid measured at 21°C is 1.744 g/ml and is compared with the density of water at 15°C, which is 0.9990 g/ml, then the specific gravity is

$$\text{sp gr}\left(\frac{21°}{15°}\,\text{C}\right) = \frac{\text{density of liquid at 21°C}}{\text{density of water at 15°C}} = \frac{1.744 \text{ g/ml}}{0.9990 \text{ g/ml}} = 1.75$$

Example 1. Calculate (a) the specific gravity of a sulfuric acid solution, (b) the volume of the flask, and (c) the density of the acid solution from the following data:

Weight of flask... 125.5 g
Weight of flask + enough water to fill it, at 21°C.............. 224.8 g
Weight of flask + enough sulfuric acid to fill it, at 21°C...... 303.5 g
The density of water at 21°C.................................... 0.998 g/ml

(a)　　　　Weight of flask + acid at 21°C　 = 303.5 g
　　　　　　Weight of flask　　　　　　　　 = 125.5 g
　　　　　　Weight of acid at 21°C　　　　　 = 178.0 g

　　　　　　Weight of flask + water at 21°C = 224.8 g
　　　　　　Weight of flask　　　　　　　　 = 125.5 g
　　　　　　Weight of water at 21°C　　　　　= 99.3 g

$$\text{sp gr of acid} = \frac{178.0 \text{ g}}{99.3 \text{ g}} = 1.791$$

(b)   Volume of flask $= \dfrac{\text{weight of water at } 21°C}{\text{density of water at } 21°C} = \dfrac{99.3 \text{ g}}{0.998 \text{ g/ml}}$

$$= 99.5 \text{ ml}$$

(c)   Density of acid $= \dfrac{\text{weight of acid at } 21°C}{\text{volume}} = \dfrac{178.0 \text{ g}}{99.5 \text{ ml}}$

$$= 1.788 \text{ g/ml}$$

or

Density of acid at $21°C$ = specific gravity $\times$ density of water at $21°C$
$$= 1.791 \times 0.998 \text{ g/ml} = 1.787 \text{ g/ml}$$

Example 2.   (a) What is the weight in pounds per gallon of processed linseed oil which has a specific gravity of 0.934?   (b) How many drums, each holding 55 gal of oil, would be required for a shipment of 4,284.5 lb of this linseed oil?   The weight of 1 gal of water is 8.34 lb.

(a) $0.934 \times 8.34 \text{ lb/gal} = 7.79 \text{ lb/gal} = $ weight of 1 gal of oil

(b) $\dfrac{4,284.5 \text{ lb}}{7.79 \text{ lb/gal}} = 550 \text{ gal} = $ volume of oil containing 4,284.5 lb

$$\frac{550 \text{ gal}}{55 \text{ gal/drum}} = 10 \text{ drums}$$

PERCENTAGE CONCENTRATION

In dealing with aqueous solutions of acids, bases, salts, and some organic solutions, it is essential to know the strength or weight concentration of these solutions.   This strength is usually expressed as percentage by weight concentration, which is the weight of solute (dissolved substance) in 100 parts by weight of solution.   Thus, a sulfuric acid solution that is 93 per cent by weight pure H_2SO_4 means that 100 g of this acid solution contains 93 g of pure H_2SO_4.   Or the *unit weight concentration* would be 0.93 g of pure H_2SO_4 in 1 g of acid solution.

In order to determine the weight of solute in 1 ml of a solution of a given percentage concentration, one must know the specific gravity (or density) of the solution.   Thus, "oil-of-vitriol" solution is a sulfuric acid solution having a specific gravity of 1.83 and containing approximately 93 per cent by weight pure H_2SO_4.   How many grams of pure H_2SO_4 will be contained in 1 ml of this oil-of-vitriol solution?

NOTE.   For convenience in expressing dimensional units, oil-of-vitriol solution is abbreviated *ovs*.

Step 1.   Convert specific gravity of *ovs* to density term, thus

$$\text{sp gr of } ovs = \frac{\text{density of } ovs}{\text{density of water at } 4°C}$$

or density of *ovs* = sp gr of *ovs* × density of water at 4°C; then density of *ovs* = 1.83 × 1 g/ml = 1.83 g/ml, or 1.83 g *ovs*/ml *ovs* (read "1.83 g oil-of-vitriol solution per milliliter of oil-of-vitriol solution").

Step 2. Since the *ovs* contains 93 per cent by weight pure H_2SO_4, or 93 g pure H_2SO_4 in 100 g *ovs*, then 0.93 g pure H_2SO_4 per 1 g *ovs* would equal the *unit weight concentration*. Then the weight of pure H_2SO_4 in 1 ml *ovs* would be

$$\underset{\text{density}}{\frac{1.83 \text{ g } ovs}{1 \text{ ml } ovs}} \times \underset{\substack{\text{unit weight} \\ \text{concentration}}}{\frac{0.93 \text{ g pure } H_2SO_4}{1 \text{ g } ovs}} = \underset{\substack{\text{weight pure solute} \\ \text{per unit volume of} \\ \text{solution}}}{\frac{1.7 \text{ g pure } H_2SO_4}{1 \text{ ml } ovs}}$$

The student should observe in the solution of the following examples how the dimensional units are carried along with the numbers and made to perform the same mathematical operations as the numbers.

Example 1. (*a*) How many grams of pure HNO_3 will be contained in 100 ml of nitric acid solution, specific gravity 1.40 and containing 65.7 per cent by weight of pure HNO_3? (*b*) How many milliliters of this acid solution will contain 63.0 g of HNO_3?

NOTE. For convenience in explanation and use of dimensional units, the term nitric acid solution is abbreviated *nas*.

(*a*) The density of *nas* = specific gravity *nas* × density of water at 4°C = 1.40 × 1 g/ml = 1.40 g/ml, or 1.40 g *nas*/ml *nas*.

Since 65.7 per cent by weight pure HNO_3 = 65.7 g pure HNO_3 per 100 g *nas*, or 0.657 g pure HNO_3 per 1 g *nas*, then

$$\frac{1.40 \text{ g } nas}{1 \text{ ml } nas} \times \frac{0.657 \text{ g pure } HNO_3}{1 \text{ g } nas} \times 100 \text{ ml } nas = 92 \text{ g pure } HNO_3$$

$$\frac{1.40 \text{ g } nas}{1 \text{ ml } nas} \times \frac{0.657 \text{ g pure } HNO_3}{1 \text{ g } nas} = \frac{0.92 \text{ g pure } HNO_3}{1 \text{ ml } nas}$$

or 0.92 g pure HNO_3/ml *nas*.

(*b*) Now to find the number of milliliters of *nas* that will contain 63 g pure HNO_3, one divides the given weight, 63 g pure HNO_3, by the number of grams of pure HNO_3 in 1 ml *nas*, or

$$\frac{63.0 \text{ g pure } HNO_3}{0.92 \text{ g pure } HNO_3/\text{ml } nas} = 63.0 \text{ g pure } HNO_3 \times \frac{1 \text{ ml } nas}{0.92 \text{ g pure } HNO_3}$$
$$= 68.5 \text{ ml } nas$$

or 68.5 ml of nitric acid solution (sp gr 1.40 and containing 65.7 per cent by weight pure HNO_3) will contain 63.0 g of pure HNO_3.

Example 2. How many grams of caustic soda (85 per cent pure NaOH) is required to prepare 1 l of a 20 per cent sodium hydroxide solution? Specific gravity of a 20 per cent sodium hydroxide solution is 1.22.

NOTE. Sodium hydroxide solution is abbreviated *shs* and caustic soda *cs* for convenience in explanation only.

From foregoing examples it follows that if sodium hydroxide solution (*shs*) has a specific gravity of 1.22, its density will be 1.22 *g shs*/ml *shs*.

A 20 per cent sodium hydroxide solution contains 20 g pure NaOH in 100 g sodium hydroxide solution, or 0.2 g pure NaOH per g *shs*; then

$$\frac{1.22 \text{ g } shs}{1 \text{ ml } shs} \times \frac{0.2 \text{ g pure NaOH}}{1 \text{ g } shs} \times \frac{1,000 \text{ ml } shs}{1 \text{ l } shs} = \frac{244 \text{ g pure NaOH}}{1 \text{ l } shs}$$

or 244 g pure NaOH is required for 1 l of a 20 per cent sodium hydroxide solution. However, the available caustic soda is 85 per cent pure NaOH, or 0.85 g pure NaOH/g *cs*; then

$$\frac{244 \text{ g pure NaOH/l } shs}{0.85 \text{ g pure NaOH/g } cs} = \frac{244 \text{ g pure NaOH}}{1 \text{ l } shs}$$

$$\times \frac{1 \text{ g } cs}{0.85 \text{ pure NaOH}} = \frac{287 \text{ g } cs}{1 \text{ l } shs}$$

or 287 g caustic soda (85 per cent pure NaOH) will be required in the preparation of 1 l of sodium hydroxide solution (sp gr 1.22 and containing 20 per cent by weight pure NaOH). That is, 287 g of caustic soda (85 per cent pure NaOH) dissolved in sufficient water to make 1 l of solution will give a sodium hydroxide solution of specific gravity 1.22 and containing 20 per cent by weight of pure NaOH.

Example 3. How many milliliters of concentrated sulfuric acid solution (specific gravity 1.83 and containing 92.1 per cent by weight of pure H_2SO_4) will be required to prepare 1 l of sulfuric acid solution that contains 37.2 per cent by weight of pure H_2SO_4 and has a specific gravity of 1.28?

NOTE. Concentrated sulfuric acid solution is abbreviated *csa* and sulfuric acid solution is abbreviated *sas*.

Step 1. Calculate the number of grams of pure H_2SO_4 that will be contained in 1 l of sulfuric acid solution (*sas*), having specific gravity 1.28 and containing 37.2 per cent by weight of pure H_2SO_4.

$$\frac{1.28 \text{ g } sas}{1 \text{ ml } sas} \times \frac{0.372 \text{ g pure } H_2SO_4}{1 \text{ g } sas} \times \frac{1,000 \text{ ml } sas}{1 \text{ l } sas} = \frac{476 \text{ g pure } H_2SO_4}{1 \text{ l } sas}$$

Step 2. Determine the number of grams of pure H_2SO_4 in 1 ml of concentrated sulfuric acid solution (*csa*).

$$\frac{1.83 \text{ g } csa}{1 \text{ ml } csa} \times \frac{0.921 \text{ g pure } H_2SO_4}{1 \text{ g } csa} = \frac{1.685 \text{ g pure } H_2SO_4}{1 \text{ ml } csa}$$

Step 3

$$\frac{476 \text{ g pure } H_2SO_4/1 \text{ } sas}{1.685 \text{ g pure } H_2SO_4/\text{ml } csa} = 282 \text{ ml } csa/1 \text{ } sas$$

or 282 ml of concentrated sulfuric acid solution diluted with sufficient water to make 1 l of solution will yield a sulfuric acid solution of specific gravity 1.28 and containing 37.2 per cent by weight of pure H_2SO_4.

Example 4. A carboy holds 12 gal of sulfuric acid solution (specific gravity 1.83 and containing 92.1 per cent by weight of pure H_2SO_4). (*a*) What is the weight of the acid solution in the carboy? (*b*) How many pounds of pure H_2SO_4 is contained in 5 gal of this acid solution? Density of water is 8.3 lb/gal.

NOTE. Sulfuric acid solution is abbreviated *sas*.

(*a*) Since 1.83×8.3 lb/gal = 15.19 lb *sas*/gal *sas* = density of *sas*, the weight of *sas* in the carboy will be

$$\frac{15.19 \text{ lb } sas}{1 \text{ gal } sas} \times 12 \text{ gal } sas = 182.3 \text{ lb } sas$$

(*b*) Since density of *sas* = 15.19 lb *sas*/gal *sas*,

$$\frac{15.19 \text{ lb } sas}{1 \text{ gal } sas} \times \frac{0.92 \text{ lb pure } H_2SO_4}{1 \text{ lb } sas} \times 5 \text{ gal } sas = 69.9 \text{ lb pure } H_2SO_4$$

Problems

2-26. The weight of 50 ml of a sulfuric acid solution is 91.5 g. What is its specific gravity? *Ans.* 1.83 g/ml.

2-27. The density of a potassium hydroxide solution is 0.238 g/ml. How many milliliters of this solution would contain 100 g of KOH? *Ans.* 420 ml.

2-28. What is the weight in grams of 25 ml of a salt solution whose specific gravity is 1.45? *Ans.* 36.2 g.

2-29. An empty bottle weighs 25.2 g. The bottle filled with water weighs 45.2 g. The bottle filled with sulfuric acid weighs 61.8 g. (*a*) What is the specific gravity of the sulfuric acid? (*b*) What would be the weight in pounds of a gallon of this sulfuric acid solution? *Ans.* (*a*) 1.83; (*b*) 15.2 lb/gal.

2-30. An empty bottle weighs 50.5 g. The bottle filled with water weighs 258.6 g. The bottle filled with an oil weighs 220.2 g. Calculate (*a*) the specific gravity of the oil and (*b*) the weight in pounds of a gallon of this oil. *Ans.* (*a*) 0.816; (*b*) 6.77 lb/gal.

2-31. A piece of glass weighs 258.6 g in air, 152.6 g in water at 4°C, and 92 g in sulfuric acid. Calculate the specific gravity of the sulfuric acid. *Ans.* 1.57.

2-32. Calculate the volume in gallons of 50 lb of linseed oil of specific gravity 0.926 One gallon of water weighs 8.34 lb. *Ans.* 6.47 gal.

2-33. A steel drum holding 55 gal is filled to its capacity with ethyl alcohol. The specific gravity of the alcohol solution is 0.804. What is the weight in pounds of the alcohol solution in the drum?   *Ans.* 367 lb.

2-34. Calculate the volume in pints of 9 lb of sulfuric acid which has a specific gravity of 1.84.   *Ans.* 4.69 pt.

2-35. A nitric acid solution has a specific gravity of 1.25 and contains 39.8 per cent by weight of pure HNO_3. What weight in grams of pure HNO_3 is contained in 100 ml of the solution?   *Ans.* 49.8 g.

2-36. A hydrochloric acid solution has a specific gravity of 1.19 and contains 39.8 per cent by weight of pure HCl. How many milliliters of this solution will contain 100 g of pure HCl?   *Ans.* 211 ml.

2-37. Storage-battery sulfuric acid solution has a specific gravity of 1.28 and contains 37 per cent by weight of pure H_2SO_4. (a) What is the weight of a gallon of storage-battery acid solution? (b) How many milliliters of storage-battery acid solution contains 71.1 g of pure H_2SO_4?
          Ans. (a) 10.6 lb; (b) 150 ml.

2-38. (a) Determine the weight in grams of pure NaOH in 5 l of sodium hydroxide solution which has a specific gravity of 1.15 and contains 14 per cent by weight of pure NaOH. (b) Calculate the number of milliliters of this caustic-soda solution that will contain 20 g of pure NaOH.
          Ans. (a) 805 g; (b) 124 ml.

2-39. (a) Calculate the weight of 10 gal of sulfuric acid solution having a specific gravity of 1.615 and containing 70 per cent by weight of pure H_2SO_4. (b) How many gallons of this acid solution will contain 184 lb of pure H_2SO_4?
          Ans. (a) 134 lb; (b) 19.6 gal.

2-40. A carboy holds 100 lb of water or 183.9 lb of sulfuric acid. (a) What is the capacity of the carboy in gallons? (b) Calculate the specific gravity of the acid at 4°C.   *Ans.* (a) 12.0 gal; (b) 1.84.

2-41. How many liters of an oil having a specific gravity of 0.926 is contained in a quantity of oil weighing 150 kg?

2-42. A pycnometer weighs 16.525 g, 35.639 g filled with water, and 42.778 g filled with a liquid. Calculate the specific gravity of the liquid.

2-43. Calculate the specific gravity of a drying oil from the following data:

Weight of pycnometer + water at 15.5°C. 60.9114 g
Weight of pycnometer + oil at 15.5°C. . . . . 59.3296 g
Weight of pycnometer. . . . . 33.0612 g

2-44. The specific gravity of a sulfuric acid solution is 1.83. This acid contains 92.1 per cent by weight of pure H_2SO_4. Calculate the number of grams of pure H_2SO_4 contained in 25 ml of this sulfuric acid.

2-45. The specific gravity of a shipment of nitric acid solution is 1.420. This acid contains 69.8 per cent by weight of pure HNO_3. Calculate the number of milliliters of this nitric acid that will contain 10 g of pure HNO_3.

2-46. The specific gravity of a potassium hydroxide solution is 1.42. This solution contains 40.9 per cent of pure KOH by weight. Calculate the number of grams of pure KOH that is contained in 50 ml of this solution.

2-47. How many milliliters of sodium hydroxide solution will contain 20 g of pure NaOH if the solution of sodium hydroxide in question has a specific gravity of 1.38 and contains 35 per cent by weight of pure NaOH?

2-48. Glacial acetic acid has a specific gravity of 1.052 and contains 99 per cent by weight of pure $HC_2H_3O_2$. (a) What weight of pure $HC_2H_3O_2$ is contained in 2.1 l of this acid solution? (b) How many milliliters of this solution will contain 25 g of pure $HC_2H_3O_2$?

2-49. A sodium hydroxide solution is prepared so that it contains 100 g of caustic soda (85 per cent pure $NaOH$) in 500 ml of solution. How many milliliters of this sodium hydroxide solution will be required to prepare 500 ml of a dilute sodium hydroxide solution (sp gr 1.11 and containing 10 per cent by weight of pure $NaOH$)?

2-50. Determine the number of liters of storage-battery acid (sp gr 1.283 and containing 37.3 per cent by weight of pure H_2SO_4) that can be prepared from 10 l of stock sulfuric acid solution of specific gravity 1.83 and containing 92 per cent by weight of pure H_2SO_4.

2-51. An acid solution is made by diluting 50 ml of sulfuric acid (sp gr 1.835 and containing 93.19 per cent by weight of pure H_2SO_4) with sufficient water to make 1 l of solution. Calculate the weight in grams of pure H_2SO_4 in 25 ml of this dilute solution.

2-52. A dilute nitric acid solution is made by diluting 64 ml of nitric acid (sp gr 1.41 and containing 70 per cent by weight of pure HNO_3) to 1 l. How many grams of pure HNO_3 would be contained in 50 ml of this dilute solution?

2-53. A solution containing 40 g of pure K_2SO_4 in 200 ml was found to have a specific gravity of 1.10. Determine the per cent by weight of K_2SO_4 in this solution.

2-54. Upon evaporation of 50 ml of a 24 per cent by weight salt solution, 15 g of salt was obtained. What is the density of the salt solution in grams per milliliter?

CHAPTER III

THE LANGUAGE OF CHEMISTRY

OUTLINE

Significance of valence; electrovalence; covalence.

Formation of compounds.

Fundamentals of chemical nomenclature; formula writing; rules for naming chemical formulas.

Significance of (1) atomic weight and (2) molecular weight.

The law of definite proportions. When elements combine to form a chemical compound, they do so in definite proportions by weight.

Percentage composition.

In beginning the study of chemistry, the student is informed of the atomic theory proposed by Dalton in 1802, followed by a presentation of the modern electronic structural theory of atoms. He also learns of the existence and discovery of 100 chemical elements, thousands of chemical compounds, and is informed of the periodic table of elements. Next comes the task of memorizing the names and chemical symbols of the more common elements, a sort of "chemical alphabet." From a study of the electronic structure of atoms the term **valence,** the combining power of atoms, comes in for consideration. Briefly, valence manifests itself in one of two ways. When atoms combine with atoms of another element (or with themselves) to form molecules, either electrons (the outermost electrons) are completely transferred from one atom to another or electrons are shared between atoms. In the transfer of electrons between atoms, the atom losing electrons forms a positive ion, and is said to have a positive (+) valence number; this is characteristic of metallic elements. The atom gaining electrons forms a negative ion and is said to have a negative (−) valence number; this is prominent in atoms of nonmetallic elements. Under these circumstances positive (+) ions (cations) and negative (−) ions (anions) are attracted to each other and held together by an electrostatic force or bond resulting in compound formation. This type of bond is called an **electrovalent bond.**

When atoms of an element unite with each other to form molecules, *e.g.*, the union of two hydrogen atoms to form a molecule of hydrogen

(H_2), the electrons from each of the hydrogen atoms are shared equally between the two atoms. Likewise, atoms of one element may share electrons with atoms of other elements. This type of bond is called a **covalent bond.** A pair of shared electrons represents **one unit of valence.** It is convenient to speak of positive and negative valence numbers of atoms in covalent compounds even though no electrostatic charge as such is involved in compound formation. Usually a positive valence number is assigned to those atoms which indicate electropositive tendencies, and a negative valence number is assigned to the atoms that show electronegative tendencies. Thus in the covalent compound carbon tetrachloride (CCl_4), the carbon is assigned a $+4$ valence number; and the chlorine being the more electronegative atom is assigned a -1 valence number. In methane (CH_4), the carbon atom is the more electronegative atom and its valence number is -4, and hydrogen has a valence number $+1$.

In a later chapter the term **oxidation number** will be introduced in connection with various oxidation states of atoms exhibiting variable valencies.

In the formation of compounds, then, there may be a transfer of valence electrons (electrovalence), or there may be a sharing of electrons (covalence). In general:

1. Elements whose atoms have 1, 2, and frequently 3 electrons in the outer shell (valence electrons)—H and metals—will lose electrons to form electrovalent compounds.

2. Elements whose atoms have 3, 4, and 5 valence electrons (C, Si, N, P) will share electrons to form covalent compounds.

3. Elements whose atoms have 6 and 7 valence electrons (O, F, Cl, Br, I) (*a*) will share electrons to form covalent compounds and (*b*) will gain electrons to form electrovalent compounds.

A diagrammatic scheme of these two types of compound formation is shown in the accompanying illustration.

1. By electron transfer (electrovalence).

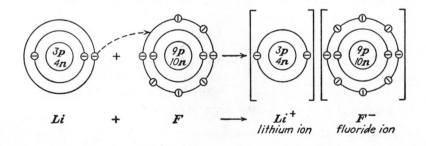

Li   +   F   ⟶   Li⁺   F⁻
                                                    lithium ion   *fluoride ion*

2. By sharing of electrons (covalence).

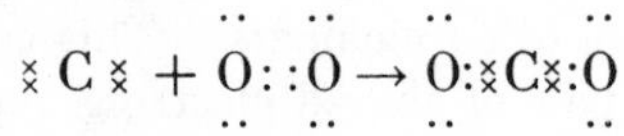

$$\overset{..}{\underset{..}{\text{×}}} \text{C} \underset{..}{\overset{..}{\text{×}}} + \overset{..}{\text{O}} \text{::} \overset{..}{\text{O}} \rightarrow \overset{..}{\text{O}} \text{:×} \text{C×} \text{:} \overset{..}{\text{O}}$$

$$\text{C} + \text{O}_2 \rightarrow \text{CO}_2$$

NOTE. Only valence electrons of carbon and oxygen are indicated in the formation of carbon dioxide, and the carbon valence electrons are represented by (x) and the oxygen electrons by (·) for convenience in representing this type of chemical action. The electrons, of course, are all alike, *i.e.*, negative charges.

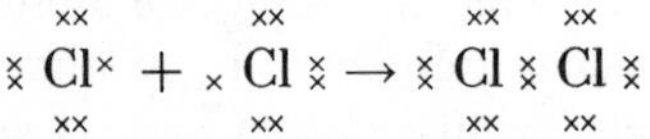

$$\overset{xx}{\underset{xx}{\text{×}}} \text{Cl}^{\times} + _\times \text{Cl} \underset{xx}{\overset{xx}{\text{×}}} \rightarrow \overset{xx}{\underset{xx}{\text{×}}} \text{Cl} \overset{xx}{\underset{xx}{\text{×}}} \text{Cl} \overset{xx}{\underset{xx}{\text{×}}}$$

$$\text{Cl} + \text{Cl} \rightarrow \text{Cl}_2$$

3. Compounds in which both types of bonds prevail. The structure of sodium sulfate (Na_2SO_4) will illustrate this type.

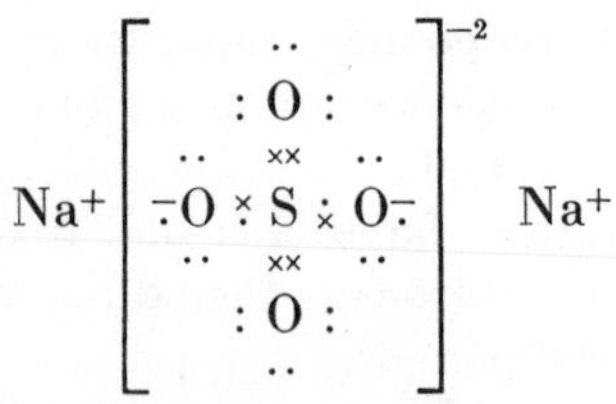

$$\text{Na}^+ \left[\begin{array}{c} \overset{..}{\text{: O :}} \\[4pt] \overset{..}{} \quad \overset{xx}{} \quad \overset{..}{} \\[-2pt] \text{:O × S × O:} \\[-2pt] \overset{..}{} \quad \underset{xx}{} \quad \overset{..}{} \\[4pt] \underset{..}{\text{: O :}} \end{array} \right]^{-2} \text{Na}^+$$

In this representation, the neutral sulfur atom has 6 valence electrons (x), and each of the neutral oxygen atoms has 6 valence electrons (·). Note that 2 of the sulfur electrons are paired with an electron from each of 2 oxygen atoms to form the true covalent bond, and the remaining 4 sulfur electrons are not paired with oxygen electrons but form two covalent bonds of a type commonly called a "coordinate covalent bond." A coordinate covalent bond is one in which the shared pair of electrons is furnished by only one of the atoms. In addition, each of the 2 sodium atoms has transferred its valence electron to the SO_4 combination which in turn acquires a negative charge of 2 or a valence of -2. Thus, 2 Na^+ ions are attached to the $(SO_4)^{-2}$ by electrovalent bonds.

NOTE. It should be mentioned that the "coordinate covalent bonds" in the SO_4^{-2} ion, as illustrated above, and similar ions of oxyacids, have been questioned by Phillips[1] and others. As an example, the suggested structure for sulfuric acid is

---

[1] Phillips and others, *J. Chem. Soc.*, 146 (1945).

$$\left[\begin{array}{c} \overset{\cdot\cdot}{:}\text{O} \\[2pt] \overset{\cdot\cdot}{:}\overset{\cdot\cdot}{\text{O}} \overset{\cdot\cdot}{\times} \overset{\times\times}{\underset{\times\times}{\text{S}}} \overset{\cdot}{\times} \text{O}\overset{\cdot\cdot}{:} \\[2pt] \overset{\cdot\cdot}{:}\text{O} \\ \cdot\cdot \end{array}\right]^{-2}$$

H+   [structure]   H+

One can observe in the above structure that the number of electrons on the sulfur atom is 12, which does not conform to the so-called rule of 8. The stability of such acids is said to be due to the formation of double bonds as shown.

FUNDAMENTALS OF CHEMICAL NOMENCLATURE

With the knowledge of names and chemical symbols of the common elements, together with their common valence numbers (Table V), the student learns of the chemical radical, a group of atoms that remain combined in many chemical reactions, and each radical also having a valence number. The names and formulas for the common radicals with their respective valences are given in Table VI.

In order to write correctly the chemical formula of a compound, the student must know the correct symbols, formulas, and valence numbers of the elements and radicals. Also chemical compounds are electrically neutral, i.e., the total number of positive charges must equal the total number of negative charges for a molecule to be neutral.

In writing the chemical formula of a binary (2-element) compound, the symbol for the positive unit with its valence number is followed by the symbol for the negative unit with its valence number. Thus, when magnesium chemically unites with oxygen the compound magnesium oxide is formed. The chemical formula for this compound is obtained in the following manner:

1. The symbols for magnesium and oxygen with their respective valence numbers are Mg^{+2} and O^{-2}.

2. It is seen that each of the two units has the same number of charges, $+2$ and -2; therefore it takes *one* Mg^{+2} unit to combine with *one* O^{-2} unit to form a neutral molecule. Then the formula would be written $Mg_1^{+2}O_1^{-2}$, where the superscript numbers are the valence numbers and the subscript numbers represent the number of each unit. However, when *one* unit, either positive or negative, is required as subscript number in a formula, the convention is to eliminate the subscript number 1, then the symbol itself stands for *one* unit. The molecular formula of magnesium oxide would be $Mg^{+2}O^{-2}$ or preferably MgO.

TABLE V. TABLE OF NAMES, SYMBOLS, ATOMIC NUMBERS, COMMON VALENCE
NUMBERS, AND ATOMIC WEIGHTS OF COMMON ELEMENTS

Name	Symbol	Atomic number	Valence numbers	Atomic weight
Hydrogen...............	H	1	+1	1.008
Oxygen.................	O	8	−2	16.00
Sulfur..................	S	16	−2, +4, +6	32.066
Selenium...............	Se	34	−2, +4, +6	78.96
Tellurium..............	Te	52	−2, +4, +6	127.61
Fluorine...............	F	9	−1	19.00
Chlorine...............	Cl	17	−1, +1, +3, +5, +7	35.457
Bromine...............	Br	35	−1, +1, +5	79.916
Iodine.................	I	53	−1, +1, +5, +7	126.91
Nitrogen...............	N	7	−3, +1, +2, +4, +5	14.008
Phosphorus............	P	15	−3, +3, +5	30.975
Arsenic*...............	As	33	−3, +3, +5	74.91
Antimony*.............	Sb	51	−3, +3, +5	121.76
Boron..................	B	5	+3	10.82
Carbon.................	C	6	−4, +4	12.011
Silicon.................	Si	14	+4	28.09
Helium.................	He	2	0	4.003
Neon...................	Ne	10	0	20.183
Argon..................	A	18	0	39.944
Krypton................	Kr	36	0	83.8
Xenon..................	Xe	54	0	131.3
Lithium................	Li	3	+1	6.940
Sodium................	Na	11	+1	22.991
Potassium..............	K	19	+1	39.100
Magnesium.............	Mg	12	+2	24.32
Calcium................	Ca	20	+2	40.08
Strontium..............	Sr	38	+2	87.63
Barium................	Ba	56	+2	137.36
Zinc....................	Zn	30	+2	65.38
Cadmium...............	Cd	48	+2	112.41
Lead...................	Pb	82	+2, +4	207.21
Manganese*............	Mn	25	+2, +4, +7	54.94
Copper.................	Cu	29	+1, +2	63.54
Mercury................	Hg	80	+1, +2	200.61
Tin*...................	Sn	50	+2, +4	118.70
Iron...................	Fe	26	+2, +3	55.85
Cobalt.................	Co	27	+2, +3	58.94
Nickel.................	Ni	28	+2, +3	58.69
Bismuth................	Bi	83	+3	209.00
Aluminum*.............	Al	13	+3	26.98
Chromium*.............	Cr	24	+2, +3, +6	52.01
Gold...................	Au	79	+1, +3	197.0
Platinum...............	Pt	78	+2, +4	195.23
Silver..................	Ag	47	+1	107.88

* Elements possessing both nonmetallic and metallic characteristics.

To write the chemical formula for aluminum oxide, one proceeds as follows:

1. The symbols for aluminum and oxygen with their respective valence numbers are Al^{+3} and O^{-2}.

TABLE VI. COMMON RADICALS WITH NAMES, FORMULAS, AND VALENCE

Name	Radical	Valence	Name	Radical	Valence
Nitrate............	NO_3^-	−1	Nitrite.............	NO_2^-	−1
Chlorate..........	ClO_3^-	−1	Chlorite...........	ClO_2^-	−1
Perchlorate........	ClO_4^-	−1	Hypochlorite.......	ClO^-	−1
Sulfate............	SO_4^{-2}	−2	Sulfite.............	SO_3^{-2}	−2
Carbonate.........	CO_3^{-2}	−2			
Chromate.........	CrO_4^{-2}	−2			
Dichromate.......	$Cr_2O_7^{-2}$	−2			
Manganate........	MnO_4^{-2}	−2			
Permanganate.....	MnO_4^-	−1			
Silicate...........	SiO_3^{-2}	−2			
Phosphate.........	PO_4^{-3}	−3			
Metaphosphate.....	PO_3^-	−1			
Pyrophosphate.....	$P_2O_7^{-4}$	−4			
Arsenate..........	AsO_4^{-3}	−3	Arsenite...........	AsO_3^{-3}	−3
Acetate............	$C_2H_3O_2^-$	−1			
Bisulfate..........	HSO_4^-	−1			
Bicarbonate.......	HCO_3^-	−1			
Cyanide...........	CN^-	−1			
Hydroxide........	OH^-	−1			
Ammonium.......	NH_4^+	+1			

2. Since the valence numbers are unequal, to equalize the number of positive units and the number of negative units necessitates taking *two* Al^{+3} units and *three* O^{-2} units. These numbers of units are written as numerical subscripts after each symbol as follows: $Al_2^{+3}O_3^{-2}$, preferably Al_2O_3, read "Al two O three." Note $2 \times +3 = +6$ and $3 \times -2 = -6$, or the total positive units equal the total negative units.

Example. Write the chemical formulas for each of the following: (a) silver bromide; (b) aluminum sulfate; (c) ammonium chloride.

(a) *Step 1.* The symbols and valence numbers of silver and bromide are Ag^{+1} and Br^{-1}.

Step 2. Since each of these units has the same number of charges, +1 and −1, only *one* unit of each is required for a neutral molecule; therefore the chemical formula of silver bromide is $Ag^{+1}Br^{-1}$, or preferably AgBr.

(b) In the chemical compound aluminum sulfate, the aluminum is the positive unit and the sulfate radical is the negative unit.

Step 1.   The symbol and valence number of aluminum is Al^{+3}; the formula and valence number of sulfate radical is SO_4^{-2}.

Step 2.   To equalize the number of positive units and the number of negative units requires *two* Al^{+3} units and *three* SO_4^{-2} units written $Al_2^{+3}(SO_4)_3^{-2}$, or preferably $Al_2(SO_4)_3$, and read "Al two SO_4 taken three times."   Note that $2 \times +3 = +6$ and $3 \times -2 = -6$.   Then $Al_2(SO_4)_3$ is the chemical formula for aluminum sulfate.

(c)   In the chemical compound ammonium chloride, the ammonium radical is the positive unit and the chloride is the negative unit.

Step 1.   The formula and valence number of ammonium radical is NH_4^+; the symbol and valence number of chloride is Cl^-.

Step 2.   Since each of these units has the same number of charges, $+1$ and -1, only *one* unit of each is required in the chemical formula or NH_4Cl.   Note that when only one radical unit is required, both the parentheses and subscript number 1 are omitted, but it is understood that *one* NH_4^+ unit combines with *one* Cl^- unit.

FUNDAMENTAL RULES OF CHEMICAL NOMENCLATURE

Rule 1.   All binary (2-element) compounds have names beginning with the positive unit followed by the negative unit with suffix *-ide*. Thus KI is potassium iod*ide*; Ag_2O is silver ox*ide*; $CaCl_2$ is calcium chlor*ide*; Bi_2S_3 is bismuth sulf*ide*; Ca_3P_2 is calcium phosph*ide*; Al_4C_3 is aluminum carb*ide*.   When the same elements form more than one *electrovalent compound*, the variable valences of the positive unit are indicated by using the suffix *-ous* to represent the *lower* valence state and the suffix *-ic* for the *higher* valence state.   Thus Cu_2O is cupr*ous* ox*ide*, CuO is cupr*ic* ox*ide*; FeS is ferr*ous* sulf*ide*, Fe_2S_3 is ferr*ic* sulf*ide*; $SnCl_2$ is stann*ous* chlor*ide*, $SnCl_4$ is stann*ic* chlor*ide*.   Note that the names of the foregoing positive units or metallic ions with variable valences have the suffix added to the Latin name of the metal.

When the same elements form more than one *covalent compound*, it is customary to use a prefix of the number of atoms before the name of the more electronegative element.   Thus CO is carbon *monoxide*, CO_2 is carbon *dioxide*; PCl_3 is phosphorus *tri*chlor*ide*, PCl_5 is phosphorus *penta*chlor*ide*; NO_2 is nitrogen *dioxide*, N_2O_5 is nitrogen *pentoxide*; SiF_4 is silicon *tetra*fluor*ide*; Cl_2O_7 is chlorine *hept*oxide.

Rule 2.   In naming compounds containing positive elements with negative radicals, one first uses the name of the positive element and then adds the name of the radical.   When the positive element possesses a variable valence, the convention of suffixes of Rule 1 applies. Refer to Table VI for formulas of common radicals and valences. Thus KNO_3 is potassium nitr*ate*, KNO_2 is potassium nitr*ite*; $BaSO_4$ is barium sulf*ate*, $BaSO_3$ is barium sulf*ite*; $Ca(ClO_3)_2$ is calcium chlor*ate*, $Ca(ClO_4)_2$ is calcium *per*chlor*ate*; $SnSO_4$ is stann*ous* sulf*ate*, $Sn(SO_4)_2$ is stann*ic* sulf*ate*; Na_3PO_4 is sodium phosph*ate*, $(NH_4)_2CO_3$ is ammonium carbon*ate*; K_2CrO_4 is potassium chrom*ate*, $K_2Cr_2O_7$ is potassium dichrom*ate*; $CaMnO_4$ is calcium mangan*ate*, $Ca(MnO_4)_2$ is calcium *per*mangan*ate*.

Rule 3.   All acids with prefix *hydro-* and suffix *-ic* form salts with suffix *-ide*.

Oxyacids with suffix *-ic* form salts with suffix *-ate*.

Oxyacids with suffix *-ous* form salts with suffix *-ite*.

Oxyacids with prefix *hypo-* and suffix *-ous* form salts with prefix *hypo-* and suffix *-ite*.

Oxyacids with prefix *per-* and suffix *-ic* form salts with prefix *per-* and suffix *-ate*.   See Table VII for typical formulas of acids and their salts.

Rule 4.   True bases contain the OH^-, or hydroxide ion, and are named by first naming the metallic ion and adding the term "hydroxide."   See Table VIII for examples.

TABLE VII. NAMES, FORMULAS OF ACIDS, AND TYPE FORMULAS OF THEIR SALTS

Name of acid	Formula of acid	Type of salt formed	Formula of type salt	Name of salt
(a) *Hydro—ic acids:*				
Hydrochloric acid.....	HCl	Chloride	KCl	Potassium chloride
Hydrobromic acid....	HBr	Bromide	NaBr	Sodium bromide
Hydriodic acid.......	HI	Iodide	LiI	Lithium iodide
Hydrofluoric acid.....	HF	Fluoride	CaF_2	Calcium fluoride
Hydrosulfuric acid....	H_2S	Sulfide	PbS	Lead sulfide
Hydrocyanic acid.....	HCN	Cyanide	NaCN	Sodium cyanide
(b) *Oxyacids* or *ternary compounds:*				
Hypochlorous acid....	HClO	Hypochlorite	KClO	Potassium hypochlorite
Chlorous acid........	$HClO_2$	Chlorite	$NaClO_2$	Sodium chlorite
Chloric acid..........	$HClO_3$	Chlorate	$Mg(ClO_3)_2$	Magnesium chlorate
Perchloric acid.......	$HClO_4$	Perchlorate	$Ba(ClO_4)_2$	Barium perchlorate
Nitric acid...........	HNO_3	Nitrate	$Fe(NO_3)_3$	Ferrous nitrate
Nitrous acid..........	HNO_2	Nitrite	KNO_2	Potassium nitrite
Acetic acid...........	$HC_2H_3O_2$	Acetate	$Pb(C_2H_3O_2)_2$	Lead acetate
Sulfuric acid.........	H_2SO_4	Sulfate	$CuSO_4$	Cupric sulfate
Sulfurous acid........	H_2SO_3	Sulfite	Ag_2SO_3	Silver sulfite
Carbonic acid........	H_2CO_3	Carbonate	$MgCO_3$	Magnesium carbonate
Chromic acid........	H_2CrO_4	Chromate	Ag_2CrO_4	Silver chromate
Orthophosphoric acid..	H_3PO_4	Orthophosphate	$Ca_3(PO_4)_2$	Calcium orthophosphate
Pyrophosphoric acid..	$H_4P_2O_7$	Pyrophosphate	$Mg_2P_2O_7$	Magnesium pyrophosphate
Metaphosphoric acid..	HPO_3	Metaphosphate	$Co(PO_3)_2$	Cobalt metaphosphate
Arsenic acid..........	H_3AsO_4	Arsenate	$Ca_3(AsO_4)_2$	Calcium arsenate
Arsenious acid........	H_3AsO_3	Arsenite	Na_3AsO_3	Sodium arsenite
Manganic acid........	H_2MnO_4	Manganate	Na_2MnO_4	Sodium manganate
Permanganic acid.....	$HMnO_4$	Permanganate	$LiMnO_4$	Lithium permanganate

TABLE VIII. FORMULAS AND NAMES OF BASES

Formula	Name
NaOH	Sodium *hydroxide*
KOH	Potassium *hydroxide*
$Ca(OH)_2$	Calcium *hydroxide*
$Ba(OH)_2$	Barium *hydroxide*
$Sr(OH)_2$	Strontium *hydroxide*
$Mg(OH)_2$	Magnesium *hydroxide*
$Pb(OH)_2$	Lead *hydroxide*
$Al(OH)_3$	Aluminum *hydroxide*
$Cr(OH)_3$	Chromium *hydroxide*
$Bi(OH)_3$	Bismuth *hydroxide*
$Fe(OH)_2$	Ferr*ous* *hydroxide*
$Fe(OH)_3$	Ferr*ic* *hydroxide*
$Sn(OH)_2$	Stann*ous* *hydroxide*
$Sn(OH)_4$	Stann*ic* *hydroxide*
NH_4OH	Ammonium *hydroxide*

NOTE. Ammonium hydroxide is in reality an aqueous solution of ammonia. This ammonia solution furnishes both ammonium and hydroxide ions, or

$$NH_3 + H_2O \rightleftharpoons NH_4OH \rightleftharpoons NH_4^+ + OH^-$$

Exercises

In each of the following exercises write (*a*) the symbol or formula together with valence after each name and (*b*) the name after each symbol or formula. Example: (*a*) Lead Pb^{+2}; (*b*) O^{-2} oxide

3-1. (*a*) Cadmium   (*b*) Na^+
       Silver Mg^{+2}
       Nitrate SO_4^{-2}
       Sulfide Sn^{+2}
       Mercuric NH_4^+

3-2. (*a*) Zinc   (*b*) Cu^+
       Lithium Bi^{+3}
       Phosphate Ba^{+2}
       Ferric I^-
       Strontium OH^-

3-3. (*a*) Calcium   (*b*) Cl^-
       Stannic ClO_3^-
       Phosphide F^-
       Arsenate CrO_4^{-2}
       Bromide Al^{+3}

3-4. (*a*) Cupric   (*b*) K^+
       Ferrous SO_3^{-2}
       Mercurous Mn^{+2}
       Carbide Cr^{+3}
       Carbonate Br^-

In each of the following exercises write (*a*) the name after each chemical formula and (*b*) the chemical formula after each name. Example: (*a*) $CaCl_2$—calcium chloride; (*b*) NaOH—sodium hydroxide

3-5. (a) NaI (b) Silver nitride
CaO Aluminum oxide
$MgCl_2$ Calcium iodide
Na_3N Hydrogen iodide
Ag_2O Aluminum nitride

3-6. (a) HCl (b) Calcium nitride
AgI Aluminum chloride
$CaCl_2$ Magnesium iodide
- Mg_3N_2 Silver chloride
AlI_3 Sodium oxide

3-7. (a) Cr_2S_3 (b) Sodium chloride
Ag_3P Silver sulfide
ZnO Strontium oxide
$MgBr_2$ Hydrogen sulfide
Al_4C_3 Calcium phosphide

3-8. (a) Hg_2O (b) Stannic phosphide
P_2S_3 Barium hydroxide
CuCl Ferric bromide
HgS Phosphorus trichloride
$Fe(OH)_2$ Carbon tetrachloride

3-9. (a) P_2O_5 (b) Mercurous sulfide
SO_3 Ferric hydroxide
$Zn(OH)_2$ Stannic oxide
FeI_2 Phosphorus pentachloride
$HgBr_2$ Carbon disulfide

3-10. (a) $Cr(NO_3)_3$ (b) Strontium carbonate
SiO_2 Silver nitrate
$SnSO_4$ Barium chlorate
As_2O_5 Bismuth sulfate
Li_3PO_4 Calcium arsenate

3-11. (a) $(NH_4)_2SO_4$ (b) Barium fluoride
CdS Zinc phosphate
$Pb_3(AsO_4)_2$ Silicon tetrachloride
$MnCO_3$ Lead chromate
NH_4CN Potassium sulfite

3-12. (a) $KMnO_4$ (b) Sodium manganate
$Cr_2(CO_3)_3$ Ammonium dichromate
$Al(ClO_3)_3$ Cadmium cyanide
$BiPO_4$ Cupric nitrate
$FeAsO_4$ Ferrous phosphate

ATOMIC WEIGHT

The actual weight of an atom of an element has not been determined directly. However, it is known that an electron has a mass of 1/1,840 times the mass of the hydrogen atom, or the mass of the hydrogen atom is 1,840 times the mass of an electron. The weight of an electron is 9×10^{-28} g; the actual weight of the hydrogen atom is $1,840 \times (9 \times 10^{-28})$ g $= 1.66 \times 10^{-24}$ g. Since the actual weights of atoms of other elements would be of the order of 10^{-24} g, an extremely small order of magnitude, it would be very cumbersome to deal with such small entities in considering weight relations of atoms, molecules, and compounds. Thus the **relative weight** or **atomic weight** of the element comes into being. An atom of oxygen is approximately 16 times as heavy as an atom of hydrogen, and on the basis of O = 16.000 the atomic weight of hydrogen is 1.008. The atomic weights of all the elements are determined on the basis of O = 16.000 and are *pure numbers*. A table of atomic weights of the elements is given on the inside of the front cover (see also Table V, page 32).

MOLECULAR WEIGHT

Since molecules of elements and compounds contain atoms of elements, one would express weights of molecules in terms of atomic weights of the elements of which the molecule is composed. The term **molecular weight** expresses the **relative weight** of the molecule. The molecule of hydrogen contains 2 atoms, or H_2; each hydrogen atom has an atomic weight of 1.008; therefore the molecular weight of hydrogen would be $2 \times 1.008 = 2.016$. A molecule of phosphorus pentoxide (P_2O_5) contains 2 atoms of phosphorus (atomic weight = 30.98) and 5 atoms of oxygen (atomic weight = 16.00). The sum of the total atomic weights of phosphorus and oxygen would be the molecular weight of this compound; thus

$$P_2 = 2 \times 30.98 = \quad 61.96$$
$$O_5 = 5 \times 16.00 = \quad 80.00$$
$$\text{Molecular weight } P_2O_5 = \overline{141.96}$$

It should be noted that the molecular weight, like the atomic weight, is a *pure number*.

Furthermore, it is a fact that the atomic-weight proportion of phosphorus and oxygen in 141.96 parts by weight of phosphorus pentoxide is always in the ratio of 61.96:80.00. If the atoms united in some other ratio, the compound would not be phosphorus pentoxide, but some other substance which would, of course, have properties entirely different from those possessed by phosphorus pentoxide. The facts are, then, **when elements combine to form a chemical compound, they do so in definite proportions by weight.** This is the fundamental **law of definite proportions.** Stated otherwise, **each compound has a constant percentage composition by weight.**

PERCENTAGE COMPOSITION

The amount of an element in any given compound may be determined from the quantitative chemical analysis of a definite weight of the substance.   This amount is usually expressed on the basis of per cent (hundredths or two decimal places).

Thus from repeated chemical analyses it has been found that 1 g of a particular oxide of carbon contains 0.4286 g of carbon and 0.5714 g of oxygen.   On the basis of per cent these weights are equivalent to 42.86 per cent C and 57.14 per cent O.   The percentages of C and of O in this oxide of carbon then represent the per cent of the total weight which each element contributes to the compound, more commonly termed the **percentage composition** of the given compound.

To determine the percentage composition of any chemical compound when the formula of the compound is given, it is necessary to proceed as follows:

1. Multiply the atomic weight of the element by the *number* of atoms of that element which is contained in the formula of the compound.   Do this for each element.

2. Take the sum of the total weights of each element in Step 1. This sum is the molecular weight of the compound.

3. Divide the total weight of each element by the molecular weight of the compound and express each as per cent (by moving the decimal point two places to the right and annexing the per cent sign %). Expressing these steps as a formula,

Per cent of an element in a compound

$$= \frac{\text{atomic weight of element} \times \text{number of atoms}}{\text{molecular weight of compound}} \times 100$$

In performing calculations involving atomic weights it is convenient to "round off" numbers to *one* digit to the right of the decimal place. Recall that the procedure of "rounding off" a number consists in dropping from a given number, one or more digits at the right as follows: (1) When the digit dropped is greater than 5, the last retained digit is increased by 1.   (2) If the digit dropped is less than 5, the last retained digit is left unchanged.   (3) When the discarded digit is exactly 5, the procedure is to round off the last retained digit to an *even* number.   Thus the atomic weight of chlorine, which is 35.457, when rounded off becomes 35.5; the atomic weight of iron, 55.85, becomes 55.8; the atomic weight of radium, 226.05, becomes 226.0; the atomic weight of vanadium, 50.95, becomes 51.0; the number 71.35 becomes 71.4.

Example 1.   Calculate the percentage composition of (*a*) silver chloride, (*b*) aluminum oxide, and (*c*) potassium sulfate.

(*a*) *Step* 1.   The formula for silver chloride is AgCl.   Atomic weights: Ag = 107.9; Cl = 35.5.

Step 2

> 1 atom Ag = 1 × 107.9 = 107.9 parts by weight of Ag
> 1 atom Cl = 1 × 35.5 = 35.5 parts by weight of Cl

Step 3. Molecular weight of AgCl = 143.4.

Step 4. Weight ratios of component parts multiplied by 100 to express per cent of each:

$$\frac{Ag}{AgCl} = \frac{107.9}{143.4} \times 100 = 75.2 \text{ per cent Ag}$$

$$\frac{Cl}{AgCl} = \frac{35.5}{143.4} \times 100 = 24.8 \text{ per cent Cl}$$

(*b*) *Step* 1. The formula for aluminum oxide is Al_2O_3. Atomic weights: Al = 27.0; O = 16.0.

Step 2

> 2 atoms Al = 2 × 27.0 = 54.0 parts by weight of Al
> 3 atoms O = 3 × 16.00 = 48.0 parts by weight of O

Step 3. Molecular weight of Al_2O_3 = 102.0.

Step 4. Weight ratios of component parts multiplied by 100 to express per cent of each:

$$\frac{2Al}{Al_2O_3} = \frac{54.0}{102.0} \times 100 = 52.9 \text{ per cent Al}$$

$$\frac{3O}{Al_2O_3} = \frac{48.0}{102.0} \times 100 = 47.1 \text{ per cent O}$$

(*c*) *Step* 1. The formula for potassium sulfate is K_2SO_4. Atomic weights: K = 39.1; S = 32.1; O = 16.0.

Step 2

> 2 atoms K = 2 × 39.1 = 78.2 parts by weight of K
> 1 atom S = 1 × 32.1 = 32.1 parts by weight of S
> 4 atoms O = 4 × 16.0 = 64.0 parts by weight of O

Step 3. Molecular weight of K_2SO_4 = 174.3.

Step 4. Weight ratios of component parts multiplied by 100 to express per cent of each:

$$\frac{2K}{K_2SO_4} = \frac{78.2}{174.3} \times 100 = 44.9 \text{ per cent K}$$

$$\frac{S}{K_2SO_4} = \frac{32.1}{174.3} \times 100 = 18.4 \text{ per cent S}$$

$$\frac{4O}{K_2SO_4} = \frac{64.0}{174.3} \times 100 = 36.7 \text{ per cent O}$$

Example 2. What is the theoretical percentage of CaO in (a) $Ca(OH)_2$ and (b) $Ca_3(PO_4)_2$. Molecular weights: $CaO = 56.1$; $Ca(OH)_2 = 74.1$; $Ca_3(PO_4)_2 = 310.3$.

(a) The formula $Ca(OH)_2$ shows that 1 molecule of $Ca(OH)_2$ contains 1 molecule of CaO, or 1 molecular weight of CaO is contained in 1 molecular weight $Ca(OH)_2$. Expressed as a ratio of molecular weights and multiplying by 100 to obtain per cent of CaO,

$$\frac{1CaO}{1Ca(OH)_2} = \frac{56.1}{74.1} \times 100 = 75.7 \text{ per cent CaO in } Ca(OH)_2$$

(b) The formula $Ca_3(PO_4)_2$ indicates that 1 molecule of $Ca_3(PO_4)_2$ contains 3 molecules of CaO, or 3 molecular weights of CaO are contained in 1 molecular weight of $Ca_3(PO_4)_2$. Expressed as a ratio of molecular weights and multiplying by 100 to obtain per cent of CaO,

$$\frac{3CaO}{1Ca_3(PO_4)_2} = \frac{3 \times 56.1}{310.3} \times 100 = 54.2 \text{ per cent CaO in } Ca_3(PO_4)_2$$

Example 3. The formula for blue vitriol is $CuSO_4 \cdot 5H_2O$. Calculate percentage of (a) $CuSO_4$ and (b) water in this compound. Molecular weights: $CuSO_4 \cdot 5H_2O = 249.6$; $CuSO_4 = 159.6$; $H_2O = 18.0$.

(a) The formula $CuSO_4 \cdot 5H_2O$ indicates 1 molecular weight of $CuSO_4$ is contained in 1 molecular weight $CuSO_4 \cdot 5H_2O$. Expressed as a ratio of molecular weights and multiplying by 100 to obtain per cent of $CuSO_4$,

$$\frac{1CuSO_4}{1CuSO_4 \cdot 5H_2O} = \frac{159.6}{249.6} \times 100 = 63.9 \text{ per cent } CuSO_4 \text{ in } CuSO_4 \cdot 5H_2O$$

(b) The formula indicates 5 molecular weights of H_2O are contained in 1 molecular weight of $CuSO_4 \cdot 5H_2O$. Expressed as a ratio of molecular weights and multiplying by 100 to obtain per cent of H_2O,

$$\frac{5H_2O}{1CuSO_4 \cdot 5H_2O} = \frac{5 \times 18.0}{249.6} \times 100 = 36.1 \text{ per cent } H_2O \text{ in } CuSO_4 \cdot 5H_2O$$

Problems

The problems in this list will require the use of atomic weights. Refer to the table of atomic weights on the inside cover of textbook. It is permissible and convenient to round off atomic-weight numbers so that there is only one digit to the right of the decimal place.

3-13. (1) Write the name for each of the compounds with following chemical formulas, and (2) check the molecular weight of each compound with the given answer: (a) KI; (b) $Fe(OH)_2$; (c) PbS; (d) Al_4C_3; (e) $MgBr_2$.

Ans. (2) (a) 166.0; (b) 89.8; (c) 239.3; (d) 144.0; (e) 184.1.

3-14. (1) Write the name for each of the compounds with following chemical formulas, and (2) check the molecular weight of each compound with the given answer: (a) CaS; (b) MgF$_2$; (c) Fe$_2$O$_3$; (d) Bi(OH)$_3$; (e) SnCl$_4$.

Ans. (2) (a) 72.2; (b) 62.3; (c) 159.6; (d) 260.0; (e) 260.7.

3-15. (1) Write the name for each of the compounds with following chemical formulas, and (2) check the molecular weight of each compound with the given answer: (a) CaCO$_3$; (b) FeI$_3$; (c) Hg$_2$S; (d) Mg$_3$(PO$_4$)$_2$; (e) CuOH.

Ans. (2) (a) 100.1; (b) 436.5; (c) 433.3; (d) 262.9; (e) 80.6.

3-16. (1) Write the name for each of the compounds with following chemical formulas, and (2) check the molecular weight of each compound with the given answer: (a) K$_3$PO$_4$; (b) Mg$_3$N$_2$; (c) H$_3$AsO$_4$; (d) Sn(SO$_4$)$_2$; (e) Cu$_2$S.

Ans. (2) (a) 212.3; (b) 100.9; (c) 141.9; (d) 310.9; (e) 159.3.

3-17. The following is a list of chemical formulas of compounds. (1) Write the name of each compound, and (2) check the molecular weight of each compound with the given answer. (a) Mg(ClO$_4$)$_2$; (b) Hg(CN)$_2$; (c) (NH$_4$)$_2$SO$_4$; (d) Fe$_2$(CO$_3$)$_3$; (e) KMnO$_4$.

Ans. (2) (a) 223.3; (b) 252.6; (c) 132.1; (d) 291.6; (e) 158.0.

3-18. (1) Write the chemical formula for each of the following compounds, and (2) check the molecular weight of each compound with the given answer: (a) cadmium oxide; (b) silicon dioxide; (c) aluminum sulfide; (d) barium chloride; (e) calcium nitride.

Ans. (2) (a) 128.4; (b) 60.1; (c) 150.3; (d) 208.4; (e) 148.3.

3-19. The following is a list of names of chemical compounds. (1) Write the chemical formula for each compound, and (2) check the molecular weight of each compound with the given answer. (a) Silver sulfide; (b) potassium oxide; (c) ferric chloride; (d) magnesium phosphide; (e) sodium iodide.

Ans. (2) (a) 247.9; (b) 94.2; (c) 162.3; (d) 134.9; (e) 149.9.

3-20. (1) Write the chemical formula for each of the following compounds, and (2) check the molecular weight of each compound with the given answer: (a) aluminum phosphate; (b) ammonium iodide; (c) silicon tetrachloride; (d) stannic oxide; (e) ferric sulfate.

Ans. (2) (a) 122.0; (b) 144.9; (c) 170.1; (d) 150.7; (e) 399.9.

3-21. The following is a list of names of chemical compounds. (1) Write the chemical formula for each compound, and (2) check the molecular weight of each compound with the given answer. (a) Silver sulfate; (b) calcium fluoride; (c) zinc carbonate; (d) ammonium chlorate; (e) lead arsenate.

Ans. (2) (a) 311.9; (b) 78.1; (c) 125.4; (d) 101.5; (e) 899.4.

3-22. The following is a list of names of chemical compounds. (1) Write the chemical formula for each compound, and (2) check the molecular weight of each compound with the given answer. (a) Phosphorus trichloride; (b) hydriodic acid; (c) iodic acid; (d) lithium carbonate; (e) manganese phosphate. *Ans.* (2) (a) 137.5; (b) 127.9; (c) 175.9; (d) 73.8; (e) 183.7.

3-23. Determine the molecular weight of each of the following compounds: (a) crystallized sodium carbonate (Na$_2$CO$_3$·10H$_2$O); (b) calcium bicarbonate [Ca(HCO$_3$)$_2$]; (c) lead acetate [Pb(C$_2$H$_3$O$_2$)$_2$]; (d) magnesium pyrophosphate (Mg$_2$P$_2$O$_7$). *Ans.* (a) 286.0; (b) 162.1; (c) 325.2; (d) 222.6.

3-24. The following are common names and formulas of salts crystallized from aqueous (water) solutions: (a) glauber salt (Na$_2$SO$_4$·10H$_2$O); (b) copperas (FeSO$_4$·7H$_2$O); (c) epsom salt (MgSO$_4$·7H$_2$O); (d) microcosmic salt [Na(NH$_4$)HPO$_4$·4H$_2$O]. What is the molecular weight of each salt?

Ans. (a) 322.1; (b) 277.9; (c) 246.4; (d) 209.0.

3-25. Calculate the percentage of iron in (a) FeO, (b) Fe_2O_3, and (c) Fe_3O_4.

$Ans.$ (a) 77.7 per cent; (b) 69.9 per cent; (c) 72.3 per cent.

3-26. Calculate the percentage composition of potassium dichromate.

$Ans.$ K, 26.6 per cent; Cr, 35.4 per cent; O, 38.0 per cent.

3-27. What is the percentage of water of crystallization in (a) $CaCl_2 \cdot 6H_2O$ and (b) $KCl \cdot MgCl_2 \cdot 6H_2O$? $Ans.$ (a) 49.3 per cent; (b) 38.8 per cent.

3-28. The mineral kaolinite has a chemical formula $Al_2O_3 \cdot 2SiO_2 \cdot 2H_2O$. What is the theoretical percentage of (a) Al_2O_3, (b) SiO_2, and (c) H_2O in this mineral?
$Ans.$ (a) Al_2O_3, 39.5 per cent; (b) SiO_2, 46.6 per cent; (c) H_2O, 13.9 per cent.

3-29. Calculate the percentage of MgO in (a) $Mg(OH)_2$, (b) $Mg_2P_2O_7$, and (c) $Mg_3(PO_4)_2$. $Ans.$ (a) 69.1 per cent; (b) 36.2 per cent; (c) 15.3 per cent.

3-30. Given the following chemical formulas of compounds, (1) write the name of each compound, and (2) determine the molecular weight of each one: (a) $BaCl_2$; (b) HgS; (c) MgI_2; (d) KBr; (e) FeO.

3-31. The following is a list of chemical formulas of compounds. (1) Write the name of each compound, and (2) determine the molecular weight of each one: (a) $MgBr_2$; (b) AgI; (c) $ZnCl_2$; (d) CaS; (e) Na_3N.

3-32. Given the following chemical formulas of compounds, (1) write the name of each compound, and (2) determine the molecular weight of each one: (a) $Zn(OH)_2$; (b) $SnBr_2$; (c) P_2O_5; (d) FeI_2; (e) Hg_2O.

3-33. Given the names of the following chemical compounds, (1) write the chemical formula for each compound, and (2) determine the molecular weight of each one: (a) Stannous iodide; (b) barium nitride; (c) phosphorus pentasulfide; (d) ferrous hydroxide; (e) mercuric bromide.

3-34. The following is a list of names of chemical compounds. (1) Write the chemical formula for each compound, and (2) determine the molecular weight of each one. (a) Zinc sulfate; (b) silver nitrate; (c) barium chlorate; (d) ferrous carbonate; (e) phosphoric acid.

3-35. Given the names of the following chemical compounds, (1) write the chemical formula for each compound, and (2) determine the molecular weight of each one: (a) Lithium hydroxide; (b) arsenic pentasulfide; (c) strontium sulfate; (d) sodium sulfite; (e) lead phosphate.

3-36. Determine the percentage of silver in (a) silver oxide and (b) silver nitrate.

3-37. What is the percentage of copper in (a) cuprous oxide and (b) cupric oxide?

3-38. Determine the percentage of iron in (a) ferrous sulfide and (b) ferric sulfide.

3-39. Calculate the percentage of lead in (a) Pb_2O_3 and (b) Pb_3O_4.

3-40. Determine (a) the percentage of lithium in lithium sulfate and (b) the percentage of aluminum in aluminum sulfate.

3-41. What is the theoretical per cent of barium oxide in (a) barium hydroxide and (b) barium carbonate?

3-42. What is the theoretical per cent of aluminum oxide in (a) aluminum sulfate and (b) aluminum hydroxide?

3-43. What is the theoretical per cent of (a) ferrous oxide in ferrous hydroxide and (b) ferric oxide in ferric hydroxide?

3-44. What is the percentage of (a) Cl, (b) Mg, (c) KCl, (d) $MgCl_2$, and (e) H_2O in the mineral carnallite $(KCl \cdot MgCl_2 \cdot 6H_2O)$?

3-45. What is the percentage of water in (a) $Al_2(SO_4)_3 \cdot 17H_2O$ and (b) $Na_2B_4O_7 \cdot 10H_2O$?

CHAPTER IV

GRAM-ATOM AND GRAM-MOLE

OUTLINE

Gram-atomic weight, or gram-atom. One gram-atom (g-atom) of an element is the weight of 6.02×10^{23} atoms of that element; 6.02×10^{23} atoms of oxygen weigh 16 g, or 1 g-atom of oxygen weighs 16 g. To determine the number of gram-atoms in a given weight of an element divide the given number of grams of the element by the number of grams per gram-atom of that element.

Gram-molecular weight, or gram-mole. One gram-mole (g-mole) of any element or compound is the weight of 6.02×10^{23} molecules of that substance. The gram-mole is the sum of the total gram-atomic weights of the elements in the substance. To determine the number of gram-moles in a given weight of substance, divide the given number of grams of the substance by the number of grams per gram-mole of that substance.

Ounce-mole; pound-mole; kilogram-mole.

GRAM-ATOMIC WEIGHT OR GRAM-ATOM

Since the atomic weight of an element is proportional to the actual weight of an atom of an element, it is customary to express the atomic weight of an element in grams, commonly termed **gram-atomic weight,** or simply a **gram-atom (g-atom).** It can be shown that a gram-atomic weight or a gram-atom of *any* element contains the same number of atoms, *viz.*, 6.02×10^{23} atoms (**the Avogadro number**), or 1 g-atom of an element is the weight of 6.02×10^{23} atoms of that element.[1] Thus

[1] There is 1.008 g of hydrogen in 1 g-atom of hydrogen. The actual weight of the hydrogen atom is 1.66×10^{-24} g. Then

$$\frac{1.008 \text{ g of hydrogen/g-atom of hydrogen}}{1.66 \times 10^{-24} \text{ g of hydrogen/atom of hydrogen}} = 6.03 \times 10^{23}$$
$$\text{atoms of hydrogen/g-atom of hydrogen}$$

This number, 6.03×10^{23}, or the more accurately determined value of 6.02×10^{23} (the Avogadro number) is the actual number of atoms in 1 g-atom of any element. It also is the number of molecules in 1 g-mole of any substance. Also, it is the number of ions in 1 g-ion of a given substance.

Since oxygen is 16 times as heavy as hydrogen, an *atom* of oxygen would be 16 times as heavy as an *atom* of hydrogen, or

$$1.66 \times 10^{-24} \text{ g/atom} \times 16 = 2.66 \times 10^{-23} \text{ g/atom}$$
$$= \text{the actual weight of an atom of oxygen}$$

1 g-atom sodium = 23.0 g = weight of 6.02×10^{23} atoms sodium

2 g-atoms sodium = 2×23.0 g = 46.0 g

To find the *number* of gram-atoms in a *given weight* of an element, one divides the given number of grams of the element by the atomic weight of the element in grams (number of grams per gram-atom). This statement can be formulated as follows

$$\text{No. of g-atoms} = \frac{G}{\text{no. of g/g-atom}}$$

where G = the given number of grams of the element and no. of g/g-atom = the atomic weight of the element in grams, or the number of grams of the element in 1 g-atomic weight.

Example 1. How many gram-atoms of sulfur are there in 80.25 g of sulfur? Atomic weight of sulfur = 32.1.

Since

$$\text{No. of g-atoms} = \frac{G}{\text{no. of g/g-atom}}$$

G = 80.25 g S   and   no. of g/g-atom = 32.1 g S/g-atom S

Let x = number of gram-atoms

$$= \frac{80.25 \text{ g}}{32.1 \text{ g S/g-atom S}} = 80.25 \text{ g S} \times \frac{1 \text{ g-atom S}}{32.1 \text{ g S}}$$

$$= 2.5 \text{ g-atoms S}$$

Example 2. How many grams of calcium are there in 3.25 g-atoms of Ca? Atomic weight of Ca = 40.1.

Since

$$\text{No. of g-atoms} = \frac{G}{\text{no. of g/g-atom}}$$

by rearranging,

$$G = \text{no. of g-atoms} \times \text{no. of g/g-atom}$$

Let x = number of grams of Ca

Then 6.02×10^{23} atoms of oxygen would weigh

2.66×10^{-23} g/atom $\times 6.02 \times 10^{23}$ atoms/g-atom = 16.00 g/g-atom

or 1 g-atom of oxygen weighs 16 g, which is the weight of 6.02×10^{23} atoms of oxygen. In the same manner one could prove that the gram-atom of any element is the weight of 6.02×10^{23} atoms of that element. Similar reasoning will show that the gram-mole of any given substance is the weight of 6.02×10^{23} molecules of that substance.

$$\text{No. of g-atoms} = 3.25 \text{ g-atoms Ca} \quad \text{and}$$

$$\text{no. of g/g-atom} = \frac{40.1 \text{ g Ca}}{1 \text{ g-atom Ca}}$$

$$x = 3.25 \text{ g-atoms Ca} \times \frac{40.1 \text{ g Ca}}{1 \text{ g-atom Ca}}$$

$$= 130 \text{ g Ca}$$

GRAM-MOLECULAR WEIGHT; GRAM-MOLE

When the atomic weight of the elements in a molecule of a substance is expressed in grams, the molecular weight is called a **gram-molecular weight,** or simply a **gram-mole (g-mole).**[1] As in the case of the gram-atom, it can be shown that a gram-molecular weight or a gram-mole of any element or compound contains the same number of molecules, *viz.*, 6.02×10^{23} molecules (the *Avogadro number*), or a gram-mole of a substance is the weight of 6.02×10^{23} molecules of that substance. The gram-mole is the sum of the total gram-atomic weights in the substance. Thus 1 g-mole of sodium sulfate (Na_2SO_4) contains

$$
\begin{array}{rcll}
Na_2 = 2 \text{ g-atoms Na} = 2 \text{ g-atoms} \times 23.0 \text{ g/g-atom} = & 46.0 \text{ g} \\
S = 1 \text{ g-atom S} = 1 \text{ g-atom} \times 32.1 \text{ g/g-atom} = & 32.1 \text{ g} \\
O_4 = 4 \text{ g-atoms O} = 4 \text{ g-atoms} \times 16.0 \text{ g/g-atom} = & \underline{64.0 \text{ g}} \\
1 \text{ g-mole } Na_2SO_4 = & \overline{142.1 \text{ g}}
\end{array}
$$

or 142.1 g Na_2SO_4/g-mole.

To find the *number* of gram-moles in a *given weight* of an element or compound, one divides the given number of grams of the substance by the molecular weight of the substance in grams (number of grams per gram-mole). This statement can be formulated

$$\text{No. of g-moles} = \frac{G}{\text{no. of g/g-mole}}$$

where G = the given number of grams of substance and no. of g/g-mole = the molecular weight of the substance in grams, or the number of grams of substance in 1 g-mole.

Example 1.   How many gram-moles of $CdCl_2$ are contained in 62.32 g $CdCl_2$? Atomic weights: Cd = 112.4; Cl = 35.5.

$$
\begin{array}{rcll}
Cd = 1 \text{ g-atom Cd} = 1 \text{ g-atom} \times 112.4 \text{ g/g-atom} = & 112.4 \text{ g} \\
Cl_2 = 2 \text{ g-atoms Cl} = 2 \text{ g-atoms} \times 35.5 \text{ g/g-atom} = & \underline{71.0 \text{ g}} \\
1 \text{ g-mole } CdCl_2 = & \overline{183.4 \text{ g}}
\end{array}
$$

---

[1] In many general chemistry textbooks, the term "mole" is used to express the gram-molecular weight. In this text, this term "mole" is intentionally omitted to avoid confusion in expressing molecular weights in other weight units.

$$\text{No. of g-moles} = \frac{G}{\text{no. of g/g-mole}}$$

where G = 62.32 g $CdCl_2$ and no. of g/g-mole = 183.4 g $CdCl_2$/g-mole.

Let x = number of gram-moles

$$= \frac{62.32 \text{ g } CdCl_2}{183.4 \text{ g } CdCl_2/\text{g-mole } CdCl_2}$$

$$= 62.32 \text{ g } CdCl_2 \times \frac{1 \text{ g-mole } CdCl_2}{183.4 \text{ g } CdCl_2}$$

$$= 0.34 \text{ g-mole } CdCl_2$$

Example 2. (*a*) How many grams of H_2SO_4 are contained in 0.25 g-mole H_2SO_4? (*b*) How many gram-atoms of H and of S are contained in 0.25 g-mole H_2SO_4? (*c*) How many grams of H and of S are contained in 0.25 g-mole H_2SO_4? Atomic weights: H = 1.0; S = 32.1; O = 16.0.

(*a*) *Step* 1. From the formula H_2SO_4, and the atomic weights of the elements, the molecular weight of H_2SO_4 is found to be 98.1, or 98.1 g H_2SO_4 is contained in 1 g-mole H_2SO_4.

Step 2

$$\text{No. of g-moles} = \frac{G}{\text{no. of g/g-mole}}$$

Upon rearranging,

$$G = \text{no. of g-moles} \times \text{no. of g/g-mole}$$

Step 3. Let x = number of grams H_2SO_4

$$= 0.25 \text{ g-mole } H_2SO_4 \times \frac{98.1 \text{ g } H_2SO_4}{1 \text{ g-mole } H_2SO_4}$$

$$= 24.5 \text{ g } H_2SO_4$$

(*b*) Since 1 g-mole H_2SO_4 contains 2 g-atoms H and 1 g-atom S, 0.25 g-mole H_2SO_4 contains 0.25 × 2 g-atoms H = 0.5 g-atom H, and 0.25 × 1 g-atom S = 0.25 g-atom S.

(*c*) It has been shown that

$$G = \text{no. of g-atoms} \times \text{no. of g/g-atom}$$

From part (*b*), 0.25 g-mole H_2SO_4 contains 0.5 g-atom H and 0.25 g-atom S.

Let x = number of grams of H

$$= 0.5 \text{ g-atom H} \times \frac{1.0 \text{ g H}}{1 \text{ g-atom H}} = 0.5 \text{ g H}$$

Let y = number of grams of S

$$= 0.25 \text{ g-atom S} \times \frac{32.1 \text{ g S}}{1 \text{ g-atom S}} = 8.0 \text{ g S}$$

Example 3.   What weight of (a) sulfur and (b) sulfur trioxide (SO_3) is contained in 10 g of sodium sulfate? Atomic weights: $Na = 23.0$; $S = 32.1$; $O = 16.0$.

(a) *Step* 1.   The formula for sodium sulfate is Na_2SO_4. The molecular weight of this compound is 142.1, or 142.1 g Na_2SO_4/g-mole Na_2SO_4.

Step 2.   Determine the number of gram-moles Na_2SO_4 in 10 g Na_2SO_4.

$$\text{Let } x = \text{number of gram-moles } Na_2SO_4$$
$$= \frac{10 \text{ g } Na_2SO_4}{142.1 \text{ g } Na_2SO_4/\text{g-mole } Na_2SO_4}$$
$$= 10 \text{ g } Na_2SO_4 \times \frac{1 \text{ g-mole } Na_2SO_4}{142.1 \text{ g } Na_2SO_4}$$
$$= 0.07 \text{ g-mole } Na_2SO_4$$

Step 3.   It is readily seen that 1 g-mole Na_2SO_4 contains 1 g-atom S, or 32.1 g S.   Then 0.07 g-mole Na_2SO_4 will contain 0.07 g-mole Na_2SO_4 $\times$ 32.1 g S/g-mole $Na_2SO_4 = 2.2$ g S.

(b) *Step* 1.   Molecular weight of $SO_3 = 80.1$. Since 1 g-mole Na_2SO_4 contains 1 g-mole SO_3, or 80.1 g SO_3, then 0.07 g-mole Na_2SO_4 will contain 0.07 g-mole $Na_2SO_4 \times 80.1$ g SO_3/g-mole $Na_2SO_3 = 5.6$ g SO_3.

Alternate Solution.   An alternate solution can be obtained on the basis of weight ratios.

(a) On this basis 1S atom is contained in 1 molecule Na_2SO_4, or a ratio of $1S:1Na_2SO_4$.

Let x = number of grams S

$$\frac{S}{Na_2SO_4} = \frac{32.1 \text{ g S}}{142.1 \text{ g } Na_2SO_4} = \frac{x}{10 \text{ g } Na_2SO_4}$$
$$x = 10 \text{ g } Na_2SO_4 \times \frac{32.1 \text{ g S}}{142.1 \text{ g } Na_2SO_4} = 2.2 \text{ g S}$$

(b) On this basis $1SO_3$ is contained in $1Na_2SO_4$, or a ratio of $1SO_3:1Na_2SO_4$.

Let y = number of grams SO_3

$$\frac{SO_3}{Na_2SO_4} = \frac{80.1 \text{ g } SO_3}{142.1 \text{ g } Na_2SO_4} = \frac{y}{10 \text{ g } Na_2SO_4}$$
$$y = 10 \text{ g } Na_2SO_4 \times \frac{80.1 \text{ g } SO_3}{142.1 \text{ g } Na_2SO_4} = 5.6 \text{ g } SO_3$$

OUNCE-MOLE; POUND-MOLE; KILOGRAM-MOLE

Thus far we have considered atomic weights and molecular weights (relative weights) in the metric system, gram-atoms and gram-moles.

It frequently becomes necessary to deal with the English system of weights, and such terms as ounce-mole (oz-mole), pound-atom (lb-atom), and pound-mole (lb-mole) come into being, particularly in industry. One **ounce-mole** of a compound can be defined as the sum of the total **ounce-atomic weights** (atomic weights expressed in ounces) of the atoms in that compound. Likewise, one pound-mole of a compound is a quantity represented by the sum of the total pound-atomic weights of the atoms in that compound. The formula weight of a compound (relative weight) can be conveniently expressed in any unit of quantity in any system of measures as gram-mole, kilogram-mole, ounce-mole, pound-mole, ton-mole.

Example. Determine the theoretical amount in pounds of lead chromate ($PbCrO_4$) that can be obtained from 1 ton of chromite ore which analyzed 28.5 per cent Cr_2O_3.

It is evident from the chemical formulas Cr_2O_3 and $PbCrO_4$ that 1 lb-mole of Cr_2O_3 will yield 2 lb-moles of $PbCrO_4$, since 2 atoms of Cr are available from Cr_2O_3, and $PbCrO_4$ contains only 1 atom of Cr. This is conveniently represented by $1Cr_2O_3 = 2PbCrO_4$.

Step 1. The chromite ore contains 28.5 per cent Cr_2O_3. This means, of course, that 100 lb of chromite contains 28.5 lb of pure Cr_2O_3. Then 1 lb of chromite contains $\frac{1}{100} \times 28.5$ lb pure Cr_2O_3 = 0.285 lb of pure Cr_2O_3. Then 2,000 lb (1 ton) of chromite will contain $2,000 \times 0.285$ lb pure Cr_2O_3 = 570.0 lb of pure Cr_2O_3.

Step 2. Determine the number of pound-moles Cr_2O_3 in 570 lb pure Cr_2O_3. Molecular weight Cr_2O_3 = 152.0.

$$\text{No. of lb-moles} = \frac{\text{lb}}{\text{no. of lb/lb-mole}}$$

where lb = given or available pounds of the pure substance and no. of lb/lb-mole = the molecular weight of the substance in pounds, or the number of pounds in 1 lb-mole of the substance. Then lb = 570 lb Cr_2O_3, and no. of lb/lb-mole = 152 lb Cr_2O_3/lb-mole Cr_2O_3.

Let x = number of pound-moles Cr_2O_3

$$= \frac{570 \text{ lb } Cr_2O_3}{152 \text{ lb } Cr_2O_3/\text{lb-mole } Cr_2O_3}$$

$$= 570 \text{ lb } Cr_2O_3 \times \frac{1 \text{ lb-mole } Cr_2O_3}{152 \text{ lb } Cr_2O_3}$$

$$= 3.75 \text{ lb-moles } Cr_2O_3$$

Step 3. Since 1 lb-mole Cr_2O_3 will yield 2 lb-moles $PbCrO_4$, 3.75 lb-moles Cr_2O_3 will yield 3.75×2 lb-moles $PbCrO_4$ = 7.5 lb-moles $PbCrO_4$.

Step 4.   Since molecular weight $PbCrO_4 = 323.0$, then

$$7.5 \text{ lb-moles } PbCrO_4 \times \frac{323.0 \text{ lb } PbCrO_4}{1 \text{ lb-mole } PbCrO_4} = 2{,}422 \text{ lb } PbCrO_4$$

Problems

4-1. How many gram-atoms of the element are contained in each of the following:
(a) 94.5 g of Al; (b) 18.2 g of Cr; (c) 983.5 g of Si; (d) 0.8505 g of Mg?
Ans. (a) 3.5 g-atoms; (b) 0.35 g-atom; (c) 35 g-atoms; (d) 0.035 g-atom.

4-2. Determine (a) the number of gram-atoms of Ba in 34.35 g of Ba and (b) the number of grams of Ba in 5 g-atoms of Ba.
Ans. (a) 0.25 g-atom; (b) 687.0 g.

4-3. Determine (a) the number of grams of Li in 2.5 g-atoms of Li and (b) the number of gram-atoms of Pb in 116.03 g of Pb.
Ans. (a) 17.2 g; (b) 0.56 g-atom.

4-4. (a) How many gram-moles of silver chloride are contained in 100.38 g of this substance? (b) How many grams of silver chloride would be contained in 2.5 g-moles of this substance? *Ans.* (a) 7 g-moles; (b) 358.5 g.

4-5. Determine (a) the number of gram-moles of barium chloride that would be contained in 114.62 g of this salt and (b) the number of grams of barium chloride contained in 3.5 g-moles of this salt.
Ans. (a) 0.55 g-mole; (b) 729.4 g.

4-6. Calculate (a) the number of grams of aluminum sulfate contained in 0.25 g-moles of this salt and (b) the number of gram-moles of aluminum sulfate in 126.65 g of this salt. *Ans.* (a) 85.6 g; (b) 0.37 g-mole.

4-7. Determine (a) the number of ounce-moles of ammonium sulfate that would be present in 343.5 oz of this salt and (b) the number of ounces of ammonium sulfate in 0.25 oz-mole of this salt. *Ans.* (a) 2.6 oz-moles; (b) 33.0 oz.

4-8. (a) Calculate the number of gram-moles of calcium oxide that could be obtained from 42.54 g of calcium carbonate, and (b) convert the number of gram-moles of calcium oxide obtained in (a) to grams of calcium oxide.
Ans. (b) 23.8 g.

4-9. (a) How many gram-moles of phosphorus pentoxide can be obtained from 5 g-atoms of phosphorus? (b) Convert the number of gram-moles of phosphorus pentoxide obtained in (a) to grams of this substance.
Ans. (b) 35.5 g.

4-10. (a) How many gram-atoms of sulfur are contained in 35.025 g of barium sulfate? (b) Convert this number of gram-atoms of sulfur to grams of sulfur. *Ans.* (b) 4.82 g.

4-11. (a) Determine the number of ounce-moles of phosphorus that can be obtained from 173.8 oz of calcium phosphate. (Note that a molecule of phosphorus contains 4 atoms.) (b) Convert the number of ounce-moles of phosphorus determined in (a) to ounces of phosphorus.
Ans. (b) 34.7 oz.

4-12. (a) Calculate the number of pound-atoms of sulfur required to prepare 2.08 tons of pure H_2SO_4. (b) Convert the number of pound-atoms of sulfur obtained in (a) to pounds of sulfur. *Ans.* (b) 1361 lb.

4-13. (a) How many pound-atoms of aluminum can be obtained from 10 tons of bauxite ore which contains 65 per cent pure aluminum oxide? (b) How many pounds of aluminum can be obtained from the number of pound-atoms of aluminum found in part (a)? *Ans.* (a) 254.8 lb-atoms.

4-14. Calculate (a) the number of ton-moles of calcium carbonate that can theoretically be obtained from 100 tons of limestone that is 95 per cent pure $CaCO_3$. (b) How many tons of quick lime (96 per cent pure CaO) can be obtained from the number of ton-moles of calcium carbonate found in (a)?

Ans. (b) 55.5 tons.

4-15. (a) Determine the number of pound-moles of phosphorus (P_4) that can be obtained from 1 ton of phosphate rock [impure $Ca_3(PO_4)_2$] that analyzes 33.5 per cent P_2O_5. (b) Convert the number of pound-moles of phosphorus found in (a) to pounds of phosphorus. *Ans.* (b) 292.6 lb.

4-16. Determine (a) the number of gram-atoms of magnesium and (b) the number of atoms in 63.2 g of Mg.

4-17. (a) How many gram-atoms of silver are contained in 59.34 g of Ag? (b) How many atoms of silver does this weight of silver represent?

4-18. Determine (a) the number of gram-moles of aluminum chloride and (b) the number of molecules in 34.71 g of this salt.

4-19. Calculate (a) the number of gram-moles of silver nitrate and (b) the number of molecules in 21.24 g of this substance.

4-20. Determine (a) the number of gram-atoms, (b) the number of gram-moles, and (c) the number of molecules in 76.9 g of phosphorus (P_4).

4-21. (a) How many pound-moles of water would be contained in 1 ton of this substance? (b) How many ounce-moles of zinc oxide would be present in 100 lb of this compound?

4-22. Calculate (a) the number of kilogram-moles of calcium chloride in 655.5 g of this salt. (b) Calculate the number of pounds of calcium chloride in 3.5 ton-moles of this salt.

4-23. (a) How many gram-atoms of iron are contained in 39.9 g of ferric oxide? (b) Convert this number of gram-atoms of iron to grams of iron.

4-24. Given 68.4 g of chromium oxide. (a) Calculate the number of gram-atoms of chromium that could be obtained from this weight of chromium oxide. (b) Convert the number of gram-atoms in (a) to grams of chromium.

4-25. Given 79.80 g of ferric oxide and 69.42 g of ferrous-ferric oxide (Fe_3O_4), (a) calculate the number of gram-atoms of iron present in each of these weights of iron oxides, and (b) convert the respective gram-atoms of iron obtainable in (a) to grams of iron.

4-26. An iron blast furnace in a day will use 1,000 tons of hematite ore that contains 50 per cent pure ferric oxide. (a) How many ton-atoms of iron can be obtained from this weight of ore? (b) Convert the number of ton-atoms of iron determined in (a) to tons of pig iron that is 94 per cent iron.

4-27. Determine the number of pounds of chromite ore containing 42 per cent Cr_2O_3 that is required to obtain 2,600 lb of chromium.

4-28. Calculate the tonnage of hematite ore containing 53.5 per cent Fe_2O_3 that will be required to make 100,000 tons of pig iron, 94 per cent Fe.

4-29. A sample of a soluble sulfate weighing 1.023 g was treated with excess barium chloride solution. The precipitate of $BaSO_4$ obtained weighed 1.509 g. Calculate the percentage of sulfur in the original sample.

4-30. A sample of brass weighing 2.6235 g is dissolved in nitric acid, and the lead, an impurity in the brass, is precipitated as $PbSO_4$. The precipitate of lead sulfate obtained weighed 0.0147 g. Calculate the percentage of lead in this sample of brass.

CHAPTER V

THE MEASUREMENT OF TEMPERATURE

OUTLINE

Measurement of temperature.
Thermometric scales.
Absolute zero.
Absolute temperature.   Kelvin scale.   Rankine scale.

The temperature of a body specifies its state with respect to its ability to transfer heat to other bodies and is usually expressed in degrees on one of the three scales: (*a*) centigrade; (*b*) Fahrenheit; (*c*) absolute.

The **centigrade** (C, from Latin *centum*, hundred, and *gradus*, degree) scale was proposed by Celsius in 1742, and is sometimes called by his name.

The **Fahrenheit** scale was suggested by Fahrenheit in 1724.

Comparison of the three scales may be made by considering on each the freezing point and boiling point of pure water, as follows:

Scale		Freezing point of pure water	Boiling point of pure water
Centigrade...........................		0°	100°
Fahrenheit...........................		32°	212°
Absolute	Kelvin......................	273.16°	373.16°
	Rankine.....................	492°	672°

The Fahrenheit scale (°F) is in common use in our domestic life. The centigrade (°C) and the absolute scales are used almost exclusively in the scientific world.

A comparison of the two most commonly used thermometric scales, *i.e.*, Fahrenheit and centigrade, may be made by considering the freezing point (fp) and the boiling point (bp) of pure water on each scale, as shown graphically in Fig. 2.

Between the freezing point and boiling point of pure water there are 100 centigrade degrees, or 180 Fahrenheit degrees; hence,

$$1°C = {}^{180}\!/_{100} = {}^{9}\!/_{5}°F$$
$$1°F = {}^{100}\!/_{180} = {}^{5}\!/_{9}°C$$

The ratio of the differences between the freezing point and the boiling point of water on the centigrade and Fahrenheit scales can be expressed by the formula

$$\frac{°C}{°F - 32} = \frac{100}{180} = \frac{5}{9}$$
$$°C = {}^{5}\!/_{9}(°F - 32)$$
$$°F = {}^{9}\!/_{5}(°C) + 32$$

To some workers the use of these formulas is considered an inconvenience, and a simplification of the method of conversion from one temperature scale to the other has been suggested,[1] based on the following: (a) that the relative magnitude of the two kinds of degrees is in the ratio of 9:5 and (b) that the number −40° expresses the same temperature on both scales. Figure 2 shows the three equivalent points on each of the two thermometric scales. It should be noted that the ratios of the degree distance between these points °F:°C (*i.e.*, 180:100 and 72:40), reduced to lowest terms, are 9:5. The simplification rule follows: (a) To the given temperature add 40; (b)

Fig. 2.

multiply this sum by ⁵⁄₉ or ⁹⁄₅; (c) from this product subtract 40. The remainder is the temperature expressed in the other scale. The proper fraction is readily selected if one realizes that there are more degrees Fahrenheit than degrees centigrade for a given interval. Thus, in converting degrees centigrade to degrees Fahrenheit the fraction is ⁹⁄₅; and, vice versa, from degrees Fahrenheit to degrees centigrade the fraction is ⁵⁄₉.

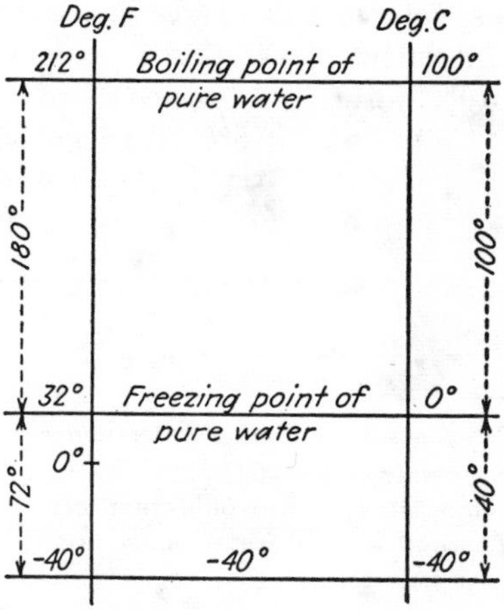

Expressed mathematically, the relation becomes

$$\frac{°F + 40}{180} = \frac{°C + 40}{100} \qquad \text{or} \qquad \frac{°F + 40}{9} = \frac{°C + 40}{5}$$

Then

$$°C = (°F + 40){}^{5}\!/_{9} - 40 \qquad \text{and} \qquad °F = (°C + 40){}^{9}\!/_{5} - 40$$

Shaw, H. G., *J. Chem. Educ.*, **8**, 729 (1931).

Example. What temperature on the centigrade scale corresponds to 120°F?

Employing the formula °C = $\frac{5}{9}$(F° − 32),

$$°C = \frac{5}{9}(120 − 32) = 48.8 \quad \text{or} \quad 120°F = 48.8°C$$

Alternate Solution. Using the formula °C = (°F + 40)$\frac{5}{9}$ − 40,

$$°C = (120 + 40)\frac{5}{9} − 40 = 48.8 \quad \text{or} \quad 120°F = 48.8°C$$

ABSOLUTE ZERO

It is a familiar fact that when a definite quantity of gas is subjected to an increase in temperature (at constant pressure), the volume will increase; and that if the temperature is lowered (at constant pressure), the volume will decrease. With a given volume of a gas at 0°C, experiment shows that it expands approximately $\frac{1}{273}$ of its volume at 0°C for each degree centigrade that it is heated. Thus, if we have 273 ml of gas at 0°C and increase the temperature to 100°C (at constant pressure), the volume will increase $\frac{100}{273}$ of its volume at 0°C, or 273 ml + ($\frac{100}{273}$ × 273) = 373 ml. Also, if we start with 273 ml

	°R	°F	°C	°K	Volume, ml
Temperature of boiling water under pressure of 1 atm	672	212	100	373	373
Temperature of an equilibrium mixture of ice and water under pressure of 1 atm	492	32	0	273	273
	460	0	−17.8	255.2	255.2
	420	−40	−40	233	233
Absolute zero	0	−460	−273	0	0

Fig. 3. Equivalent points on thermometric scales.

of gas at 0°C and it is cooled to −100°C (at constant pressure), the volume will be decreased by $\frac{1}{273}$ for each degree that it is cooled; *i.e.*, 273 ml − ($\frac{100}{273}$ × 273) = 173 ml. Again, if we have 273 ml of gas at 0°C and could lower the temperature to −273°C, the volume would be zero. This point (−273°C or, more accurately, −273.16°C) on the centigrade scale is called the **absolute zero**. . Figure 3 shows the relationship between the volume and temperature changes (at constant pressure) when 273 ml of a gas is confined at 0°C. This, of course, leads directly to the well-known law of Charles: **With pressure remaining constant, the volume of a gas is directly proportional to the absolute temperature (Kelvin).**

All gases liquefy before the temperature of $-273°C$ is reached, and the volume then becomes the volume of the substance in the liquid state. This is small and changes only slightly with further decrease in temperature.

ABSOLUTE TEMPERATURE

A temperature scale which has the **absolute zero** for its starting point is called an "absolute scale." There are two methods employed to express temperatures on the absolute scale: (*a*) the **Kelvin scale** (**°K**), which begins at absolute zero (0°K) with degrees expressed the same as on the centigrade scale, and (*b*) the **Rankine scale** (**°R**), which begins at absolute zero (0°R) with degrees expressed as on the Fahrenheit scale. The **Kelvin scale**, or thermodynamic scale, of temperature is the **absolute centigrade scale**; and the **Rankine scale** of temperature is the **absolute Fahrenheit scale**.

Thus $0°K = -273.16°C$ (usually rounded off to $-273°C$) and $273°K = 0°C$.

Also $0°R = -459.69°F$ (usually rounded off to $-460°F$) and $460°R = 0°F$.

To convert a temperature reading in degrees centigrade to a reading in degrees absolute on the Kelvin scale, it is only necessary to *add algebraically* 273 to the given centigrade reading, or

$$t°C = (t°C + 273)°K \qquad \text{or} \qquad °K = °C + 273$$

To convert a temperature reading in degrees Fahrenheit to a reading in degrees absolute on the Rankine scale, one needs only to *add algebraically* 460 to the given reading on Fahrenheit scale, or

$$t°F = (t°F + 460)°R \qquad \text{or} \qquad °R = °F + 460$$

It has been shown that the ratios of the differences between the temperature of boiling water and the temperature at which water freezes on the centigrade $(100 - 0)$ and Fahrenheit scales $(212 - 32 = 180)$ are expressed as

$$\frac{°C}{°F - 32} = \frac{100}{180} \qquad \text{or} \qquad \frac{°C}{100} = \frac{°F - 32}{180}$$

Since $°K = °C + 273$, or $°C = °K - 273$, it follows that

$$\frac{°C}{100} = \frac{°K - 273}{100}$$

Also $°R = °F + 460$ or $°F = °R - 460$ and $°F - 32 = °R - 492$; then

$$\frac{°F - 32}{180} = \frac{°R - 492}{180}$$

From the foregoing, the relationship for these equivalent points on the various thermometric scales can be expressed as follows:

$$\frac{°C}{100} = \frac{°F - 32}{180} = \frac{°R - 492}{180} = \frac{°K - 273}{100}$$

Example 1.   Convert 68°C to (a) °K and (b) °R.
(a) Since

$$\frac{°C}{100} = \frac{°K - 273}{100} \quad \text{or} \quad °C = °K - 273 \quad \text{or} \quad °K = °C + 273$$

$$68°C = (68 + 273)°K = 341°K$$

(b) Since

$$\frac{°C}{100} = \frac{°R - 492}{180}$$

$$\frac{68}{100} = \frac{°R - 492}{180}$$

$$°R = \tfrac{180}{100}(68) + 492 = 614.4°$$

Alternate Solution.   68°C = 154.4°F.
Since °R = °F + 460,

$$154.4°F = (154.4 + 460)°R = 614.4°R$$

Example 2.   Convert 100°F to (a) °K and (b) °R.
(a) Since

$$\frac{°F - 32}{180} = \frac{°K - 273}{100}$$

$$\frac{100 - 32}{180} = \frac{°K - 273}{100}$$

$$°K = \tfrac{100}{180}(68) + 273 = 310.8°$$

Alternate Solution.   100°F = 37.8°C.
Since °K = °C + 273,

$$37.8°C = (37.8 + 273)°K = 310.8°K$$

(b) Since

$$\frac{°F - 32}{180} = \frac{°R - 492}{180} \quad \text{or} \quad °F - 32 = °R - 492$$

$$°F = °R - 460$$

or

$$°R = °F + 460$$

then

$$100°F = (100 + 460)°R = 560°R$$

It should be emphasized that the freezing point of pure water (1 atm) is 0°C, or 32°F. These temperatures expressed on the two absolute temperature scales would be

$$0°C = (0 + 273)°K = 273°K$$
$$32°F = (32 + 460)°R = 492°R$$

Problems

5-1. Convert 160°C to (a) °F, (b) °K, and (c) °R.
Ans. (a) 320°F; (b) 433°K; (c) 780°R.

5-2. Convert −180°C to (a) °F; (b) °K, and (c) °R.
Ans. (a) −292°F; (b) 93°K; (c) 168°R.

5-3. Make the following temperature conversions of 86°F to (a) °C, (b) °K, and (c) °R. *Ans.* (a) 30°C; (b) 303°K; (c) 546°R

5-4. Make the following temperature conversions of −90°F to (a) °C, (b) °K and (c) °R. *Ans.* (a) −67.8°C; (b) 205.2°K; (c) 370°R.

5-5. Convert 298°K to (a) °C, (b) °F, and (c) °R.
Ans. (a) 25°C; (b) 77°F; (c) 537°R.

5-6. Convert 223°K to (a) °C, (b) °F, and (c) °R.
Ans. (a) −50°C; (b) −58°F; (c) 402°R.

5-7. Convert 552°R to (a) °F, (b) °C, and (c) °K.
Ans. (a) 92°F; (b) 33.3°C; (c) 306.3°K.

5-8. Convert 330°R to (a) °F, (b) °C, and (c) °K.
Ans. (a) −130°F; (b) −90°C; (c) 183°K.

5-9. Calculate the temperature on the Fahrenheit scale that corresponds to exactly five times the reading on the centigrade scale. *Ans.* +50°F.

5-10. Ethyl alcohol (1) freezes at −117.6°C and (2) boils at 78.4°C. Determine the corresponding temperatures on (a) the Kelvin scale and (b) the Rankine scale. *Ans.* (1b) 280.3°R; (2b) 633.1°R.

5-11. During an experiment, a Fahrenheit thermometer showed a temperature change of 30°. Calculate the value of this temperature change in centigrade degrees. *Ans.* 16.66°C.

5-12. Convert 100°F to (a) °C, (b) °K, and (c) °R.

5-13. Convert 1750°F to (a) °C, (b) °K, and (c) °R.

5-14. Convert 212°C to (a) °F, (b) °R, and (c) °K.

5-15. Convert 32°C to (a) °F, (b) °R, and (c) °K.

5-16. Convert 343°K to (a) °C, (b) °F, and (c) °R.

5-17. Convert 83°K to (a) °C, (b) °F, and (c) °R.

5-18. Convert 475.6°R to (a) °F, (b) °C, and (c) °K.

5-19. Convert 60°R to (a) °F, (b) °C, and (c) °K.

5-20. The melting point of tungsten is 3370°C. Express this temperature on (a) the Fahrenheit scale, and (b) the Rankine scale.

5-21. Liquid oxygen boils at −297.4°F. Express this temperature on (a) the centigrade scale and (b) the Kelvin scale.

5-22. The melting point of magnesia (MgO) is 5072°F. Express this temperature on (a) the centigrade scale and (b) the Kelvin scale.

5-23. In the blank spaces supply the temperature conversion for the following:
(a) −40°F corresponds to _____°C, _____°K, _____°R.
(b) 173°K corresponds to _____°C, _____°F, _____°R.

5-24. In the blank spaces supply the temperature conversion for the following:
(a) −50°C corresponds to _____°F, _____°K, _____°R.
(b) 610°R corresponds to _____°F, _____°C, _____°K.

5-25. Determine whether −100°C is a higher or lower temperature than −166°F.

5-26. Given the two readings 1760°C and 3164°F, which is the lower temperature reading?

5-27. Determine whether 800°F is a higher or lower temperature than 460°C.

5-28. Of the two readings −5°C and 20°F, which represents the higher temperature?

5-29. Determine whether 1073°K is a higher or lower temperature than 1490°F.

5-30. Of the two readings 403°K and 708°R, which represents the higher temperature?

5-31. Determine whether 4470°R is a higher or lower temperature than 2473°K.

5-32. The temperature of the hydrogen-fluorine flame is said to be about 8000°F, and is capable of melting every known substance on earth. What is the corresponding reading on (a) the centigrade, (b) Kelvin, and (c) Rankine scales?

CHAPTER VI

EFFECT OF CHANGES IN PRESSURE AND TEMPERATURE ON THE VOLUME OF GASES

OUTLINE

Boyle's law.   Volume of a gas is inversely proportional to the pressure if temperature is kept constant.

Standard pressure.

Charles' law.   Volume of a gas is directly proportional to the absolute temperature if pressure is kept constant.

Standard temperature.

Standard conditions (STP).

Effect of changes of both pressure and temperature on the volume of gases.

Density of gases.   Effect of changes in pressure and temperature on the density of a gas.

Dalton's law.   Partial pressure.   The total pressure of a mixture of gases may be regarded as the sum of the pressures that each gas would exert if it alone occupied the entire space.

Vapor pressure of water.   Correction for difference in levels.

BOYLE'S LAW

Very careful measurements have indicated that the molecules of which substances are composed are very nearly incompressible; *i.e.*, when subjected to tremendous pressure each molecule contracts only a very small amount in size.   Solids and liquids decrease only slightly in volume when subjected to tremendous pressure.   This indicates that in solids and liquids the molecules are packed closely together. In the case of gases, one naturally assumes that the molecules are separated from one another.   This assumption is confirmed by the fact that the volume of a gas is decreased by increasing the pressure on the gas.   It is known that the molecules of gases are moving, that they are traveling in sensibly straight lines at high speeds, colliding, rebounding, and continuing their travel in other directions.   It is assumed that they are perfectly elastic, in accord with the fact that no energy is lost by the collisions.   A great many of the molecules are, of course, continually colliding with the walls of the vessel.   These repeated collisions exert a pressure (the force per unit area) on the walls and balance the pressure acting on the gas.   Thus, consider a gas contained in a cylinder subject to a pressure P as shown in Fig. 4.

The pressure caused by the collision of the particles against the walls balances the pressure P and prevents the piston from moving

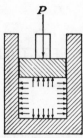

down. The speed of a molecule is dependent on the temperature. The higher the temperature, the greater the speed of the molecule, and consequently the greater the energy that it possesses. If a gas is heated, the speed of the molecules is increased, the energy is increased, the number of collisions per minute is increased, and the pressure on the walls, due to collisions with the walls, is increased. If the temperature is decreased, the speed of the molecules is decreased, their energy is decreased, the number of collisions per minute on the walls is decreased, and the pressure on the walls is decreased. Thus, the pressure of the gas varies directly with temperature, or P is proportional to T.

Fig. 4

If the temperature of the gas is kept constant and the pressure increased, the molecules will be crowded together; *i.e.*, the volume of the gas will be decreased. Because of this crowding, the collisions will become more frequent as the molecules are brought closer together, and the increased number of collisions will cause increased pressure on the walls sufficient to balance the increased external pressure.

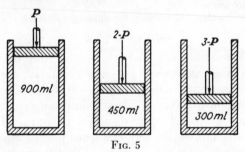

Fig. 5

The numerical effect of increase of pressure upon the volume of gases was first found by Boyle in 1660. Boyle compressed air in the short closed leg of a U tube, using varying amounts of mercury as a compressing agent. He concluded from his experiments that, temperature remaining constant, the volume of a given mass of gas is inversely proportional to the pressure, or V is proportional to $1/P$. This relation is known as the law of Boyle. It may be illustrated as follows:

Consider a cylinder (Fig. 5) containing 900 ml of a gas at a stated temperature, under a pressure P. If the pressure is doubled (temperature remaining constant), the gas will be compressed until it occupies one-half its original volume; *i.e.*, its volume under a pressure $2P$ will be

450 ml. If the pressure is increased to $3P$ (temperature remaining constant), the volume will be reduced to 300 ml, and so on.

It will be noticed from the foregoing illustration that, at constant temperature, the pressure multiplied by the volume of a mass of gas is constant, or $P \times V =$ constant.

STANDARD PRESSURE

It is a familiar fact that the pressure of the atmosphere fluctuates from day to day. The instrument used for measuring atmospheric pressures is known as a **barometer** and originated in 1644 with E. Torricelli. In its simplest form a barometer consists of a straight glass tube about 8.5 mm in diameter and 80 to 85 cm in length, closed at one end. It is completely filled with purified mercury, which is boiled in the tube in order to eliminate any entrapped air or moisture and then with a stopper held against its open end it is placed under the surface of the mercury in a shallow open vessel and the tube inverted. It will be noticed that the mercury falls in the tube to a height of approximately 76 cm (29.92 in.) above the level of the mercury in the dish. The space in the tube above the mercury is familiarly known as "Torricelli's vacuum." It is of interest to note that Torricelli concluded that the column of mercury was maintained at this height (76 cm) by the atmosphere pressing down on the surface of the mercury in the open vessel.

Since the pressure of the atmosphere varies greatly with altitude and with varying weather conditions, it follows naturally that volumes (and densities) of gas are subjected to changes. As a basis for comparison of volumes (and densities) of gases, it is customary to refer to the **normal,** or **standard, pressure.** This is equal to the pressure exerted by the weight of a column of mercury of unit cross-sectional area and 760 mm high at sea level, which is approximately the average pressure of the atmosphere at sea level, and is called "one atmosphere" (atm).

The pressure exerted by any column of liquid is equal to the height multiplied by the density of liquid. In the cgs system:

Height (cm) $\times$ density of liquid (g/cu cm)
$\qquad\qquad$ = pressure in g/sq cm, or grams per square centimeter

Thus a column of mercury (density 13.596 g/cu cm) 76 cm in height exerts a pressure of 1 atm, or

$$1 \text{ atm} = 76 \text{ cm} \times 13.596 \text{ g/cu cm} = 1{,}033.3 \text{ g/sq cm}$$

In the English system:

Height (in.) × density of liquid (lb/cu in.)
          = pressure in lb/sq in., or pounds per square inch (psi)

Since 76 cm Hg = 29.92 in. Hg, and the density of mercury is 0.490 lb/cu in.

1 atm = 29.92 in. × 0.490 lb/cu in. = 14.7 lb/sq in., or 14.7 psi

In 1940, the United States Weather Bureau adopted the procedure of expressing barometric pressure in terms of pressure units (force per unit area), in addition to the usual practice of expressing pressure in terms of units of length, *i.e.*, inches of mercury and millimeters of mercury. The absolute pressure unit adopted by meteorologists was the **bar,** which is a force of one million dynes per square centimeter. The working unit is the **millibar** (**mb**) which is 0.001 bar, and 1,000 mb falls within the range of normal atmospheric pressures. Thus

1 atm (sea level) = 760 mm Hg = 29.92 in. Hg = 1,013.25 mb

or

1,000 mb = 1 bar = 750 mm Hg

Table IX will serve as a convenient source for conversion of pressure units. It is based on a pressure of 1 atm.

TABLE IX. CONVERSION TABLE FOR PRESSURE

Pounds per square inch	Pounds per square foot	Inches of mercury	Milli-meters of mercury	Centi-meters of mercury	Feet of water	Inches of water
14.7	2,116.8	29.92	760.0	76.0	33.91	406.9
1.0	144.0	2.036	51.706	5.1706	2.307	27.68
0.00694	1.0	0.01413	0.359	0.0359	0.01602	0.19224
0.4913	70.75	1.0	25.40	2.54	1.1322	13.59
0.01934	2.785	0.03937	1.0	0.10	0.0446	0.5352
0.1934	27.85	0.3937	10.0	1.0	0.446	5.352
0.433	62.40	0.8819	22.40	2.24	1.0	12.00
0.03611	5.20	0.0735	1.866	0.1866	0.0833	1.0

EFFECT OF TEMPERATURE

It has been found by experiment that a gas if kept at constant pressure will expand $\frac{1}{273}$ of the volume it occupies at 0°C (273°K) for each 1°C it is heated. Similarly, it will contract $\frac{1}{273}$ of its volume at 0°C for each 1°C it is cooled (pressure kept constant). Thus:

273 ml of any gas at 0°C (273°K)

becomes

274 ml. . . . . at 1°C (274°K)
275 ml. . . . . at 2°C (275°K)
373 ml. . . . . at 100°C (373°K)
272 ml. . . . . at −1°C (272°K)
271 ml. . . . . at −2°C (271°K)
173 ml. . . . . at −100°C (173°K)
 73 ml. . . . . at −200°C (73°K)
 23 ml. . . . . at −250°C (23°K)

If one deals with degrees Fahrenheit, the gas (at constant pressure) will expand $\frac{1}{492}$ of the volume it occupied at 32°F (492°R) for each 1°F it is heated. Also, it will contract $\frac{1}{492}$ of its volume at 32°F (at constant pressure) for each 1°F it is cooled.

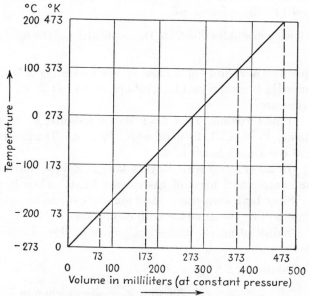

FIG. 6. Graph illustrating the law of Charles.

This relationship between changes in volume with changes in temperature, at constant pressure, led to the following statement: **Pressure remaining constant, the volume of a given mass of gas is directly proportional to the absolute temperature.** It is known as the **law of Charles** (Fig. 6). V is proportional to T and $V/T = a$ constant, if pressure and mass remain fixed.

STANDARD TEMPERATURE

From the foregoing statements of Boyle's law and Charles' law, which relate the interdependency in changes of volume with variations of temperature and pressure, it is customary, for scientific purposes, to reduce all gas volumes to 0°C (32°F) or 273°K (492°R), the temperature of an equilibrium mixture of ice and water under 1 atm pressure, or 760 mm Hg (29.92 in. Hg, or 14.7 psi, or 1,013.25 mb). These temperature and pressure conditions, *i.e.*, 0°C and 760 mm Hg, are called "standard (or normal) conditions of temperature and pressure," and abbreviated STP. Thus, **standard conditions (STP)** for various temperature scales and the common pressure units can be expressed as follows:

0°C and 1 atm
0°C and 760 mm or 76 cm Hg
0°C and 1,013.25 mb
32°F and 29.92 in. Hg
32°F and 14.7 lb/sq in., or psi

The following examples illustrate the application of the fundamental gas laws.

Example 1. A volume of a mass of gas measuring 2.5 l at 21°C and 700 mm Hg is compressed to a volume of 0.5 l at 21°C. What is the final pressure?

Step 1. Initial volume, $V_i = 2.5$ l; initial pressure, $P_i = 700$ mm. Final volume, $V_f = 0.5$ l; final pressure, $P_f = x$. Temperature and mass of gas remain unchanged.

Step 2. In accordance with Boyle's law, $P \times V =$ constant, provided temperature and mass of gas remain fixed. Then $P_i \times V_i = P_f \times V_f$. Since both temperature and mass of gas remain unchanged, the constant will be the same for both conditions.

Step 3. Substituting the numerical values in this expression and solving, let $x = P_f$.

$$700 \text{ mm} \times 2.5 \text{ l} = x \times 0.5 \text{ l}$$

$$x = 700 \text{ mm} \times \frac{2.5 \text{ l}}{0.5 \text{ l}} = 3,500 \text{ mm}$$

It should be noted that since the 2.5 l of gas is compressed to 0.5 l without change in temperature and mass of gas, the final pressure must increase in order to cause the initial volume of gas to occupy a smaller volume; therefore *the initial pressure must be multiplied by a volume fraction which is greater than* 1, *i.e.*, the numerator is greater than the denominator.

Example 2. A gas occupies 3 l, measured at 32°C and atmospheric pressure. What volume will it occupy if the temperature is changed to 18°C, the pressure remaining unchanged?

Step 1.   Express temperature readings to corresponding readings on absolute scale, in this case degrees centigrade to degrees Kelvin. Since °K = °C + 273, then

$$32°C = 32° + 273 = 305°K \qquad \text{and} \qquad 18°C = 18° + 273 = 291°K$$

Step 2.   Initial volume, V_i = 3 l; initial temperature, T_i = 305°K. Final volume, V_f = x; final temperature, T_f = 291°K.   The pressure and mass of gas remain fixed during these changes.

Step 3.   In accordance with Charles' law, V is proportional to T and V/T = constant, provided pressure and mass of gas remain unchanged.   Note that T is expressed in degrees on an absolute scale. Then $V_i/T_i = V_f/T_f$, since the constant is the same for both conditions.   (If pressures were different and the masses were different, the constants would be different.)

Step 4.   Substituting the numerical values for each volume and temperature and solving, one obtains

$$\frac{3 \text{ l}}{305°K} = \frac{x}{291°K}$$

where $x = V_f$.

$$x = 3 \text{ l} \times \frac{291°K}{305°K} = 2.86 \text{ l} = \text{final volume}$$

Note that the gas is cooled from 305 to 291°K, which causes it to contract, provided pressure and mass of gas remain fixed (Charles' law).   Therefore *the initial volume must be multiplied by a temperature fraction less than* 1, *i.e.*, the numerator is smaller than the denominator.

EFFECT OF CHANGES OF BOTH TEMPERATURE AND PRESSURE

The effect of both temperature and pressure changes on the volume of a given mass of gas may be determined by combining the formulas for Boyle's law and Charles' law as follows:

$$\frac{V_i}{V_f} = \frac{T_i \times P_f}{T_f \times P_i}$$

The following examples illustrate these effects.

Example 1.   A certain weight of gas occupies 250 ml at 20°C and 700 mm Hg.   Calculate the volume that this gas will occupy at 5°C and 740 mm Hg.

Step 1.   Express temperature readings to corresponding readings on the absolute scale, in this case degrees centigrade to degrees Kelvin. Since °K = °C + 273, then 20°C = 293°K and 5°C = 278°K.

Step 2. Initial volume, $V_i = 250$ ml; initial temperature, $T_i = 293°K$; initial pressure, $P_i = 700$ mm Hg. Final volume, $V_f = x$; final temperature, $T_f = 278°K$; final pressure, $P_f = 740$ mm Hg.

Step 3. Substituting the numerical values for each of the components in the combined gas-laws formula, one obtains

$$\frac{250 \text{ ml}}{x} = \frac{293°K}{278°K} \times \frac{740 \text{ mm}}{700 \text{ mm}}$$

or

$$x = 250 \text{ ml} \times \frac{278°K}{293°K} \times \frac{700 \text{ mm}}{740 \text{ mm}} = 224 \text{ ml} = \text{final volume}$$

It should also be noted that since the temperature is lowered, this causes the volume to decrease, provided the pressure is unchanged. Thus, *the initial volume is multiplied by a temperature fraction less than* 1. However, the pressure changes from a lower to higher value; then this increase in pressure causes a further decrease in volume and the expression (250 ml $\times$ $278°K/293°K$) *must be multiplied by a pressure fraction less than* 1. Since both fractions are less than 1, the final volume most certainly must be smaller than the initial volume.

Example 2. A certain quantity of a gas measured 500 ml at a temperature of $15°C$ and 750 mm Hg. What pressure is required to compress this quantity of gas into a 400-ml vessel at a temperature of $50°C$?

Step 1. Express temperature readings to corresponding readings on absolute scale, in this case degrees centigrade to degrees Kelvin. Since $°K = °C + 273$, then $15°C = 288°K$ and $50°C = 323°K$.

Step 2. Initial volume, $V_i = 500$ ml; initial temperature, $T_i = 288°K$; initial pressure, $P_i = 750$ mm Hg. Final volume, $V_f = 400$ ml; final temperature, $T_f = 323°K$; final pressure, $P_f = x$.

Step 3. Substituting the numerical values for each of the components in the combined gas-laws expression, one obtains

$$\frac{500 \text{ ml}}{400 \text{ ml}} = \frac{288°K}{323°K} \times \frac{x}{750 \text{ mm}}$$

$$x = 750 \text{ mm} \times \frac{323°K}{288°K} \times \frac{500 \text{ ml}}{400 \text{ ml}} = 1{,}051 \text{ mm}$$

The following logic may be employed to check the foregoing solution. The temperature is raised from 288 to $323°K$. If the volume is kept constant, raising the temperature creates a rise in pressure (P is proportional to T). Thus, *the original pressure must be multiplied by a fraction greater than* 1, or 750 mm $\times$ $323°K/288°K$.

Now, at the higher temperature, 500 ml of the gas is compressed to a volume of 400 ml. In order to accomplish this, the pressure must be *proportionately increased* (if the temperature is kept the same); therefore, to take into account both effects, the pressure must be made 500 ml/400 ml of its former value.

Example 3.   An expansion tank holds 2.5 cu ft of a gas at 72°F and 30 in. Hg.   What temperature, expressed in degrees Fahrenheit, is required to cause the gas to expand to 3.0 cu ft at a pressure of 29.5 in. Hg?

Step 1.   Express temperature reading to corresponding reading on the absolute scale, in this case degrees Fahrenheit to degrees Rankine. Since °R = °F + 460, then 72°F = 532°R.

Step 2.   Initial volume, V_i = 2.5 cu ft; initial temperature, T_i = 532°R; initial pressure, P_i = 30 in. Hg.   Final volume, V_f = 3.0 cu ft; final temperature = x; final pressure, P_f = 29.5 in. Hg, where x = degrees Rankine, °R.

Step 3.   Substituting the numerical values for each of the components in the combined gas-laws expression, one obtains

$$\frac{2.5 \text{ cu ft}}{3.0 \text{ cu ft}} = \frac{532°\text{R}}{x} \times \frac{29.5 \text{ in.}}{30 \text{ in.}}$$

$$x = 532°\text{R} \times \frac{3.0 \text{ cu ft}}{2.5 \text{ cu ft}} \times \frac{29.5 \text{ in.}}{30 \text{ in.}} = 627°\text{R}$$

Step 4.   Since °F = °R − 460, then °F = 627° − 460 = 167°F.

The following logic may be employed to check the foregoing solution.

First, consider the change in temperature with change in volume with constant pressure.   Since the initial volume increases from 2.5 cu ft to 3.0 cu ft, the temperature must increase if pressure is constant.   Then *the initial temperature* (532°R) *must be multiplied by a volume fraction greater than* 1, or 532°R × 3.0 cu ft/2.5 cu ft.

Second, consider the change in temperature with change in pressure. Since the initial pressure decreases from 30 in. Hg to 29.5 in. Hg, and T is proportional to P, *the intermediate temperature*, 532°R × 3.0 cu ft/2.5 cu ft, *must be multiplied by a pressure fraction less than* 1, or 29.5 in./30 in.

Problems

6-1. A volume of helium measuring 550 ml at a pressure of 758 mm Hg is subjected to a pressure of 1½ times the original pressure, the temperature remaining constant.   What will be the new volume?   *Ans.*   367 ml.

6-2. A gas occupying a volume of 500 ml at a pressure of 755 mm Hg was allowed to expand until the volume measured 755 ml, the temperature remaining constant.   What is the final pressure of the gas?   *Ans.*   500 mm Hg.

6-3. A volume of oxygen measuring 360 ml at 27°C is cooled to −23°C, the pressure remaining constant.   Determine the final volume.   *Ans.*   300 ml.

6-4. If 253 ml of a gas at 20°C is heated to 100°C, the pressure remaining constant, what will be the final volume?   *Ans.*   322 ml.

6-5. A container holds 11.5 cu ft of gas at 72°F and 1 atm pressure. What would this volume measure at standard conditions? *Ans.* 10.6 cu ft.

6-6. If 149 ml of a gas is measured at 25°C and 755 mm Hg, what will be the volume of the gas at standard conditions? *Ans.* 136 ml.

6-7. A gas occupying a volume of 333 ml at 25°C exerts a pressure of 750 mm Hg. If the conditions are changed to −11°C and 730 mm Hg, what will be the new volume? *Ans.* 301 ml.

6-8. A cylinder holds 10 cu ft of hydrogen under a pressure of 1,650 psi and at a temperature of 85°F. What volume would this hydrogen occupy at 32°F and 14.7 psi (STP)? *Ans.* 1,013 cu ft.

6-9. A volume of gas measuring 700 ml at 30°C and 745 mm Hg is compressed to a volume of 350 ml at 20°C. Calculate the new pressure to which the gas must be subjected. *Ans.* 1,441 mm.

6-10. What pressure in atmospheres must be applied to a body of gas in order that its volume may measure 100 ml at 21°C, when its volume at 18°C and 758 mm Hg is 250 ml? *Ans.* 2.51 atm.

6-11. Calculate the temperature necessary to expand 200 ml of a gas at 0°C and pressure of 750 mm Hg to a volume of 250 ml at 740 mm Hg. *Ans.* 63.7°C.

6-12. Calculate the temperature (°C) necessary to reduce 250 ml of dry air at 22°C and 755 mm Hg to a volume of 100 ml at a pressure of 700 mm Hg. *Ans.* −164°C.

6-13. Calculate the volume of nitrogen, collected at a temperature of 77°F and a pressure of 14.7 psi, required to fill 10 steel cylinders, each cylinder having a capacity of 2 cu ft and holding the gas under a pressure of 2,000 psi at 70°F. *Ans.* 2,757 cu ft.

6-14. Acetylene is obtainable in steel cylinders (holding 2.75 cu ft), which are packed with a porous filler saturated with acetone in which the acetylene is dissolved under a pressure of 250 psi at 70°F. Calculate the volume in cubic feet of acetylene at 70°F and pressure of 14.7 psi necessary to fill one of these cylinders. *Ans.* 46.8 cu ft.

6-15. Calculate the number of steel cylinders, each holding 200 cu ft of helium under a pressure of 1,800 psi at 70°F, required to furnish sufficient helium to fill a dirigible of 2,500,000 cu ft capacity at a pressure of 14.7 psi at 77°F. *Ans.* 100.6 cylinders.

6-16. A container holding a volume of air measuring 2.5 cu ft at 68°F was heated to 300°F at constant pressure. What would be the volume of the heated air?

6-17. What volume will 40 cu ft of hydrogen, measured at a pressure of 30 in. Hg, occupy under a pressure of 28 in. Hg, the temperature remaining constant?

6-18. A volume of gas measures 200 ml at 21°C and 760 mm Hg. If the volume is increased 2½ times the initial volume without change in pressure, what temperature must be attained?

6-19. A volume of hydrogen measures 2.5 l at standard conditions. What will the volume measure at 21°C and 750 mm Hg?

6-20. Given 100 ml of a gas at 32°C and 760 mm Hg, what will be the volume at −10°C and 750 mm Hg?

6-21. A volume of hydrogen sulfide measures 5 cu ft at 20°F and 30.3 in. Hg. What will the volume measure at standard conditions?

6-22. If 270 cu ft of air at 65°F and 30.7 in. Hg is cooled to −10°F and 29.0 in. Hg, what is the new volume?

6-23. A flask can stand an internal pressure equivalent to 2,500 mm Hg. It is filled with a gas at 21°C and 758 mm Hg. Above what temperature will it burst?

6-24. A volume of gas measuring 200 ml at 200°C and a pressure of 700 mm Hg was cooled to 2°C, and the volume increased to 400 ml. Calculate the new pressure.

6-25. Calculate the decrease in temperature (°C) necessary to reduce 370 ml of argon at 21°C and 755 mm Hg to a volume of 200 ml at a pressure of 745 mm Hg.

6-26. A glass flask having a volume of 200 ml is filled with helium at a pressure of 725 mm Hg at 21°C. The flask is heated to 200°C. Calculate the internal pressure on the flask.

6-27. A volume of gas measuring 700 ml at 30°C and 745 mm Hg is compressed to a volume of 350 ml at 20°C. Calculate the new pressure to which the gas must be subjected.

6-28. Calculate the pressure that must be applied to a gas at a temperature of 18°C in order that its volume may remain the same as it does under standard conditions.

6-29. A volume of nitrogen under a pressure of 10 atm is allowed to expand to twice its original volume, at a pressure of 1 atm. After the expansion the temperature of the gas is 10°F. What was its original temperature in degrees centigrade?

6-30. A flask while open to the air is heated from room temperature (21°C) to 200°C, and the barometric pressure is 755 mm. The flask is then stoppered and cooled to 28°C. Calculate the final pressure in the flask.

6-31. A balloon is filled with helium at 20°C and 1 atm pressure. The balloon rises until its volume is doubled. The temperature at this altitude is −5°C. What is the pressure in millimeters of mercury at this altitude?

DENSITY OF GASES

The **density** of a gas is the weight in grams of 1 l of the gas at standard conditions of temperature and pressure.

Since 1 l of air at 0°C and 760 mm Hg (STP) weighs 1.293 g, the density of air is then 1.293 g/l (STP).

Example 1. The density of air at STP is 1.293 g/l. What is the density expressed in ounces per cubic foot at 32°F and 760 mm Hg (STP)?

Since 1 g = 0.0352 oz and 1 cu ft = 28.3 l, the *conversion factors* are 0.0352 oz/g and 28.3 l/cu ft, then

$$\frac{1.293 \text{ g}}{1 \text{ l}} = \frac{1.293 \text{ g}}{1 \text{ l}} \times \frac{0.0352 \text{ oz}}{1 \text{ g}} \times \frac{28.3 \text{ l}}{1 \text{ cu ft}} = \frac{1.29 \text{ oz}}{1 \text{ cu ft}}$$

Example 2. A volume of carbon dioxide measuring 2,600 ml at STP was found to weigh 5.148 g. Calculate the density (g/l at STP) of carbon dioxide.

$$\text{Density} = \text{mass per unit volume} = \frac{5.148 \text{ g}}{2.6 \text{ l(STP)}} = 1.98 \text{ g/l(STP)}$$

EFFECT OF CHANGES IN PRESSURE AND TEMPERATURE
ON THE DENSITY OF A GAS

In previous paragraphs it has been stated that the volume of a gas varies directly with the absolute temperature (V is proportional to T, Charles' law) and inversely with pressure (V is proportional to $1/P$, Boyle's law). The density of a gas will also vary with changes in temperature and pressure, since density is defined as mass per unit volume, and any change in volume will cause a change in the density of the gas.

When a gas is compressed at constant temperature, the volume decreases proportionately. The weight remains the same, *i.e.*, the same weight of gas occupies a smaller volume, density (mass per unit volume) thereby being increased. Thus, suppose that the 900 ml of gas (Fig. 5) in the cylinder weighs 4.5 g. The density is 4.5 g/900 ml = 0.005 g/ml, or 5 g/l.

When the volume is decreased to 450 ml by doubling the pressure, the density becomes 4.5 g/450 ml = 0.01 g/ml, or 10 g/l. The total weight of the gas remains the same, 4.5 g; therefore, by doubling the pressure the density is doubled. Thus the **density of a gas is directly proportional to the pressure,** or D is proportional to P, at constant temperature.

It can be shown that changes in temperature also affect the density of gases. Everyone is familiar with the fact that in a warm room the air found close to the ceiling is warmer than that near the floor. Warm air has a lower density than cold air. Hence it rises.

Increase in temperature causes the volume of a given mass of gas to increase. The *mass per unit volume*, *i.e.*, the density of the gas, will therefore decrease as the temperature is raised. However, the total weight of the gas remains the same. Stated otherwise, the **density of a gas varies inversely as the absolute temperature,** or D is proportional to $1/T$.

The combined effect of changes in both temperature and pressure on the density of a gas can be formulated as follows.

Initial density = D_i, final density = D_f, initial temperature in absolute degrees = T_i, final temperature in absolute degrees = T_f, initial pressure = P_i, and final pressure = P_f. Keeping in mind that D is proportional to $1/T$ and D is proportional to P,

$$\frac{D_i}{D_f} = \frac{T_f}{T_i} \times \frac{P_i}{P_f} \quad \text{or} \quad D_f = D_i \times \frac{T_i}{T_f} \times \frac{P_f}{P_i}$$

Example 1. The density of helium is 0.1782 g/l at STP. Calculate the density of this gas at 25°C and 740 mm Hg.

Step 1. Express temperature readings to corresponding readings on absolute scale, in this case degrees centigrade to degrees Kelvin, or $°K = °C + 273$. Standard temperature $= 0°C = 273°K$, and $25°C = 298°K$.

Step 2. Initial density, $D_i = 0.1782$ g/l; final density, $D_f = x$; initial temperature, $T_i = 273°K$; final temperature, $T_f = 298°K$; initial pressure, $P_i = 760$ mm Hg; final pressure, $P_f = 740$ mm Hg.

Step 3. Substituting the numerical values for each of the components in the expression giving the change in density with changes in temperature and pressure, one obtains

$$x = \frac{0.1782 \text{ g}}{1 \text{ l}} \times \frac{273°K}{298°K} \times \frac{740 \text{ mm}}{760 \text{ mm}} = 0.1588 \text{ g/l}$$

$$= \text{density He at } 25°C \text{ and } 740 \text{ mm Hg}$$

The following reasoning may be employed in solving the foregoing problem. The temperature is raised from 273 to 298°K. This will cause the initial density of the gas to decrease. To accomplish this numerically, *the initial density must be multiplied by a temperature fraction less than* 1, or 0.1782 g/l $\times 273°K/298°K$.

Now simultaneous with this increase in temperature is a decrease in pressure which causes the density to become still smaller, or 0.1782 g/l $\times 273°K/298°K$ *must be multiplied by a pressure fraction less than* 1, or 740 mm/760 mm. Since both fractions are numerically less than 1, the final density must be numerically smaller than the initial density.

Example 2. A certain cylinder contains 6 cu ft of argon at a pressure of 1,725 psi and temperature of 72°F. What is the weight in pounds of argon in the cylinder? The density of argon is 0.1114 lb/cu ft at STP.

Step 1. Convert degrees Fahrenheit to degrees Rankine, using the expression $°R = °F + 460$, or standard temperature $= 32°F = 492°R$ and $72°F = 532°R$.

Step 2. Initial density, $D_i = 0.1114$ lb/cu ft; final density, $D_f = x$; initial temperature, $T_i = 492°R$; final temperature $= T_f = 532°R$; initial pressure (standard pressure), $P_i = 14.7$ psi; final pressure, $P_f = 1,725$ psi.

Step 3. Substituting the numerical values for each of the components in the expression for obtaining the change in density with changes in temperature and pressure, one obtains

$$x = \frac{0.1114 \text{ lb}}{1 \text{ cu ft}} \times \frac{492°R}{532°R} \times \frac{1,725 \text{ psi}}{14.7 \text{ psi}} = 12.1 \text{ lb/cu ft}$$

$$= \text{density of gas at } 72°F \text{ and } 1,725 \text{ psi}$$

Step 4. There is 6 cu ft of argon in the cylinder at 72°F and 1,725 psi; then

$$\frac{12.1 \text{ lb}}{1 \text{ cu ft}} \times 6 \text{ cu ft} = 72.6 \text{ lb} = \text{weight of argon in cylinder}$$

To check the solution in determining the final density, the following reasoning may be employed. First, consider the effect of temperature change on the density. The temperature is increased from 492 to 532°R. This increase in temperature will cause the initial density to decrease; therefore *the initial density must be multiplied by a temperature fraction less than* 1, or 0.1114 lb/cu ft × 492°R/532°R.

Second, consider the effect caused by a change in pressure. Since the pressure is increased from 14.7 psi to 1,725 psi, the density of the gas will increase, or 0.1114 lb/cu ft × 492°R/532°R *must be multiplied by a pressure fraction greater than* 1, or 1,725 psi/14.7 psi.

Alternate Solution on a Volume Basis. A check on the foregoing solution by solving the problem on a volume basis follows:

$$6 \text{ cu ft} \times \frac{492°\text{R}}{532°\text{R}} \times \frac{1,725 \text{ psi}}{14.7 \text{ psi}} \times \frac{0.1114 \text{ lb}}{1 \text{ cu ft}} = 72.6 \text{ lb}$$

$$= \text{weight of argon in cylinder}$$

Problems

6-32. The density of chlorine is 3.22 g/l at STP. At what pressure will 1 l of this gas weigh 1 g, the temperature remaining constant at 0°C?   *Ans.*   236 mm.

6-33. At what temperature will 1 l of oxygen weigh 1 g if the pressure remains constant at 760 mm? The density of oxygen is 1.429 g/l at STP.

                                         Ans.   117°C.

6-34. A liter of air at standard conditions weighs 1.293 g. At what temperature will 200 ml of air weigh 0.1 g, the pressure remaining fixed at 1 atm?

                                         Ans.   433°C.

6-35. A volume of chlorine measuring 450 ml (STP) is allowed to expand to a volume measuring 900 ml at a constant temperature. The density of chlorine is 3.22 g/l at STP. Calculate the weight of 100 ml of the expanded gas.   *Ans.*   0.161 g.

6-36. A volume of oxygen measuring 300 ml at standard conditions was compressed until the volume was 130 ml, the temperature remaining constant. Calculate the weight of 30 ml of the compressed gas. The density of oxygen is 1.429 g/l at STP.   *Ans.*   0.099 g.

6-37. A volume of chlorine measuring 500 ml at standard conditions is heated to a temperature of 25°C, constant pressure being maintained during the expansion. Calculate the density of the expanded gas. The weight of 1 l of chlorine at 0°C and 760 mm Hg is 3.22 g.   *Ans.*   2.94 g/l.

6-38. Calculate the weight of 1 l of nitrogen collected at 21°C and 750 mm Hg. One liter of this gas at standard conditions weighs 1.25 g. *Ans.*   1.14 g.

6-39. The density of chlorine is 3.22 g/l at STP. What weight of this gas is contained in a flask of 100 ml capacity at a temperature of 24°C and 750 mm Hg? *Ans.* 0.292 g.

6-40. Under standard conditions of temperature and pressure, 1 cu ft of hydrogen sulfide weighs 1.539 oz. Calculate the weight in ounces of the gas contained in a gasometer holding 2.5 cu ft of gas at a temperature of 20°C and pressure of 770 mm Hg. *Ans.* 3.63 oz.

6-41. The density of chlorine at STP is 3.22 g/l. What is its density at STP, expressed in pounds per cubic foot?

6-42. The density of ammonia at STP is 0.771 g/l. Determine its density at STP, expressed in pounds per cubic foot.

6-43. A glass cylinder contains 2.15 g of air at a pressure of 750 mm Hg. At what pressure will the cylinder contain 4.1 g of air, the temperature remaining constant?

6-44. A quantity of chlorine in a container measures 50 ml at 80°C and 750 mm Hg. The density of chlorine is 3.22 g/l at STP. Calculate the weight of the gas in the container.

6-45. The density of hydrogen sulfide is 0.0961 lb/cu ft at STP. Calculate the weight in ounces of this gas in a gasometer holding 100 cu ft of gas at a temperature of 22°C and a pressure of 762 mm Hg.

6-46. Calculate the weight in ounces of hydrogen contained in a steel cylinder holding 6.2 cu ft at 70°F and a pressure of 1,800 psi. The density of hydrogen is 0.0899 oz/cu ft at STP.

6-47. Determine the weight in pounds of helium needed to fill 100 tanks, each tank holding 2 cu ft of helium at a pressure of 1,650 psi and a temperature of 75°F. The density of helium is 0.1785 oz/cu ft at STP.

6-48. A volume of gas weighing 8 g was allowed to expand at constant temperature until the pressure of the gas was reduced to one-half its former value. It was determined that 500 ml of the rarefied gas weighed 1.25 g. (*a*) What was the original volume of the gas? (*b*) Determine the original density of the gas in grams per liter at STP.

PARTIAL PRESSURES

The total pressure of a mixture of gases may be regarded as the sum of the pressures that each would exert if it alone occupied the whole space. This is known as **Dalton's law of partial pressures.** This law finds application in correcting the pressure of a gas when collected over water. Consideration of this detail is given in the following paragraphs.

VAPOR PRESSURE OF WATER

When a gas is collected over water at a given temperature (*i.e.*, the gas is in contact with liquid water), the stage is ultimately reached when the gas becomes saturated with water vapor, *i.e.*, a condition of equilibrium has been established. This water vapor in the gas has a partial pressure of its own and at equilibrium exerts a maximum vapor pressure at the given temperature. This maximum vapor pressure at the given temperature is commonly called the vapor pressure of water. It is expressed in millimeters of mercury and varies with the temperature, but it always has the same value for the same temperature when the gas is saturated with water vapor. See Table X, page 75, for vapor pressure of water in millimeters of mercury.

When a gas is collected over water, the total pressure of the gas in the receiver consists of the sum of (a) vapor pressure of water and (b) the pressure of the gas itself. The actual pressure exerted by the gas alone (dry) is determined by subtracting the vapor pressure of water (millimeters of mercury) at the given temperature from the atmospheric pressure or the barometric pressure (millimeters of mercury) at the same temperature.

It is appropriate to mention at this point that when gases are collected over mercury, it is not necessary to make a correction for the vapor pressure of mercury at a given temperature. This is because of the exceedingly low vapor pressure of mercury at ordinary temperatures (less than 0.0002 mm at 0°C, 0.008 mm at 40°C, 0.270 mm at 100°C), and thus its influence as far as the partial pressure of mercury vapor is concerned is negligible.

Example. A quantity of gas contained in a receiver and collected over water measured 130 ml at a temperature of 22°C and a barometric pressure of 753 mm Hg. The vapor pressure of water at 22°C is 19.66 mm Hg. What volume will the gas occupy at standard conditions?

Step 1. Correction for vapor pressure of water: vapor pressure of water at 22°C is 19.66 mm Hg. This represents the partial pressure of the water vapor in the atmosphere at 22°C, and is always subtracted from the gas pressure (when gases are collected over water) in order to obtain the actual pressure of the gas under dry conditions. Thus

Pressure of gas (plus vapor pressure of water)..........	753 mm Hg
Vapor pressure of water at 22°C.....................	19.7 mm Hg
Actual pressure of dry gas...........................	733.3 mm Hg

Step 2. The gas now occupies a volume of 130 ml at 22°C and 733 mm Hg. What volume will it occupy at 0°C and 760 mm Hg (STP)?

$$22°C = 295°K \qquad 0°C = 273°K$$

Since the temperature is lowered from 295 to 273°K, the volume (130 ml) will be decreased $273°K/295°K \times 130$ ml (pressure being constant). However, the pressure is increased from 733 mm Hg to 760 mm Hg; this change would cause a further decrease in volume.

Combining these changes of temperature and pressure, the following expression is arrived at:

$$130 \text{ ml} \times \frac{273°\text{K}}{295°\text{K}} \times \frac{733 \text{ mm}}{760 \text{ mm}} = 116 \text{ ml}$$

which is the volume of gas at standard conditions.

Table X gives the values of the vapor pressure of water (maximum vapor pressure) at temperatures ranging from 0 to 110°C.

TABLE X. VAPOR PRESSURE OF WATER IN MILLIMETERS OF MERCURY

$t°$C	Pressure, mm Hg	$t°$C	Pressure, mm Hg	$t°$C	Pressure, mm Hg
0	4.6	21	18.5	60	149.4
1	4.9	22	19.7	70	233.7
2	5.3	23	20.9	80	355.1
3	5.7	24	22.2	90	525.8
4	6.1	25	23.5	95	633.9
5	6.5	26	25.0	96	657.6
6	7.0	27	26.5	97	682.1
7	7.5	28	28.1	98	707.3
8	8.0	29	29.8	99	733.2
9	8.6	30	31.6	99.2	738.5
10	9.2	31	33.4	99.4	743.8
11	9.8	32	35.4	99.6	749.2
12	10.5	33	37.4	99.8	754.6
13	11.2	34	39.6	100	760.0
14	11.9	35	41.9	100.2	765.4
15	12.7	36	44.6	100.4	770.9
16	13.6	37	47.1	100.6	776.4
17	14.5	38	49.7	100.8	782.0
18	15.4	39	52.4	101	787.5
19	16.4	40	55.3	105	906.1
20	17.4	50	92.5	110	1074.6

Correction for Difference in Levels.   It is customary when collecting gases over water or mercury to adjust the receivers so that the level of the liquid inside the receiver is the same as that on the outside. Under these conditions the gas in the receiver will be under the same pressure as the atmosphere, *i.e.*, the barometric pressure.   Where it is not possible to adjust the receiver so that the levels of the liquid will be the same, it is necessary to make a correction for this difference in levels.   Consider that a gas is collected over mercury; if the mercury inside the receiver is at a higher level than that on the outside, the pressure of the gas is less than atmospheric pressure by a column of mercury equal in height to the distance from the level inside the receiver to the level outside.

Example. A quantity of gas collected in a graduated tube over mercury measured 75 ml at a temperature of 25°C and a barometric pressure of 760 mm Hg. The level of the mercury inside the tube was 25 mm above that on the outside. What volume would this gas occupy at standard conditions?

Step 1. Correction for difference in levels: Since the level of mercury is 25 mm above that on the outside, the pressure of the gas in the tube is lower than the barometric pressure by an amount equal to 25 mm, or 760 mm Hg − 25 mm Hg = 735 mm Hg = actual or initial pressure of the gas.

Step 2. The initial volume of gas is 75 ml at 25°C and 735 mm Hg. What volume will the gas occupy at standard conditions?

$$V_i = 75 \text{ ml} \qquad T_i = 298°\text{K} \qquad P_i = 735 \text{ mm Hg}$$
$$V_f = x \qquad T_f = 273°\text{K} \qquad P_f = 760 \text{ mm Hg}$$

Since the temperature is lowered from 298 to 273°K, the volume must decrease, or 75 ml × 273°K/298°K at constant pressure. However, since the pressure is increased from 735 mm to 760 mm, this change will cause the volume to decrease still further. Combining the effects of these changes in temperature and pressure, the following expression is obtained:

$$75 \text{ ml} \times \frac{273°\text{K}}{298°\text{K}} \times \frac{735 \text{ mm}}{760 \text{ mm}} = 66.4 \text{ ml}$$

or 66.4 ml is the volume of the gas at standard conditions.

Problems

6-49. A volume of gas contained in a graduated tube measured 80 ml over mercury at 22°C and a barometric pressure of 76.0 cm. The level of the mercury inside the measuring tube was 2.0 cm above that on the outside. Determine the volume the gas would occupy at standard conditions.
Ans. 72 ml.

6-50. A volume of gas collected in a tube over mercury measured 75 ml at 25°C and barometer reading of 755 mm. The level of the mercury inside the tube was 55 mm above that on the outside. What volume would this gas occupy at 30°C and 750 mm Hg?
Ans. 71 ml.

6-51. A volume of gas collected over water measured 85.5 ml at 22°C and 759.7 mm Hg. How many milliliters will the dry gas occupy at standard conditions?
Ans. 77.0 ml.

6-52. A volume of gas collected over water at 68°F and 760.4 mm Hg measured 760 ml. What volume would the dry gas occupy at 95°F and 760 mm Hg?
Ans. 781 ml.

6-53. A volume of dry gas measures 85 ml at 21°C and 758 mm Hg.   What volume would this gas occupy if collected over water at 755.5 mm Hg at 25°C?

Ans.   89 ml.

6-54. Dry air contains, by volume, 78.03 per cent nitrogen, 20.9 per cent oxygen, 0.9 per cent argon, 0.04 per cent carbon dioxide.   Calculate the partial pressure of each of these constituents at 758 mm Hg.

Ans. N_2, 591.46 mm; O_2, 158.4 mm; A, 6.8 mm; CO_2, 0.3 mm.

6-55. A 250-ml flask was evacuated, and into it was forced 150 ml of hydrogen under a pressure of 750 mm, 75 ml of oxygen under a pressure of 350 mm, and 50 ml of nitrogen under a pressure of 250 mm.   Determine (a) the partial pressure of each gas after mixing and (b) the total pressure of the mixture.

Ans.   (a) 450 mm for H_2; 105 mm for O_2; 50 mm for N_2; (b) 605 mm.

6-56. A volume of gas collected in an inverted tube measured 64 ml over mercury at a temperature of 75°F and a pressure of 26.8 in. Hg.   The level of the mercury inside the measuring tube was 3.9 in. above that on the outside. Calculate the volume of the gas at standard conditions.

6-57. A container holds 400 ml of nitrogen collected over water at 77°F and a pressure of 1 atm.   Calculate the volume of nitrogen at standard conditions.

6-58. A gasometer holds 500 cu m of gas collected over water at 26°C and 755 mm Hg.   What volume will the dry gas occupy at 10°C and 760 mm Hg?

6-59. A graduated tube holds 40 ml of nitrogen collected over water at 21°C and a pressure of 1 atm.   The level of the water inside the container is 15 cm above the outside level.   What is the volume of the dry gas at standard conditions?

6-60. The volume of a dry gas measures 76 ml at 77°F and 755 mm Hg.   What volume would this gas occupy if collected over water at 764.4 mm Hg and 68°F?

6-61. A glass vessel contains 3.5 l of CO_2, and another vessel holds 5.5 l of N_2; both gases are at the same temperature and under a pressure of 2.6 and 1.5 kg/sq cm, respectively.   Both are now mixed together in a vessel having a capacity of 5 l.   There is no change in temperature.   Calculate the pressure of the mixture in the last vessel.

6-62. Each of two glass vessels contains 5 l of gas, one being under a pressure of 750 mm Hg and the other under a pressure of 730 mm Hg, both gases kept at a temperature of 70°C.   The two vessels are placed in communication with each other, and all the gas compressed into one of the vessels.   During this operation the temperature is increased to 120°C.   What will be the pressure of the gaseous mixture in this vessel?

CHAPTER VII

MOLE-WEIGHT-GAS-VOLUME RELATIONS

OUTLINE

Gay-Lussac's law of volumes. When chemical reaction takes place between gases, the volumes of reacting gases, and volumes of any gaseous products formed, may be expressed in the ratio of simple whole numbers.

Law of Avogadro. Equal volumes of gases under the same conditions of temperature and pressure contain the same number of molecules.

Proof that the elementary gases, hydrogen and chlorine, contain 2 atoms in each molecule of these gases, respectively. The molecular formulas of these gases should be written H_2 and Cl_2.

Molar volume. One gram-mole of any gas occupies approximately 22.4 l at standard conditions (STP).

Numerical relationship between weight and volume units in English system and metric system.

"What a molecular chemical formula stands for."

To express gram-moles of a gas of any given volume (liters at STP), divide the given number of liters at STP by 22.4 l (STP) per gram-mole.

Molecular-weight determinations of gases from density.

Molecular-weight determination of volatile liquids by Victor Meyer method.

Molecular-weight determination by boiling-point and freezing-point methods.

GAY-LUSSAC'S LAW OF VOLUMES

It has been stated that when elements combine chemically to form compounds, they do so in *definite proportions by weight* (law of definite proportions). This statement is valid irrespective of whether the elements are solids, liquids, or gases. In dealing with chemical reactions of gases, one concerns himself with *volumes* of reacting gases and gaseous products, rather than with the weight relations of these substances. It is much more convenient to measure volumes of gases than to weigh them. Any weight relations of gases, however, may be determined from the densities of the gases.

The fundamental **law of volumes**, proposed by Gay-Lussac (1805), states: **When chemical reaction takes place between gases, the volumes of reacting gases, and volumes of any gaseous products formed, may be expressed in the ratio of simple whole numbers.** Thus, when chemical combination occurs between hydrogen and chlorine to form hydrogen chloride, the facts are expressed as follows:

1 vol hydrogen + 1 vol chlorine → 2 vol hydrogen chloride

Similarly

1 vol oxygen + 2 vol hydrogen → 2 vol steam
1 vol nitrogen + 3 vol hydrogen → 2 vol ammonia

When solids are decomposed to yield gaseous products, Gay-Lussac's law applies only to the volumes of gases and is not applicable to solids or liquids. Thus, the decomposition of the red oxide of mercury may be expressed as follows:

Mercuric oxide (*solid*) + heat → 2 vol mercury vapor + 1 vol oxygen

Similarly

1 vol ammonia + 1 vol hydrogen chloride

→ ammonium chloride (*solid*)

Also, other reactions between solids and gases may be considered as follows:

1. Carbon burning in air or oxygen:

$$\text{Carbon (\textit{solid}) + 1 vol oxygen} \xrightarrow[\text{burning}]{} \text{1 vol carbon dioxide}$$

and

Red-hot carbon (*solid*) + 1 vol carbon dioxide

→ 2 vol carbon monoxide

2. The burning of ethyl alcohol, a liquid:

$$\text{Ethyl alcohol + 3 vol oxygen} \xrightarrow[\text{burning}]{} \text{2 vol CO}_2 \text{ + 3 vol steam}$$

In 1811, Avogadro volunteered an explanation for the facts presented by the law of Gay-Lussac and put forth the following assumption: **Equal volumes of gases under the same conditions of temperature and pressure contain the same number of molecules.** This hypothesis is now generally accepted as a true generalization. It is now known as the **law of Avogadro.**

By applying Gay-Lussac's law of volumes and Avogadro's law, it is possible to determine the number of atoms present in a molecule of each of the elementary gases, hydrogen, oxygen, nitrogen, and chlorine. For example, it is an experimental fact that 1 volume of hydrogen unites with 1 volume of chlorine and forms 2 volumes of hydrogen chloride (Gay-Lussac's law). According to Avogadro's law, these equal volumes of gases contain the same number of molecules. For convenience, assume that each volume of gas contains 1,000 molecules; then

Hydrogen   +   chlorine   = hydrogen chloride
□   □   □ □
1,000 molecules + 1,000 molecules = 2,000 molecules

Each of the 2,000 molecules of hydrogen chloride must contain at least 1 atom of hydrogen and at least 1 atom of chlorine; a fractional atom is nonexistent. Therefore, in 2,000 molecules of hydrogen chloride there are at least 2,000 atoms of hydrogen. Originally there were 1,000 molecules of hydrogen before combination with chlorine took place. The 2,000 atoms of hydrogen must be derived from 1,000 molecules of hydrogen, or 2 atoms of hydrogen from each molecule of hydrogen. Therefore, 1 molecule of hydrogen must contain at least 2 atoms of hydrogen, which is represented by the molecular formula H_2. Similar reasoning applies to prove that the chlorine molecule contains 2 atoms of chlorine, or Cl_2. Similar proofs will justify the conclusion that the elementary gases oxygen and nitrogen are diatomic molecules and have the molecular formulas O_2 and N_2, respectively. In the case of the inert gases He, Ne, A, Kr, and Xe the molecules are monatomic, and the symbols of these elements not only represent atoms, but also the molecular formulas of these elements.

The formula O_2 stands for a molecule of oxygen. It is the molecular formula for oxygen. It also represents one molecular weight, such as one gram-molecular weight or 1 g-mole of oxygen. Since there are 2 g-atoms of oxygen in 1 g-mole of oxygen (2 g-atoms/g-mole), and 1 g-atom of oxygen = 16.0 g (16.0 g/g-atom), then

$$\frac{2 \text{ g-atoms}}{1 \text{ g-mole}} \times \frac{16 \text{ g}}{1 \text{ g-atom}} = \frac{32 \text{ g}}{1 \text{ g-mole}}$$

or 32 g of oxygen per gram-mole (32 g O_2/g-mole).

The density of oxygen = 1.429 g/l (STP). If one divides the number of grams per gram-mole (molecular weight in grams) by the density, grams per liter (STP) of gas, the volume at STP occupied by 1 g-mole of the gas is obtained.

Let x = volume at STP occupied by 1 g-mole of oxygen

$$= \frac{32 \text{ g/g-mole}}{1.429 \text{ g/l (STP)}} = \frac{32 \text{ g}}{1 \text{ g-mole}} \times \frac{1 \text{ l (STP)}}{1.429 \text{ g}}$$

$$= \frac{22.4 \text{ l (STP)}}{1 \text{ g-mole}}$$

or 22.4 l (STP) is the volume occupied by 1 g-mole of oxygen.

Similarly 1 g-mole of nitrogen (N_2), contains 28 g of N_2.

The density of nitrogen = 1.2505 g/l (STP). If x = volume occupied by 1 g-mole of nitrogen, then

$$x = \frac{28.0 \text{ g/g-mole}}{1.2505 \text{ g/l (STP)}} = \frac{22.4 \text{ l (STP)}}{1 \text{ g-mole}}$$

or 22.4 l (STP) is the volume occupied by 1 g-mole of nitrogen.

Thus, if one divides the weight of 1 g-mole of any gas (g/g-mole) by its density (g/l at STP), a value approximately 22.4 l at STP/g-mole is obtained for each gas. This is one of the most useful principles to find wide application in chemical calculations in which volumes and weights of gases are concerned. The relationship is usually expressed as follows: **1 g-mole of any gas occupies approximately 22.4 l at STP.** This volume is generally referred to as the **molar volume.** This principle makes possible a further extension of what the chemical formula stands for; namely, the molecular formula for any gas also represents the *molar volume* or 22.4 l at STP per gram-mole of that gas.

Since 1 g-mole contains 6.02×10^{23} molecules, and the volume of 1 g-mole of any gas is 22.4 l (STP), it follows that 6.02×10^{23} molecules of a gas will occupy 22.4 l (STP).

Note there are deviations from the gas laws, such as that caused by the attraction of the molecules of a gas for one another: the molar volume will in some cases become slightly less than 22.4 l at STP. The slight error involved in using the number 22.4 in such cases is negligible for most calculations where the principle is useful.

NUMERICAL RELATIONSHIP BETWEEN WEIGHT AND VOLUME UNITS IN ENGLISH SYSTEM AND METRIC SYSTEM

A. There is 28.35 g in 1 oz (avdp) and 28.31 l in 1 cu ft; that is to say, the number of grams in 1 oz (avdp) is practically the same as the number of liters in a cubic foot.

It can be stated that 1 g-mole of CO_2 or 44 g CO_2 occupies 22.4 l at STP. The following relationship will maintain:

$$\frac{44 \text{ g } CO_2}{28.35 \text{ g/oz}} \text{ occupies } \frac{22.4 \text{ l (STP)}}{28.31 \text{ l/cu ft}}$$

or 44 oz CO_2 occupies 22.4 cu ft (STP).

Since 44 oz CO_2 is 1 oz-mole of CO_2, it follows that 1 *oz-mole of any gas occupies* 22.4 *cu ft at STP.*

B. There is 35.26 oz (avdp) in 1 kg and 35.31 cu ft in 1 cu m. Since 1 oz-mole or 44 oz of CO_2 occupies 22.4 cu ft at STP, then

$$\frac{44 \text{ oz } CO_2}{35.26 \text{ oz/kg}} \text{ occupies } \frac{22.4 \text{ cu ft (STP)}}{35.31 \text{ cu ft/cu m}}$$

or 44 kg of CO_2 occupies 22.4 cu m at STP.

Since 44 kg of CO_2 is 1 kg-mole of CO_2, it follows that 1 *kg-mole of any gas occupies* 22.4 *cu m at STP.*

Another proof to verify this last statement, using only units in the metric system follows.

There are 1,000 g in 1 kg and 1,000 l in 1 cu m.

$$\frac{44 \text{ g } CO_2}{1,000 \text{ g/kg}} \text{ occupies } \frac{22.4 \text{ l (STP)}}{1,000 \text{ l/cu m}}$$
$$44 \text{ kg } CO_2 \text{ occupies } 22.4 \text{ cu m at STP}$$

or 1 kg-mole (44 kg) of CO_2 occupies 22.4 cu m at STP.

C. There is 28.0 lb in 1 lb-mole of nitrogen, or 28.0 lb of N_2/lb-mole. The density of nitrogen = 0.07807 lb/cu ft at STP. The volume occupied by 1 lb-mole of nitrogen is

$$\frac{28.0 \text{ lb/lb-mole}}{0.07807 \text{ lb/cu ft at STP}} = 358 \text{ cu ft at STP/lb-mole}$$

or 1 *lb-mole of any gas occupies* 358 *cu ft at STP.*

Summarizing the information of preceding sections on "what a molecular chemical formula stands for," and using carbon dioxide as a typical substance, it can be stated that the formula CO_2 now stands for the following facts:

1. That 1 atom of carbon is chemically combined with 2 atoms of oxygen.

2. That 1 g-atom of C (12.0 g) combines with 2 g-atoms of oxygen (2 × 16.0 g) and that the gram-molecular weight of carbon dioxide is 12.0 g + (2 × 16.0 g) = 44 g, or that 1 g-mole of CO_2 is 44 g, expressed as 44 g of CO_2/g-mole.

3. That 44 g of CO_2, or 1 g-mole of CO_2, occupies 22.4 l at STP, or 22.4 l of CO_2 at STP/g-mole.

4. Also that 44 kg of CO_2, or 1 kg-mole of CO_2, occupies 22.4 cu m at STP, or 22.4 cu m of CO_2 at STP/kg-mole.

5. And 44 oz of CO_2, or 1 oz-mole of CO_2, occupies 22.4 cu ft at STP, or 22.4 cu ft of CO_2 at STP/oz-mole.

6. Also 44 lb of CO_2, or 1 lb-mole of CO_2, occupies 358 cu ft at STP, or 358 cu ft of CO_2 at STP/lb-mole.

In a previous section it has been stated: To express a given weight G of a substance in terms of gram-moles, one may use the relationship

$$\text{No. of g-moles} = \frac{G}{\text{no. of g/g-mole}}$$

Since 1 g-mole of any gas occupies 22.4 l (STP), one can determine the number of gram-moles of a gas in terms of volume units (liters at STP) from the following

$$\text{No. of g-moles of a gas} = \frac{L}{22.4 \text{ l (STP)/g-mole}}$$

where L = number of liters of gas at STP and 22.4 l (STP)/g-mole = the molar volume, or the volume (STP) occupied by 1 g-mole of gas.

Also the number of liters (STP) of gas, or L, can be determined by L = no. of g-moles of gas × 22.4 l (STP)/g-mole.

Example 1. Express 123.2 l (STP) of ammonia in terms of (a) gram-moles and (b) grams of ammonia.

(a) *Step* 1

$$\text{No. of g-moles of a gas} = \frac{L}{22.4 \text{ l (STP)/g-mole}}$$

Step 2. Let x = number of g-moles of ammonia (NH_3) and L = the given liters (STP) of ammonia = 123.2 l (STP).

$$x = \frac{123.2 \text{ l (STP)}}{22.4 \text{ l (STP)/g-mole}} = 123.2 \text{ l (STP)} \times \frac{1 \text{ g-mole}}{22.4 \text{ l (STP)}}$$
$$= 5.5 \text{ g-moles } NH_3$$

(b) *Step* 1. Molecular weight of ammonia: NH_3 = 17.0, or 17.0 g NH_3 in 1 g-mole NH_3.

Step 2

$$5.5 \text{ g-moles} \times \frac{17.0 \text{ g } NH_3}{1 \text{ g-mole}} = 93.5 \text{ g } NH_3$$

Example 2. How many liters at STP are contained in 46.86 g of chlorine? Atomic weight Cl = 35.5, or 35.5 g Cl/g-atom.

Step 1. Determine the number of gram-moles of chlorine in 46.86 g of chlorine. There are 2 g-atoms Cl in 1 g-mole Cl, or

$$\frac{2 \text{ g-atoms}}{1 \text{ g-mole}} \times \frac{35.5 \text{ g Cl}}{1 \text{ g-atom}} = 71.0 \text{ g/g-mole}$$

Let x = number of gram-moles in 46.86 g of chlorine

$$= \frac{46.86 \text{ g Cl}}{71.0 \text{ g Cl/g-mole}} = 46.86 \text{ g Cl} \times \frac{1 \text{ g-mole}}{71.0 \text{ g Cl}}$$
$$= 0.66 \text{ g-mole}$$

Step 2. From the fact that

$$L = \text{no. of g-moles of gas} \times \frac{22.4 \text{ l (STP) gas}}{1 \text{ g-mole gas}}$$
$$= 0.66 \text{ g-mole} \times \frac{22.4 \text{ l (STP)Cl}}{1 \text{ g-mole}} = 14.8 \text{ l (STP)Cl}$$

NOTE. The foregoing *steps* may be combined as follows:

$$L = 46.86 \text{ g Cl} \times \frac{1 \text{ g-mole}}{71.0 \text{ g Cl}} \times \frac{22.4 \text{ l (STP)Cl}}{1 \text{ g-mole}} = 14.8 \text{ l (STP)Cl}$$

Example 3. Determine (a) the number of ounce-moles and (b) the number of ounces in 30.6 cu ft H_2S at 21°C and 750 mm Hg.

(a) *Step* 1. Convert 30.6 cu ft H_2S at 21°C and 750 mm Hg to standard conditions (0°C and 760 mm Hg).

$$21°C = 294°K \quad \text{and} \quad 0°C = 273°K$$

$$30.6 \text{ cu ft} \times \frac{273°K}{294°K} \times \frac{750 \text{ mm}}{760 \text{ mm}} = 28 \text{ cu ft (STP)}$$

Step 2. Determine the number of ounce-moles of H_2S in 28 cu ft (STP), employing the following relationship:

$$\text{No. of oz-moles gas} = \frac{\text{no. of cu ft (STP) gas}}{22.4 \text{ cu ft (STP) gas/oz-mole gas}}$$

Let x = number of ounce-moles of H_2S in 28 cu ft (STP) H_2S

$$= \frac{28 \text{ cu ft (STP)}}{22.4 \text{ cu ft (STP)/oz-mole}}$$

$$= 28 \text{ cu ft (STP)} \times \frac{1 \text{ oz-mole}}{22.4 \text{ cu ft (STP)}}$$

$$= 1.25 \text{ oz-moles}$$

(b) Molecular weight of H_2S = 34.1, or 34.1 oz H_2S in 1 oz-mole. From part (a), 30.6 cu ft H_2S at 21°C and 750 mm Hg = 1.25 oz-moles H_2S, then

$$1.25 \text{ oz-moles} \times \frac{34.1 \text{ oz } H_2S}{1 \text{ oz-mole}} = 42.6 \text{ oz } H_2S$$

or, combining Step 2 in part (a) and part (b), one obtains

$$28 \text{ cu ft (STP)} \times \frac{1 \text{ oz-mole}}{22.4 \text{ cu ft (STP)}} \times \frac{34.1 \text{ oz } H_2S}{1 \text{ oz-mole}} = 42.6 \text{ oz } H_2S$$

Example 4. Calculate the volume in cubic feet at 86°F and 30.1 in. Hg of 1.5 lb-moles of nitrogen.

Step 1. Determine the number of cubic feet of nitrogen at STP in 1.5 lb-moles N from the following relationship:

$$\text{No. of lb-moles gas} = \frac{\text{no. of cu ft (STP) gas}}{358 \text{ cu ft (STP)/lb-mole gas}}$$

Let x = number of cubic feet of nitrogen at STP

$$1.5 \text{ lb-moles} = \frac{x}{358 \text{ cu ft (STP)/lb-mole}}$$

$$x = 1.5 \text{ lb-moles} \times \frac{358 \text{ cu ft (STP)}}{1 \text{ lb-mole}} = 537 \text{ cu ft (STP)}$$

or 537 cu ft at 32°F and 29.9 in. Hg (STP).

Step 2.   Convert 537 cu ft N at STP to 86°F and 30.1 in. Hg.

$$86°F = (86 + 460)°R = 546°R \qquad 32°F = (32 + 460)°R = 492°R$$

$$537 \text{ cu ft} \times \frac{546°R}{492°R} \times \frac{29.9 \text{ in.}}{30.1 \text{ in.}} = 592 \text{ cu ft}$$

or 592 cu ft = volume of 1.5 lb-moles N at 86°F and 30.1 in. Hg.

Example 5.   Calculate the weight in kilograms of 1,000 cu m of carbon dioxide at 25°C and pressure of 5 atm.

The student should note that the solution of this problem actually involves three distinct steps: Step 1, the conversion of 1,000 cu m CO_2 at 25°C and 5 atm to standard conditions (0°C and 1 atm); Step 2, the conversion of volume (STP) CO_2 to kilogram-moles CO_2; Step 3, the conversion of kilogram-moles CO_2 to kilograms CO_2. These three steps may be combined in one expression and all dimensional units except kilograms of CO_2 cancel out in the operation.

$$1,000 \text{ cu m } CO_2 \times \frac{273°K}{298°K} \times \frac{5 \text{ atm}}{1 \text{ atm}} \times \frac{1 \text{ kg-mole } CO_2}{22.4 \text{ cu m (STP) } CO_2}$$
$$\times \frac{44 \text{ kg } CO_2}{1 \text{ kg-mole } CO_2} = 8,976 \text{ kg } CO_2$$

Problems

7-1. Determine (a) the number of gram-atoms, (b) the number of gram-moles, and (c) the number of molecules in 51.2 g of oxygen.
Ans.   (c) 9.63×10^{23} molecules.

7-2. Find (a) the number of gram-atoms, (b) the number of gram-moles, and (c) the number of molecules in 39.2 g of nitrogen.
Ans.   (c) 8.43×10^{23} molecules.

7-3. Calculate the weight of 1 molecule of carbon dioxide.   *Ans.* 7.3×10^{-23} g.

7-4. What is the gram-molecular weight of the compound if 1.505×10^{24} molecules of the substance weighs 70 g?   *Ans.*   28.

7-5. Express 145.6 l (STP) of chlorine in terms of (a) gram-moles and (b) grams of chlorine.   *Ans.*   (a) 6.5 g-moles; (b) 462 g.

7-6. How many liters (STP) are contained in 240 g of oxygen?
Ans.   168 l (STP).

7-7. Express 23.52 cu m (STP) of CH_4 gas in terms of (a) kilogram-moles and (b) kilograms of CH_4.   *Ans.*   (a) 1.05 kg-moles; (b) 168 kg.

7-8. Determine (a) the number of kilogram-moles and (b) the number of liters (STP) contained in 248.5 kg of chlorine.
Ans.   (a) 3.5 kg-moles; (b) 78.4 cu m (STP).

7-9. Express 257.6 cu ft (STP) of nitrogen dioxide in terms of (a) ounce-moles and (b) ounces of nitrogen dioxide.   *Ans.*   (a) 11.5 oz-moles; (b) 529 oz.

7-10. Determine (a) the number of pound-moles and (b) the number of pounds contained in 895 cu ft (STP) of chlorine.
Ans.   (a) 2.5 lb-moles; (b) 178 lb.

7-11. Find (a) the number of cubic feet (STP) and (b) the number of pounds contained in 0.15 lb-mole of nitrogen.   *Ans.*   (a) 54 cu ft (STP); (b) 4.2 lb.

7-12. Determine (a) the number of gram-moles and (b) the number of grams in 30.25 l (STP) of NH_3 at 22°C and 760 mm Hg.

Ans. (a) 1.26 g-moles; (b) 21.4 g.

7-13. Calculate (a) the volume in liters at 25°C and 755 mm Hg and (b) the weight in grams of 5.5 g-moles of sulfur dioxide. *Ans.* (a) 135 l; (b) 352 g.

7-14. Determine (a) the number of pound-moles and (b) the weight in pounds of 500 cu ft of propane (C_3H_8) at 72°F and 30.2 in. Hg. *Ans.* (b) 573 lb.

7-15. Calculate (a) the number of kilogram-moles and (b) the weight in kilograms of 1,000 cu m of helium at 21°C and 758 mm Hg. *Ans.* (b) 166 kg.

7-16. Determine (a) the number of gram-moles and (b) the number of liters (STP) in 25.6 g of methane (CH_4).

7-17. Calculate (a) the number of gram-moles and (b) the number of grams contained in 35.84 l (STP) of monosilane (SiH_4).

7-18. Determine (a) the number of ounce-moles and (b) the number of cubic feet contained in 110 g of propane (C_3H_8).

7-19. Express 56 l (STP) of acetylene (C_2H_2) in terms of (a) gram-moles and (b) grams of acetylene.

7-20. Express 14.78 cu ft (STP) of nitrous oxide (N_2O) in terms of (a) ounce-moles and (b) ounces of nitrous oxide.

7-21. How many (a) pound-moles and (b) pounds are represented by 1,611 cu ft (STP) of carbon dioxide?

7-22. Determine (a) the number of gram-moles and (b) the weight in grams of 1,000 l of oxygen at 25°C and 1 atm.

7-23. Calculate (a) the number of kilogram-moles and (b) the weight in kilograms of 1,000 cu m of nitrogen at 75°F and 29.5 in. Hg.

7-24. Express 100 cu ft of hydrogen sulfide at 72°F and 756 mm Hg in terms of (a) ounce-moles and (b) ounces of hydrogen sulfide.

7-25. Calculate (a) the number of pound-moles and (b) the weight in pounds of 1,000 cu ft of ammonia at 80°F and 30.3 in. Hg.

7-26. Calculate (a) the volume in liters and (b) the weight in grams of 10 g-moles of nitrogen at 20°C and 760 mm Hg.

7-27. Determine (a) the volume in cubic meters and (b) the weight in kilograms of 2 kg-moles of ammonia at 21°C and 765 mm Hg.

7-28. Calculate (a) the volume in cubic feet and (b) the weight in pounds of 10 lb-moles of acetylene (C_2H_2) at 80°F and 28.5 in. Hg.

7-29. Determine (a) the number of gram-moles and (b) the volume in liters of 100 g of oxygen at 25°C and 755 mm Hg.

7-30. (a) How many kilogram-moles and (b) how many cubic meters are contained in 1,000 kg of carbon dioxide at 22°C and 750 mm Hg?

MOLECULAR WEIGHT FROM DENSITY OF GASES

Since the molar volume (22.4 l at STP) was derived for various gases from their densities (g/l at STP), it follows that the density of a gas multiplied by the molar volume gives the molecular weight of that gas, or

$$\underbrace{\frac{\text{Grams of any gas}}{1\ \text{l (STP) gas}}}_{\text{density}} \times \underbrace{\frac{22.4\ \text{l (STP) gas}}{1\ \text{g-mole gas}}}_{\text{molar volume}} = \underbrace{\frac{\text{grams of any gas}}{1\ \text{g-mole gas}}}_{\text{gram-molecular weight}}$$

or grams per gram-mole of gas which is the gram-molecular weight.

Also, if the gram-molecular weight (g/g-mole) of a gas is known, to find its density [g/l (STP)], one divides the gram-molecular weight by 22.4 l (STP).

Example 1. The density of hydrogen is 0.0899 g/l (STP). What is the weight of 1 g-mole of hydrogen?

$$\frac{0.0899 \text{ g H}}{1 \text{ l (STP)}} \times \frac{22.4 \text{ l (STP)}}{1 \text{ g-mole}} = \frac{2.01 \text{ g}}{1 \text{ g-mole}}$$

or 2.01 g/g-mole.

Example 2. The molecular weight of nitric oxide is 30.0. Calculate its density in grams per liter (STP).

$$\underset{\text{molar volume}}{\overset{\text{gram-molecular weight}}{\frac{30.0 \text{ g/g-mole}}{22.4 \text{ l (STP)/g-mole}}}} = \frac{30.0 \text{ g}}{1 \text{ g-mole}} \times \frac{1 \text{ g-mole}}{22.4 \text{ l (STP)}} = \underset{\text{density}}{1.34 \text{ g/l (STP)}}$$

Example 3. What is the molecular weight of a gas 200 ml (STP) of which weighs 2.58 g?

$$200 \text{ ml (STP) gas} = 0.2 \text{ l (STP) gas}$$

$$\underset{\text{density}}{\frac{2.58 \text{ g}}{0.2 \text{ l (STP)}}} \times \underset{\text{molar volume}}{\frac{22.4 \text{ l (STP)}}{1 \text{ g-mole}}} = \underset{\substack{\text{gram-molecular}\\\text{weight}}}{\frac{289 \text{ g}}{1 \text{ g-mole}}}$$

or the molecular weight of the gas is 289.

Example 4. Calculate the molecular weight of a gas, 2.5 cu ft (STP) of which weighs 0.731 lb.

$$\frac{0.731 \text{ lb}}{2.5 \text{ cu ft (STP)}} \times \frac{358 \text{ cu ft (STP)}}{1 \text{ lb-mole}} = \frac{105 \text{ lb}}{1 \text{ lb-mole}}$$

The molecular weight of the gas is 105.

Example 5. A volume of gas measuring 280 ml at 90°F and 780 mm Hg weighs 0.344 g. Calculate the molecular weight of the gas.

Step 1. Change 280 ml at 90°F and 780 mm Hg to standard conditions

$$90°F = (90 + 460)°R = 550°R \qquad 32°F = (32 + 460)°R = 492°R$$

$$280 \text{ ml} \times \frac{492°R}{550°R} \times \frac{780 \text{ mm}}{760 \text{ mm}} = 256 \text{ ml (STP)} = 0.256 \text{ l (STP)}$$

then 0.256 l (STP) of gas will weigh the same as 0.28 l at 90°F and

780 mm Hg, since these volumes will contain the same number of molecules. Then

$$\frac{0.344 \text{ g}}{0.256 \text{ l (STP)}} \times \frac{22.4 \text{ l (STP)}}{1 \text{ g-mole}} = 30.1 \text{ g/g-mole}$$

or the molecular weight of the gas is 30.1.

Problems

7-31. Calculate the approximate molecular weights of (a) tungsten fluoride [density of vapor = 12.9 g/l (STP)] and (b) methyl chloride [200 ml (STP) of vapor weighs 0.4616 g].   *Ans.* (a) 289; (b) 51.7.

7-32. Calculate the approximate molecular weights of (a) cyanogen [density of vapor = 2.335 g/l (STP)] and (b) the gas, 130 ml (STP) of which weighs 0.755 g.   *Ans.* (a) 52; (b) 130.

7-33. The molecular weight of nitrous oxide (a) is 44 and of nitrogen dioxide (b) is 46. Determine the weight in grams of 250 ml (STP) of each of these gases.   *Ans.* (a) 0.49 g.

7-34. The molecular weight of chloroform (a) is 119.5 and of diethyl ether (b) is 74. Determine the weight in grams of 200 ml (STP) of the vapor of each of these two substances.   *Ans.* (a) 1.07 g.

7-35. If 0.50 g of a gas occupies 150 ml at 20°C and 750 mm Hg, what is the molecular weight of the gas?   *Ans.* 81.

7-36. Determine the molecular weight of a gas when 120 ml of the gas at 27°C and 740 mm Hg weighs 0.80 g.   *Ans.* 169.

7-37. A sample of a volatile liquid, weighing 0.08 g when heated, yielded 32 ml of vapor measured at 27°C and 740 mm Hg. Calculate the molecular weight of the substance.   *Ans.* 63.

7-38. Calculate the molecular weight of a gas 0.091 g of which occupies 33.5 ml at 100°C and 740 mm Hg.   *Ans.* 85.

7-39. It was found that 0.1225 g of a gas occupied 110 ml when measured over water at 22°C and 743 mm Hg. Calculate the molecular weight of the gas.   *Ans.* 28.3.

7-40. What weight in grams of oxygen will occupy the same volume as 0.504 g of hydrogen, both gases at standard conditions?   *Ans.* 8 g.

7-41. The molecular weight of a gas is 26.0. Calculate the weight in grams of 1 l of the gas at 24°C and 742 mm Hg.   *Ans.* 1.04 g.

7-42. The molecular weight of argon is 39.9. What is the weight in grams of 1 l of the gas at 21°C and 745 mm Hg?   *Ans.* 1.62 g.

7-43. Calculate the weight in ounces of hydrogen sulfide in a gasometer which holds 1.5 cu ft of the gas under a pressure of 762 mm Hg and a temperature of 22°C.   *Ans.* 2.1 oz.

7-44. What weight in ounces of carbon dioxide will be contained in a gas cylinder which holds 2 cu ft of the gas under a pressure of 15.6 psi and a temperature of 21°C?   *Ans.* 3.9 oz.

THE DETERMINATION OF THE MOLECULAR WEIGHT OF VOLATILE LIQUIDS

The molecular weight of liquid substances that can be vaporized without decomposition is obtained by the Victor Meyer method.

This method assumes the molecular weight of the substance in the liquid phase to be the same as that in the vapor phase. The essential details of the method are as follows: A weighed amount of the liquid substance contained in the small ampoule C (Fig. 7) is vaporized in the jacketed tube filled with air. The vapor displaces a volume of air equal to its own volume. This air, in turn, displaces its own volume of water in the eudiometer A, which corresponds to the volume of the vapor of the liquid substance whose molecular weight is to be determined. The volume of air displaced is noted by observing the water displaced. Also, the temperature and barometric pressure are

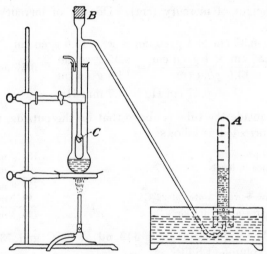

FIG. 7. Victor Meyer method for molecular-weight determination of volatile liquids.

recorded. Then corrections are made for the difference in levels of the water inside the eudiometer and in the trough, as well as for vapor pressure of water at the temperature of the experiment. This is followed by reducing the measured volume of air to standard conditions of temperature and pressure and by the calculation of the weight of 22.4 l of the vapor, which equals the molecular weight of the liquid substance.

Example 1. A volatile liquid weighing 0.686 g placed in a Victor Meyer apparatus displaced 113 ml of air (over water) at 22°C and 757.7 mm of Hg. The level of water inside the measuring tube was 2.5 in. above that on the outside. Calculate the molecular weight of the liquid.

Recall the statement in a preceding paragraph that the vapor of the liquid displaces a volume of air equal to its own volume, and the air in turn displaces a volume of water which corresponds to the volume of the vapor from the sample of liquid.

Step 1.   Correction of pressure for differences in levels and the vapor pressure of water at 22°C.

$$2.5 \text{ in. } H_2O = 2.5 \text{ in. } \times 2.54 \text{ cm/in.} = 6.35 \text{ cm } H_2O$$
$$\text{Pressure of } H_2O = \text{pressure of Hg}$$
Height of water (cm) × density of water (g/cu cm)
$$= \text{height of mercury (cm)} \times \text{density of mercury (g/cu m)}$$

Let x = height of mercury (cm).   Density of mercury = 13.6 g/cu cm.

$$6.35 \text{ cm} \times 1 \text{ g/cu cm} = x \times 13.6 \text{ g/cu cm}$$
$$x = \frac{6.35 \text{ cm} \times 1 \text{ g/cu cm}}{13.6 \text{ g/cu cm}} = \frac{6.35 \text{ g/sq cm}}{13.6 \text{ g/cu cm}} = 0.47 \text{ cm Hg}$$
$$0.47 \text{ cm Hg} = 4.7 \text{ mm Hg}$$

Since water inside the tube is above that on the outside, the original pressure is corrected as follows:

Original pressure...............................	757.7 mm Hg
Difference in levels.............................	4.7 mm Hg
	753.0 mm Hg
Vapor pressure of water at 22°C.................	19.7 mm Hg
Actual pressure of dry air.......................	733.3 mm Hg

Step 2.   The volume of air is 113 ml at 22°C and 733 mm Hg. What is the volume at STP?

$$22°C = 22°C + 273 = 295°K \qquad 0°C = 273°K$$
$$113 \text{ ml} \times \frac{273°K}{295°K} \times \frac{733 \text{ mm}}{760 \text{ mm}} = 100 \text{ ml at STP} = 0.1 \text{ l at STP}$$

The 100 ml (STP) of air corresponds to 100 ml (STP) of vapor obtained from the liquid.   Then 100 ml (STP) of vapor will weigh the same as 113 ml of vapor at 22°C and 733 mm Hg, since these volumes contain the same number of molecules.   Then 100 ml (STP), or 0.1 l (STP), of vapor weighs 0.686 g.   Then

$$\frac{0.686 \text{ g}}{0.1 \text{ l (STP)}} \times \frac{22.4 \text{ l (STP)}}{1 \text{ g-mole}} = \frac{154 \text{ g}}{1 \text{ g-mole}}$$

or 154 g/g-mole.   The molecular weight of the liquid is 154.

It should be noted that when gases are collected over water, one should adjust the level of water inside the measuring tube, whenever it is possible, so that it coincides with the level of the water on the outside. Under these conditions the gas in the receiver will be at atmospheric pressure.

Example 2. What weight of an organic volatile liquid (whose molecular weight is 58.0) will be necessary to displace 30 ml of air (over water) in a Victor Meyer apparatus, at 26°C and a barometer reading of 760 mm Hg?

Step 1. Reduce 30 ml of air (over water) at 26°C and 760 mm Hg to standard conditions.

Correction for vapor pressure of water at 26°C:

Barometer reading...............................	760 mm Hg
Vapor pressure of water at 26°C...................	25 mm Hg
Actual pressure of dry gas........................	735 mm Hg

$$26°C = 299°K \qquad 0°C = 273°K$$

$$30 \text{ ml} \times \frac{273°K}{299°K} \times \frac{735 \text{ mm}}{760 \text{ mm}} = 26.5 \text{ ml (STP)} = 0.0265 \text{ l (STP)}$$

Step 2. Molecular weight of liquid = 58.0, or 58 g/g-mole.

$$\frac{58 \text{ g/g-mole}}{22.4 \text{ l (STP)/g-mole}} \times 0.0265 \text{ l (STP)}$$

$$= \frac{58 \text{ g}}{1 \text{ g-mole}} \times \frac{1 \text{ g-mole}}{22.4 \text{ l (STP)}} \times 0.0265 \text{ l (STP)} = 0.0686 \text{ g}$$

Weight of liquid required = 0.0686 g.

Problems

7-45. Calculate the molecular weight of a volatile liquid from the following data:

Weight of liquid used.................................	0.4618	g
Volume of vapor obtained.............................	265.4	ml
Temperature...	75.0	°C
Barometer reading in mm Hg.........................	760.0	mm

Ans. 49.7.

7-46. A volatile liquid, weighing 0.125 g when vaporized, yielded 31 ml of vapor, measured over mercury at 100°C and 735 mm Hg. The level of the mercury in the measuring tube was 20 cm above the level of the mercury in the trough. Neglecting the vapor pressure of mercury at 100°C, calculate the molecular weight of the liquid. *Ans.* 175.

7-47. A volume of gas measuring 70 ml collected over water at 27°C and 756.5 mm Hg is found to weigh 0.08 g when dry. Determine the molecular weight of the gas. *Ans.* 29.

7-48. A gas measuring 67.8 ml collected over water at 24°C and 754.2 mm Hg weighed 0.075 g when dry. Calculate the molecular weight of the gas. *Ans.* 28

7-49. Determine the molecular weight of a volatile liquid, using the Victor Meyer apparatus, from the following data:

Weight of liquid used..................................	0.2016	g
Volume of air displaced...............................	44.0	ml
Temperature..	20	°C
Barometer reading (mm Hg)...........................	760.4	mm
Vapor pressure of water at 20°C (mm Hg)..............	17.4	mm

Ans. 113.

7-50. In a laboratory experiment for the determination of the molecular weight of oxygen, a student noted that a test tube, containing a mixture of potassium chlorate and manganese dioxide, after heating, had lost 0.48 g.   The oxygen evolved in the reaction was collected over water and measured 377 ml at 21°C and 747.4 mm Hg.   (*a*) What was the molecular weight determined by the student?   (*b*) What was his percentage error?

Ans. (*a*) 32.1; (*b*) 0.3 per cent.

7-51. It was noted in a laboratory experiment that after a mixture of potassium chlorate and manganese dioxide had been heated in a test tube, a loss in weight of 0.5 g was obtained.   The oxygen evolved in the reaction and collected in a vessel over water measured 375 ml at 28°C and 749 mm. Hg.   The level of water inside the vessel was 2 in. above that on the outside.   Calculate the following: (*a*) the density of oxygen in grams per liter at STP; (*b*) the approximate molecular weight of oxygen; (*c*) the percentage error of the experiment.   *Ans.*   (*a*) 1.55 g/l at STP; (*b*) 34.7; (*c*) 8.4 per cent.

7-52. Calculate the molecular weight of a volatile liquid from the following data:

Weight of volatile liquid used.........................	0.181	g
Volume of vapor obtained.............................	71.9	ml
Temperature..	100.0	°C
Barometer reading (mm Hg)...........................	752.0	mm

7-53. Calculate the weight of 1 g-mole of a volatile liquid from the following data obtained by the Victor Meyer method:

Weight of compound taken.............................	0.208	g
Volume of air displaced...............................	33.9	ml
Temperature..	21	°C
Barometer reading (mm Hg)...........................	750	mm
Vapor pressure of water at 21°C (mm Hg)..............	18.5	mm

7-54. In a molecular-weight determination by the Victor Meyer method, 240 mg of a volatile substance displaced 40 ml of air, measured at 27°C and 765 mm Hg.   What is the weight of 1 g-mole of the compound?

7-55. A glass bulb of 250 ml capacity is filled with vapor which weighs 625 mg measured at 273°C and pressure of 1 atm.   Calculate the weight of 2 g-moles of the vapor.

7-56. A quantity of gas weighing 2.5 g with a density of 1.25 g/l at STP is collected over water at 20°C and 750 mm Hg.   Calculate the volume occupied by the gas under these conditions.

7-57. Calculate the volume occupied by 0.2016 g of hydrogen when measured in a container over water at 24°C and 755 mm Hg.

7-58. Determine the weight of a sample of chloroform ($CHCl_3$) that will be necessary to displace 25 ml of air, measured at a temperature of 22°C and a barometer reading of 750 mm, using a Victor Meyer apparatus.

7-59. What weight of carbon tetrachloride (CCl_4) will be required to displace 22.4 ml of air, measured at 21°C and pressure of 1 atm, using a Victor Meyer apparatus?

7-60. Calculate the volume of vapor, measured at 75°C and 755 mm Hg, that can be obtained from 200 mg of acetone, 1 g-mole of which weighs 58.05 g.

MOLECULAR-WEIGHT DETERMINATION BY BOILING-POINT AND FREEZING-POINT METHODS

Experimentation has shown that in dealing with soluble, nonvolatile, and non-ionized solutes dissolved in water (1) the freezing point of the solvent (water) is lowered and (2) the boiling point of the solvent is raised. Also, the freezing-point lowering and the boiling-point rise are proportional to the number of molecules dissolved. Thus, 1 g-mole (6.02×10^{23} molecules), or 62 g, of ethylene glycol [$C_2H_4(OH)_2$] dissolved in 1,000 g of water lowers the freezing point 1.86°C, *i.e.*, the solution would freeze at a temperature of −1.86°C, rather than at 0°C. Furthermore, the boiling point of the water would be increased 0.52°C, *i.e.*, the solution would boil at a temperature of 100.52°C instead of 100°C.

Then a solution containing 1 g-mole (342 g) of cane sugar ($C_{12}H_{22}O_{11}$) dissolved in 1,000 g of water would boil at 100.52°C and it would freeze at −1.86°C. If 2 g-moles of cane sugar were dissolved in 1,000 g of water, the boiling-point rise would be 2×0.52°C, or 1.04°C, and the freezing-point lowering would be 2×1.86°C, or 3.72°C.

The boiling-point rise ΔT or the freezing-point lowering ΔT is proportional to the number of gram-moles of solute in a given weight of solvent.

The boiling-point rise or freezing-point lowering ΔT is proportional to the weight w of the solute, or to the number of gram-moles of solute w/M, where M is the molecular weight of the solute.

The boiling-point rise or freezing-point lowering ΔT is inversely proportional to the weight W of solvent or to the number of gram-moles W/M_1 of solvent, where M_1 is the molecular weight of the solvent. M_1 is, of course, known.

If one number (ΔT) is proportional to another, it equals some constant K_1 times the other.

$$\Delta T = \frac{K_1 \dfrac{w}{M}}{\dfrac{W}{M_1}}$$

Transposing,

$$M = \frac{K_1 M_1}{\Delta T} \frac{w}{W}$$

Since it is customary to use the number of gram-moles of solute in 1,000 g of solvent, and since M_1 is a known number, let $K = K_1 M_1 / 1,000$; then

$$M = 1,000 \frac{K}{\Delta T} \frac{w}{W}$$

The foregoing expression for molecular-weight determination by either the boiling-point or freezing-point method can be formulated with dimensional units as follows:

$$M = 1,000 \text{ g solvent} \times \frac{K°}{\text{g-mole solute}} \times \frac{1}{\Delta T°} \times \frac{\text{g solute } (w)}{\text{g solvent } (W)}$$

where $\dfrac{K°}{\text{g-mole solute}}$ = freezing-point or boiling-point constant per gram-mole of solute

$\Delta T°$ = observed freezing-point lowering or boiling-point rise

A convenient form for solving problems involving these methods is

$$\Delta T° : \frac{K°}{\text{g-mole solute}} = \left(\frac{\text{g solute}}{\text{g solvent}} \times 1,000 \text{ g solvent} \right) : \frac{\text{g solute}}{\text{g-mole solute}}$$

where $\dfrac{K°}{\text{g-mole solute}}$ for water = 1.86° for freezing-point method, and

0.52° for boiling-point method

$\dfrac{\text{g solute}}{\text{g-mole}}$ = molecular weight

The value of K, the proportionality factor, or constant, can be determined by dissolving a measured weight of a substance whose

TABLE XI. BOILING-POINT AND FREEZING-POINT CONSTANTS FOR VARIOUS SOLVENTS

Substance	Boiling point at 1 atm	K for boiling-point method	Freezing point at 1 atm	K for freezing-point method
Acetic acid (CH_3COOH).........	118.1°C	3.07	16.7°C	3.9
Acetone (CH_3COCH_3)...........	56.5	1.71		
Benzene (C_6H_6)...............	80.09	2.67	5.5	5.12
Carbon tetrachloride (CCl_4).....	76.8	5.03	−24.0	
Chloroform ($CHCl_3$)...........	61.26	3.63	−61.0	4.68
Ether ($C_2H_5OC_2H_5$).............	34.6	2.02	....	1.79
Ethyl alcohol (C_2H_5OH)........	78.4	1.22		
Phenol (C_6H_5OH)..............	181.4	3.56		
Water......................	100.0	0.52	0.0	1.86

molecular weight is known, in a known weight or volume of the solvent to be used. Then, in the foregoing relationship, every factor is known except K, and one can solve for K. Considering benzene as a solvent in the determination of the molecular weight of a material, say an oil, we dissolve 0.2 g of a known material such as anthracene ($C_{14}H_{10}$, molecular weight = 178) in 25 g of benzene and find that the boiling point of the solution is 0.120° higher than that of pure benzene.

$$M = 1,000 \frac{Kw}{\Delta TW}$$

$$K = \frac{M\Delta TW}{1,000w} = \frac{178 \times 0.120 \times 25 \text{ g}}{1,000 \times 0.2 \text{ g}} = 2.670$$

It should be stated that acids, bases, and salts, or electrolytes in general, ionize in solution to various degrees and thus give rise to larger numbers of individual particles than would be assumed from the weight of the substance used. Electrolytes therefore give abnormal boiling-point elevations and abnormal freezing-point depressions.

Example 1. When 15.3 g of glycerin is added to 500 g of water, the freezing point of the solution is $-0.62°C$. What is the approximate molecular weight of glycerin?
Since

$$\Delta T : \frac{K°}{1 \text{ g-mole}} = \left(\frac{\text{no. of g solute}}{\text{no. of g H}_2\text{O}} \times 1,000 \text{ g H}_2\text{O} \right) : \frac{\text{g solute}}{1 \text{ g-mole}}$$
$$\Delta T = 0.62° \qquad K° = 1.86°$$

Let x = number of grams of solute per gram-mole, or the molecular weight

$$0.62° : \frac{1.86°}{1 \text{ g-mole}} = \left(\frac{15.3 \text{ g solute}}{500 \text{ g H}_2\text{O}} \times 1,000 \text{ g H}_2\text{O} \right) : x$$

$$x = \frac{1.86°}{1 \text{ g-mole}} \times \frac{15.3 \text{ g solute}}{500 \text{ g H}_2\text{O}} \times 1,000 \text{ g H}_2\text{O} \times \frac{1}{0.62°}$$

$$= \frac{92 \text{ g solute}}{1 \text{ g-mole}}$$

or the molecular weight = 92.

Example 2. What weight of methyl alcohol (CH_3OH) is needed to lower the freezing point of 1,000 g of water to $-10°C$?
Since

$$\Delta T : \frac{K°}{1 \text{ g-mole}} = \left(\frac{\text{no. of g solute}}{\text{no. of g H}_2\text{O}} \times 1,000 \text{ g H}_2\text{O} \right) : \frac{\text{g solute}}{1 \text{ g-mole}}$$

Molecular weight CH_3OH = 32 or 32 g solute/g-mole

$$\Delta T = 10° \qquad K° = 1.86°$$

Let x = number of grams of solute needed

$$10°:\frac{1.86°}{1 \text{ g-mole}} = \left(\frac{x}{1,000 \text{ g H}_2\text{O}} \times 1,000 \text{ g H}_2\text{O}\right):\frac{32 \text{ g solute}}{1 \text{ g-mole}}$$

$$x = 10° \times \frac{32 \text{ g solute}}{1 \text{ g-mole}} \times \frac{1 \text{ g-mole}}{1.86°}$$

$$= \frac{320}{1.86} \text{ g solute} = 172 \text{ g solute} = 172 \text{ g CH}_3\text{OH needed}$$

Example 3.   An antifreeze solution having a specific gravity of 1.05 and containing 20 per cent by weight of a solute freezes at $-4.8°$C. Determine the approximate molecular weight of the solute.

NOTE.   For purpose of convenience in dealing with dimensional units, "antifreeze solution" is abbreviated *as*.   The specific gravity is 1.05, or expressed in terms of density, 1.05 kg *as*/l *as*, or 1,050 g *as*/l *as*.

$$\frac{1,050 \text{ g } as}{1 \text{ l } as} \times \frac{0.2 \text{ g pure solute}}{1 \text{ g } as} = \frac{210 \text{ g pure solute}}{1 \text{ l } as}$$

Since 1 l of antifreeze solution weighs 1,050 g of which 210 g is pure solute, then 1,050 g *as* − 210 g pure solute = 840 g water in *as*, or there is 210 g pure solute in 840 g of water which makes up the antifreeze solution.

Let x = molecular weight of solute

$$4.8°:\frac{1.86°}{1 \text{ g-mole}} = \left(\frac{210 \text{ g solute}}{840 \text{ g H}_2\text{O}} \times 1,000 \text{ g H}_2\text{O}\right):x$$

$$x = \frac{1.86°}{1 \text{ g-mole}}\left(\frac{210 \text{ g solute}}{840 \text{ g H}_2\text{O}} \times 1,000 \text{ g H}_2\text{O}\right) \times \frac{1}{4.8°}$$

$$= \frac{96.8 \text{ g solute}}{1 \text{ g-mole}}$$

or 96.8 = molecular weight.

Example 4.   What is the boiling point of an aqueous solution containing 20 per cent by weight ethylene glycol $[C_2H_4(OH)_2]$?

$$20 \text{ per cent} = \frac{20 \text{ g C}_2\text{H}_4(\text{OH})_2}{100 \text{ g solution}}$$

or 20 g $C_2H_4(OH)_2$ in 80 g of water.

$$\text{Molecular weight C}_2\text{H}_4(\text{OH})_2 = 62$$

or 62 g solute/g-mole.

Since

$$\Delta T:\frac{K°}{1 \text{ g-mole}} = \left(\frac{\text{g solute}}{\text{g H}_2\text{O}} \times 1,000 \text{ g H}_2\text{O}\right):\frac{\text{g solute}}{1 \text{ g-mole}}$$

Let x = boiling-point rise ΔT; $K°$ for water = $0.52°$

$$x : \frac{0.52°}{1 \text{ g-mole}} = \left(\frac{20 \text{ g solute}}{80 \text{ g H}_2\text{O}} \times 1{,}000 \text{ g H}_2\text{O}\right) : \frac{62 \text{ g solute}}{1 \text{ g-mole}}$$

$$x = \frac{0.52°}{1 \text{ g-mole}} \times \left(\frac{20 \text{ g solute}}{80 \text{ g H}_2\text{O}} \times 1{,}000 \text{ g H}_2\text{O}\right) \times \frac{1 \text{ g-mole}}{62 \text{ g solute}}$$

$$= \frac{0.52° \times 20 \times 1{,}000}{80 \times 62} = 2.1° = \text{boiling-point rise}$$

The solution will boil at 102.1°C.

Problems

7-61. Determine the freezing point of 11.3 per cent ethyl alcohol (C_2H_5OH) solution. *Ans.* −5.0°C.

7-62. Calculate the weight of glycerin [$C_3H_5(OH)_3$] dissolved in 2,500 g of water that will be required to have the same freezing point as a solution containing 2.5 g of cane sugar ($C_{12}H_{22}O_{11}$) dissolved in 125 g of water. *Ans.* 1.3 g.

7-63. An antifreeze solution has a specific gravity of 1.013 and contains 10 per cent by weight of pure glycol [$C_2H_4(OH)_2$]. What is the freezing point of this solution? *Ans.* −3.3°C.

7-64. (*a*) If one uses a 30 per cent ethylene glycol [$C_2H_4(OH)_2$] solution as an antifreeze in an automobile radiator, what is the lowest safe temperature at which the automobile may be operated without freezing the radiator solution? (*b*) At what temperature would this radiator solution "boil over"? *Ans.* (*a*) Above −12.8°C.

7-65. It was determined that 0.365 g of a substance dissolved in 90 g of benzene gave a freezing-point depression of 0.45°C. Calculate the molecular weight of the substance. *Ans.* 46.

7-66. It was found that 1.0 g of a solute dissolved in 250 g of water gave a solution freezing at −0.123°C. What is the molecular weight of the solute? *Ans.* 60.5.

7-67. It was found that 30 g of an organic compound dissolved in 500 g of water gave a boiling point of 100.173°C. What is the molecular weight of the substance? *Ans.* 180.

7-68. The freezing point of a solution containing 23 g of ethyl alcohol in 1,000 g of water is −0.98°C. What is the molecular weight of the alcohol? *Ans.* 46.

7-69. When 7.0 g of glycerin is added to 228 g of water, the freezing point of the solution is −0.62°C. What is the molecular weight of glycerin? *Ans.* 92.

7-70. It was found that a solution containing 9.3 g of a substance in 150 g of water boiled at 212.93°F. What is the molecular weight of the substance? *Ans.* 62.

7-71. What weight of glucose ($C_6H_{12}O_6$) dissolved in 500 ml of water is necessary to give a freezing-point lowering of 0.15°C? *Ans.* 7.26 g.

7-72. Calculate the weight of ethyl alcohol (C_2H_5OH) dissolved in 200 g of water that will give a freezing-point depression of 0.12°C. *Ans.* 0.6 g.

7-73. Determine the boiling point of a 5 per cent ethylene glycol [$C_2H_4(OH)_2$] solution. *Ans.* 100.14°C.

CHAPTER VIII

DERIVATION OF CHEMICAL FORMULAS

OUTLINE

Each chemical compound has a definite chemical formula which can be derived from its percentage composition.

The percentage composition of a substance is derived from a qualitative chemical analysis followed by a quantitative analysis of it.

To determine the relative numbers of atoms in a molecule of a substance: First, divide the weight per cent of each element in the substance by its atomic weight, which gives the number of gram-atoms of each element in the molecule. Second, express the number of gram-atoms of each element in the proportion of lowest integers. These whole numbers represent the *relative* number of atoms in the molecule. This gives rise to the *simple* or *empirical formula.*

The molecular formula represents the *actual* number of atoms of each element in 1 molecule of the compound. To establish the molecular formula, it is necessary to know the molecular weight of the compound or to be able to determine the molecular weight of it.

Chemical formulas of minerals are empirical formulas.

Chemical formulas of hydrated compounds and complex ammonia compounds.

EMPIRICAL OR SIMPLE CHEMICAL FORMULA

In the preceding chapters the importance and significance of the chemical formula have been stressed. It has been stated that a given chemical compound is characterized by having a constant and definite percentage composition by weight. It follows that each chemical compound has a definite chemical formula which can be derived from its percentage composition. The composition of a given material is obtained usually by, first, a qualitative chemical analysis, followed by a quantitative analysis of it. The qualitative analysis gives information as to the nature of the various constituents present in the unknown material. The quantitative analysis establishes the proportion by weight of the elements in the compound, and this proportion is usually expressed as the percentage composition of these constituents. To derive the chemical formula of a given substance from its percentage composition, it is necessary to determine the relative numbers of atoms in the molecule and to express these numbers in the proportion of the lowest integers. This gives rise to the **simple** or **empirical formula.** The method follows:

1. Determine the relative number of atoms by dividing the weight per cent of each element by its atomic weight. It is customary to express weight per cent on a gram basis and the atomic weight as grams per gram-atom. The quotient obtained will be the number of gram-atoms of each element in 100 g of the given substance.

2. Express the numbers of gram-atoms of each element in the proportion of lowest integers. These whole numbers represent the relative number of atoms in the molecule.

Example 1. Three compounds of iron and sulfur have the following compositions: (a) Fe = 46.56 per cent, S = 53.44 per cent; (b) Fe = 63.53 per cent, S = 36.47 per cent; (c) Fe = 53.73 per cent, S = 46.27 per cent. Atomic weights: Fe = 55.8; S = 32.1. Derive the simplest formula for each compound.

(a) Since

$$Fe = \frac{46.56 \text{ g}}{55.8 \text{ g/g-atom}} = 0.833 \text{ g-atom}$$

$$S = \frac{53.44 \text{ g}}{32.1 \text{ g/g-atom}} = 1.666 \text{ g-atoms}$$

Fe:S = 0.833 g-atom:1.666 g-atoms = 1:2. The simplest or empirical formula is FeS_2. This is the formula for iron pyrites.

NOTE. In expressing gram-atom ratios in terms of whole numbers, one divides each term of the ratio of gram-atoms by the smallest term. In the foregoing example, 0.833 is the smallest term.

(b) Since

$$Fe = \frac{63.53 \text{ g}}{55.8 \text{ g/g-atom}} = 1.14 \text{ g-atoms}$$

$$S = \frac{36.47 \text{ g}}{32.1 \text{ g/g-atom}} = 1.14 \text{ g-atoms}$$

Fe:S = 1.14 g-atoms:1.14 g-atoms = 1:1. The simplest formula of this compound is FeS, which is the formula for ferrous sulfide.

(c) Since

$$Fe = \frac{53.73 \text{ g}}{55.8 \text{ g/g-atom}} = 0.962 \text{ g-atom}$$

$$S = \frac{46.27 \text{ g}}{32.1 \text{ g/g-atom}} = 1.443 \text{ g-atoms}$$

Fe:S = 0.962 g-atom:1.443 g-atoms = 1:1.5. Note that this ratio was obtained by dividing each term of the ratio of gram-atoms by the smallest term. The ratio 1:1.5 must be expressed in terms of whole numbers since fractional parts of an atom do not exist. This is accomplished by multiplying both terms in the ratio by 2. Therefore

$1:1.5 = 2:3$, and the formula for this compound is Fe_2S_3, which is ferric sulfide.

Example 2. In the various oxides of lead, it is found that the weights of lead and of oxygen that enter into chemical combination are as follows: (a) in plumbous oxide, 59.412 g of Pb is combined with 4.588 g of O; (b) in lead sesquioxide, 179.24 g of Pb is combined with 20.76 g of O; (c) in plumbic oxide, 129.93 g of Pb is combined with 20.07 g of O; (d) in red lead, 93.24 g of Pb is combined with 9.60 g of O. Derive the simplest formula for each compound. Atomic weights: $Pb = 207.2$; $O = 16.0$.

(a) Since

$$Pb = \frac{59.412 \text{ g}}{207.2 \text{ g/g-atom}} = 0.286 \text{ g-atom}$$

$$O = \frac{4.588 \text{ g}}{16.0 \text{ g/g-atom}} = 0.286 \text{ g-atom}$$

$Pb:O = 0.286$ g-atom$:0.286$ g-atom $= 1:1$. The simplest formula for plumbous oxide is PbO. This is the formula for litharge.

(b) Since

$$Pb = \frac{179.24 \text{ g}}{207.2 \text{ g/g-atom}} = 0.865 \text{ g-atom}$$

$$O = \frac{20.76 \text{ g}}{16.0 \text{ g/g-atom}} = 1.298 \text{ g-atoms}$$

$Pb:O = 0.865$ g-atom$:1.298$ g-atoms $= 1:1.49$. To express the ratio of $1:1.49$ in terms of lowest integer, multiply both terms by 2. Then $Pb:O = 2:3$. The simplest formula for lead sesquioxide is Pb_2O_3.

(c) Since

$$Pb = \frac{129.93 \text{ g}}{207.2 \text{ g/g-atom}} = 0:627 \text{ g-atom}$$

$$O = \frac{20.07 \text{ g}}{16.0 \text{ g/g-atom}} = 1.25 \text{ g-atoms}$$

$Pb:O = 0.627$ g-atom$:1.25$ g-atoms $= 1:2$. The simplest formula for plumbic oxide is PbO_2. This is also called lead dioxide.

(d) Since

$$Pb = \frac{93.24 \text{ g}}{207.2 \text{ g/g-atom}} = 0.45 \text{ g-atom}$$

$$O = \frac{9.60 \text{ g}}{16.0 \text{ g/g-atom}} = 0.60 \text{ g-atom}$$

$Pb:O = 0.45$ g-atom$:0.60$ g-atom $= 1:1.33$. The ratio $1:1.33$ was obtained by dividing each term of the gram-atom ratio by the smallest number, or 0.45. However, to express this ratio in terms of lowest integers, it is necessary to multiply each term by 3, which gives $Pb:O = 1:1.33 = 3:3.99$, or $Pb:O = 3:4$. The formula for red lead is Pb_3O_4.

MOLECULAR OR TRUE CHEMICAL FORMULA

In the foregoing examples the formulas derived for each of the various substances represent the empirical formulas for these solid substances; they are also considered to be their true formulas. However, to establish the **true** or **molecular formula** of a compound, it is necessary to know not only the percentage composition by weight but also the molecular weight of that substance, or to have sufficient data at hand to enable one to determine the molecular weight by one of the various methods described in Chap. VII. However, these methods apply only to gases, liquids, and solids that are readily vaporized (volatile). In the case of solids that are nonvolatile and insoluble, there is no direct method available by which the molecular weight of the substance can be determined. It is possible to obtain knowledge concerning the molecular weight of crystalline substances whose ultimate crystal structure is known from information obtainable by X-ray crystal analysis. This is beyond the scope of this text. In dealing with nonvolatile solids, then, the empirical formula is considered to be the molecular formula for a particular solid. The *molecular formula* represents not only the relative numbers of atoms in 1 molecule of the substance, but also the *actual number of atoms* of each element in the molecule of the compound.

Example 1. The percentage composition of a gaseous hydrocarbon is 85.62 per cent carbon and 14.38 per cent hydrogen. The density of this gas is 1.260 g/l at STP. Determine the molecular formula of this hydrocarbon.

Step 1. Determine the empirical formula.

$$C = 85.62 \text{ per cent} \qquad H = 14.38 \text{ per cent}$$

or 100 g of hydrocarbon contains 85.62 g of C and 14.38 g of H. Atomic weights: $C = 12.00$; $H = 1.008$.

$$C = \frac{85.62 \text{ g}}{12.00 \text{ g/g-atom}} = 7.135 \text{ g-atoms}$$
$$H = \frac{14.38 \text{ g}}{1.008 \text{ g/g-atom}} = 14.265 \text{ g-atoms}$$

$C:H = 7.135$ g-atoms$:14.265$ g-atoms $= 1:2$. The empirical formula for this hydrocarbon is CH_2.

Step 2.   Calculate the molecular weight.

Density = 1.260 g/l at STP

1.260 g/l at STP × 22.4 l at STP/g-mole = 28.224 g/g-mole

Molecular weight of the hydrocarbon = 28.224.

Step 3.   Determine the molecular formula.   The molecular weight of empirical formula CH_2 is 14.016.   However, the calculated molecular weight is 28.224, which is about twice the weight represented by the empirical formula.   Therefore, there must be 2 times as many atoms of carbon and of hydrogen in the molecule, or its molecular formula must be C_2H_4.   This formula corresponds to a molecular weight of 28.032.   The discrepancy between the calculated molecular weight and the molecular weight corresponding to the molecular formula may be attributed to slight errors in the chemical analysis and in the density determination.   However, the calculated molecular weight is sufficiently accurate to establish beyond question that the molecular formula for this hydrocarbon is C_2H_4, and not any other multiple of CH_2 such as C_3H_6.

Alternate Solution.   Step 1.   Calculate the molecular weight.

For convenience, gaseous hydrocarbon is abbreviated *gas*.

1.26 g *gas*/l at STP × 22.4 l at STP/g-mole = 28.224 g/g-mole
= molecular weight

Step 2.   Reduce percentages to grams per gram of *gas*.   Thus

C = 85.62 per cent = 0.8562 g/g of *gas*
H = 14.38 per cent = 0.1438 g/g of *gas*

Step 3.   Determine the number of gram-atoms per gram of *gas* and multiply this by the number of grams of *gas* per gram-mole, or

$$\frac{\text{g/g of } gas}{\text{g/g-atom}} \times \text{g of } gas\text{/g-mole} = \text{g-atom/g-mole} = \text{atom/mole}$$

$$C = \frac{0.8562 \text{ g/g of } gas}{12 \text{ g/g-atom}} \times 28.224 \text{ g of } gas\text{/g-mole} = 2 \text{ atoms/mole}$$

$$H = \frac{0.1438 \text{ g/g of } gas}{1.008 \text{ g/g-atom}} \times 28.224 \text{ g of } gas\text{/g-mole} = 4 \text{ atoms/mole}$$

Note that this solution arrives at the actual number of atoms in the formula, or C_2H_4.

Example 2.   The chemical analysis of a volatile liquid organic compound gave the following percentage composition: C = 40.00 per cent; H = 6.70 per cent; O = 53.30 per cent.   It was found that a 300-mg sample of the liquid yielded 166.7 ml of vapor at 130°C and

755 mm Hg. From this information establish the true molecular formula of the compound.

Step 1. Establish the empirical formula.

From the analysis, 100 g of the compound contains 40.00 g of C, 6.70 g of H, and 53.30 g of O.

$$C = \frac{40.00 \text{ g}}{12.00 \text{ g/g-atom}} = 3.33 \text{ g-atoms}$$

$$H = \frac{6.70 \text{ g}}{1.008 \text{ g/g-atom}} = 6.65 \text{ g-atoms}$$

$$O = \frac{53.30 \text{ g}}{16.00 \text{ g/g-atom}} = 3.33 \text{ g-atoms}$$

C:H:O = 3.33 g-atoms:6.65 g-atoms:3.33 g-atoms = 1:2:1. The empirical formula of the compound is CH_2O.

Step 2. Calculate the molecular weight of the substance.

The sample of liquid = 300 mg = 0.3 g yielded 166.7 ml of vapor at 130°C and 755 mm Hg. Reduce this volume to STP.

$$130°C = 130°C + 273 = 403°K \qquad 0°C = 273°K$$

$$166.7 \text{ ml} \times \frac{273°K}{403°K} \times \frac{755 \text{ mm}}{760 \text{ mm}} = 112 \text{ ml, or } 0.112 \text{ l at STP}$$

0.112 l at STP weighs 0.3 g.

0.3 g/0.112 l at STP $\times$ 22.4 l at STP/g-mole = 60.0 g/g-mole

Molecular weight of compound = 60.0.

The empirical formula CH_2O gives a molecular weight of 30.016. The calculated molecular weight is 60.0, which is twice the weight represented by the empirical formula. Then the molecular formula of the compound is $C_2H_4O_2$. This is the formula for acetic acid ($HC_2H_3O_2$ or CH_3COOH).

Alternate Solution. *Step* 1. Calculate the molecular weight of substance from given data. This was done in Step 2 of the preceding solution. The calculated molecular weight of this compound was 60.0.

Step 2. Reduce percentages to basis of gram per gram of compound.

$$C = 40.0 \text{ per cent} = 0.40 \text{ g/g of } compd$$
$$H = 6.7 \text{ per cent} = 0.067 \text{ g/g of } compd$$
$$O = 53.3 \text{ per cent} = 0.533 \text{ g/g of } compd$$

Step 3. Set up the number of gram-atoms per gram of compound for each element and multiply each by the number of grams of compound per gram-mole (gram-molecular weight).

$$C = \frac{0.40 \text{ g/g of } compd}{12 \text{ g/g-atom}} \times 60 \text{ g of } compd/\text{g-mole} = 2 \text{ g-atoms/g-mole}$$
$$= 2 \text{ atoms/mole}$$

$$H = \frac{0.067 \text{ g/g of } compd}{1.008 \text{ g/g-atom}} \times 60 \text{ g of } compd/\text{g-mole} = 4 \text{ g-atoms/g-mole}$$
$$= 4 \text{ atoms/mole}$$

$$O = \frac{0.533 \text{ g/g of } compd}{16.0 \text{ g/g-atom}} \times 60 \text{ g of } compd/\text{g-mole} = 2 \text{ g-atoms/g-mole}$$
$$= 2 \text{ atoms/mole}$$

Step 4. $C:H:O = 2:4:2$, or molecular formula $= C_2H_4O_2$.

It should be noted here that molecular formulas of liquid substances that can be vaporized without decomposition, as in the foregoing example, are obtainable by assuming the molecular weight of the substance in the liquid phase to be the same as that in the vapor phase.   The Victor Meyer method, described and illustrated in Chap. VII, is useful in the determination of the molecular weight of these types of substances.   Molecular-weight determinations of substances that cannot be vaporized without decomposition but can be dissolved in some solvent are made by the freezing-point or the boiling-point method.

FORMULAS OF MINERALS

A mineral may be defined as any chemical element or compound occurring in nature and usually possessing a definite crystalline structure.   The elements sulfur, carbon (in the form of diamond and graphite), copper, gold, and silver found in the earth's crust are examples of simple element minerals.   The various silicate, carbonate, and sulfate rocks are typical examples of the more complex type of inorganic minerals.   Anthracite and bituminous coal and asphalt are naturally occurring organic minerals.   The silicate minerals are of considerable interest to almost everyone.   They are widely distributed over the earth and, to be sure, are crystallographically complicated and of complex chemical composition.   Great credit is due to W. H. Bragg and W. L. Bragg, who have pioneered in the field of X-ray analysis of silicate minerals, for their classification into a very few groups of all the silicates whose crystal structures are known.   A chemical analysis of a mineral will give some idea of the constituents present in it.   It does not give information as to how the atoms are combined or arranged in the structure.   It is the purpose in this text to concern ourselves with a few examples of how chemical formulas may be assigned to minerals from the percentage composition of the mineral. Since the molecular weight of a mineral cannot be determined directly, the formula established for its composition will of necessity be the empirical one.

The following example deals with a mineral made up of a chemical combination of elements.

Example 1. The chemical analysis of a specimen of arsenopyrite, or mispickel, from Czechoslovakia by Palmer[1] gave the following results:

Fe = 34.30 per cent   As = 45.51 per cent   S = 19.75 per cent

From this analysis 100 g of the mineral contains

$$\text{Fe} = \frac{34.30 \text{ g}}{55.8 \text{ g/g-atom}} = 0.614 \text{ g-atom}$$

$$\text{As} = \frac{45.51 \text{ g}}{74.9 \text{ g/g-atom}} = 0.608 \text{ g-atom}$$

$$\text{S} = \frac{19.75 \text{ g}}{32.1 \text{ g/g-atom}} = 0.615 \text{ g-atom}$$

The weight ratios of the various atoms in this mineral, then, Fe:As:S = 0.614:0.608:0.615, are in the nearest whole-number ratio of 1:1:1. Therefore, the empirical formula of arsenopyrite is FeAsS and is sometimes written as $FeS_2 \cdot FeAs_2$.

The slight discrepancy in the foregoing ratios is due, undoubtedly, to small amounts of impurities in the mineral and also to the fact that the percentage composition from chemical analysis is only a close approximation to the true composition. One is justified, therefore, in reducing the weight ratios to the nearest whole numbers to establish the chemical formula of the mineral.

The chemical composition of a great many minerals, of greater complexity than the preceding example, is indicated by expressing the various elements combined with oxygen in terms of percentages of various oxides present. As an example of this type of mineral, consider the widely distributed material known as kaolinite, a hydrated aluminum silicate. It is used in large quantities in the manufacture of ceramic materials such as chinaware, porcelain, tiles, insulators, and refractory products.

Example 2. The chemical analysis of kaolinite, the composition of which is expressed in terms of the various oxides, is silica (SiO_2) = 46.06 per cent; alumina (Al_2O_3) = 39.63 per cent; water (H_2O) = 14.31 per cent. What is its empirical formula?

[1] *U.S. Geol. Survey Bull.*, **878,** 84.

In representing the formula of the mineral, we express the weight ratios in terms of the ratios of gram-moles of the oxides present. Thus

$$1 \text{ g-mole } SiO_2 = 60.06 \text{ g } SiO_2$$
$$1 \text{ g-mole } Al_2O_3 = 101.94 \text{ g } Al_2O_3$$
$$1 \text{ g-mole } H_2O = 18.016 \text{ g } H_2O$$

From the analysis, 100 g of kaolinite contains

$$SiO_2 = \frac{46.06 \text{ g}}{60.06 \text{ g/g-mole}} = 0.767 \text{ g-mole}$$

$$Al_2O_3 = \frac{39.63 \text{ g}}{101.94 \text{ g/g-mole}} = 0.388 \text{ g-mole}$$

$$H_2O = \frac{14.31 \text{ g}}{18.016 \text{ g/g-mole}} = 0.794 \text{ g-mole}$$

The weight ratios of the various oxides follow: $SiO_2:Al_2O_3:H_2O = 0.767:0.388:0.794$. These numbers are in the nearest whole-number ratios of $2:1:2$. The empirical formula of kaolinite would be written $2SiO_2 \cdot Al_2O_3 \cdot 2H_2O$ or, more correctly, $Al_2(Si_2O_5)(OH)_4$.

When a mineral contains small amounts of other oxides that are similar in chemical nature to the several oxides present in major amounts, these small amounts are regarded as impurities. It is assumed that these oxides have replaced chemically equivalent amounts of the principal oxides. The relative numbers of molecules of these are added in with the number of molecules of the oxides that they probably replaced, thus giving the relative numbers of molecules of the major oxides before replacement took place. This procedure removes unnecessary complications of the formula of the mineral and, at the same time, compensates for the effect of the small amounts of oxides which are regarded as impurities.

HYDRATED COMPOUNDS AND COMPLEX AMMONIA COMPOUNDS

Example 1. A hydrated calcium phosphate contained 7.14 per cent water of crystallization. The molecular weight of this phosphate is 252.2. The percentage composition is Ca = 15.89 per cent; P = 24.60 per cent; H = 2.40 per cent; O = 57.11 per cent. What is the molecular formula of this compound?

Step 1. Reduce percentages to gram per gram of compound.

$$Ca = 15.39 \text{ per cent} = 0.1589 \text{ g/g } compd$$
$$H = 2.40 \text{ per cent} = 0.024 \text{ g/g } compd$$
$$P = 24.60 \text{ per cent} = 0.246 \text{ g/g } compd$$
$$O = 57.11 \text{ per cent} = 0.5711 \text{ g/g } compd$$
$$H_2O = 7.14 \text{ per cent} = 0.0714 \text{ g/g } compd$$

Step 2. Set up the number of gram-atoms per gram of compound for each element and the number of gram-moles of H_2O per gram of compound. Multiply each of these values by the number of grams of compound per gram-mole (gram-molecular weight).

$$Ca = \frac{0.1589 \text{ g/g } compd}{40.1 \text{ g/g-atom}} \times 252.2 \text{ g } compd/\text{g-mole}$$
$$= 1 \text{ g-atom/g-mole} = 1 \text{ atom/mole}$$

$$H = \frac{0.024 \text{ g/g } compd}{1.008 \text{ g/g-atom}} \times 252.2 \text{ g } compd/\text{g-mole}$$
$$= 6 \text{ g-atoms/g-mole} = 6 \text{ atoms/mole}$$

$$P = \frac{0.246 \text{ g/g } compd}{31.0 \text{ g/g-atom}} \times 252.2 \text{ g } compd/\text{g-mole}$$
$$= 2 \text{ g-atoms/g-mole} = 2 \text{ atoms/mole}$$

$$O = \frac{0.5711 \text{ g/g } compd}{16.0 \text{ g/g-atom}} \times 252.2 \text{ g } compd/\text{g-mole}$$
$$= 9 \text{ g-atoms/g-mole} = 9 \text{ atoms/mole}$$

$$H_2O = \frac{0.0714 \text{ g/g } compd}{18.0 \text{ g/g-mole}} \times 252.2 \text{ g } compd/\text{g-mole}$$
$$= 1 \text{ g-mole/g-mole} = 1 \text{ mole/mole}$$

$Ca:H:P:O = 1:6:2:9$.

The analysis gives the total hydrogen and oxygen content of the phosphate without regard to the water of crystallization, and only 1 g-mole of H_2O is contained in the molecule. The salt must be an acid phosphate, since not all the hydrogen is combined with the oxygen to form water. Of the 6 atoms of hydrogen in the molecule, only 2 are combined with 1 oxygen atom, thus leaving 4 atoms of H and 8 atoms of O in the main body of the formula. Thus the molecular formula of the phosphate from the foregoing calculations is shown to be $CaH_4P_2O_8 \cdot H_2O$, or, preferably, $Ca(H_2PO_4)_2 \cdot H_2O$, which is the formula for primary calcium orthophosphate.

Example 2. A complex cobalt compound has the following composition: $Co = 22.58$ per cent; $H = 5.79$ per cent; $N = 32.20$ per cent; $O = 12.26$ per cent; $Cl = 27.17$ per cent. When this compound is heated, it loses ammonia to the extent of 32.63 per cent of its weight. (*a*) How many molecules of ammonia are present in the complex? (*b*) Derive the empirical formula for the compound.

Step 1. Since the molecular weight of the compound is not given, one first sets up the number of gram-atoms of each element and the gram-moles of ammonia.

$$Co = \frac{22.58 \text{ g}}{58.9 \text{ g/g-atom}} = 0.383 \text{ g-atom}$$

$$N = \frac{32.20 \text{ g}}{14.0 \text{ g/g-atom}} = 2.30 \text{ g-atoms}$$

$$H = \frac{5.79 \text{ g}}{1.008 \text{ g/g-atom}} = 5.74 \text{ g-atoms}$$

$$O = \frac{12.26 \text{ g}}{16.0 \text{ g/g-atom}} = 0.766 \text{ g-atom}$$

$$Cl = \frac{27.17 \text{ g}}{35.5 \text{ g/g-atom}} = 0.766 \text{ g-atom}$$

$$NH_3 = \frac{32.63 \text{ g}}{17.0 \text{ g/g-mole}} = 1.94 \text{ g-moles}$$

$Co:N:H:O:Cl:NH_3 = 1:6:15:2:2:5$.   These whole numbers are obtained by dividing each gram-atom and gram-mole term by the smallest number (0.383).   (a) There would be 5 NH_3 molecules in the complex.   (b) Its empirical formula would be written $[Co(NH_3)_5(NO_2)]Cl_2$.

Problems

Answers are purposely omitted in these problems.

8-1. Derive the empirical formula of the compound of the following composition: 16.08 per cent K, 40.15 per cent Pt, 43.76 per cent Cl.

8-2. Derive the empirical formula of the substance that gave on analysis 30.75 per cent K, 25.21 per cent S, 44.04 per cent O.

8-3. Derive the empirical formula of the substance that has the following percentage composition: 36.79 per cent N, 5.30 per cent H, 15.77 per cent C, 42.13 per cent S.

8-4. Derive the empirical formula of the compound that gave on analysis 75.07 per cent Al and 24.93 per cent C.

8-5. Derive the empirical formula of the substance that gave on analysis 32.54 per cent K, 26.67 per cent S, 39.94 per cent O, 0.84 per cent H.

8-6. Derive the empirical formula of the substance that gave on analysis 16.63 per cent Si and 83.36 per cent Cl.

8-7. A substance on analysis gave the following percentage composition: C = 10.05 per cent; H = 0.84 per cent; Cl = 89.10 per cent.   Derive the empirical formula of the substance.

8-8. Derive the empirical formula of the substance that gave on analysis 18.28 per cent Ca, 32.36 per cent Cl, 49.36 per cent H_2O.

8-9. In one chloride of copper it is found that 31.5 g of copper is combined with 17.57 g of chlorine.   In another different chloride of copper, it is found that 40.38 g of copper is combined with 45.05 g of chlorine.   What are the simplest formulas for these chlorides?

8-10. Phosphorus forms two chlorides in which (a) 1.00 g of P is combined with 3.43 g of Cl and (b) 1.00 g of Cl is combined with 0.175 g of P.   What is the simplest formula for each of these substances?

8-11. Chromium forms two oxides.   In the acidic oxide, 3.45 g of Cr is combined with 3.184 g of O.   In the basic oxide, 5.25 g of Cr is combined with 2.423 g of O.   Derive the empirical formulas of these two oxides.

8-12. It is found that in mercurous chloride 1.00 g of Hg is combined with 0.1767 g of Cl and in mercuric chloride 1.00 g of Cl is combined with 2.8285 g of Hg. (a) Derive the simplest formula for each of these chlorides. (b) If the molecular weight of mercurous chloride is about 472, what is the molecular formula for this compound?

8-13. Isoprene (a) and benzene (b) have the following percentage compositions: (a) C = 88.158 per cent, H = 11.842 per cent; (b) C = 92.252 per cent, H = 7.748 per cent. Derive the empirical formula for each of these hydrocarbons. If benzene has a molecular weight of 78, what would be its molecular formula?

8-14. An oxide of nitrogen contains 4.0185 g of N combined with 11.4815 g of O. The molecular weight of this oxide is 108. Derive its molecular formula.

8-15. Derive the molecular formula of the substance that by analysis gave 2.24 per cent H, 26.6 per cent C, 71.09 per cent O. This compound has a molecular weight of 90.016.

8-16. Derive the molecular formula of that substance which contains N = 12.27 per cent; S = 28.09 per cent; H = 3.53 per cent; O = 56.09 per cent. The substance has a molecular weight of 228.184.

8-17. One liter of phosgene at 0°C and 760 mm Hg weighs 4.416 g. The percentage composition is C = 12.13 per cent, O = 16.17 per cent, Cl = 71.69 per cent. Derive the true formula of the substance.

8-18. An oxide of nitrogen contains 30.44 per cent N and 69.56 per cent O; 250 ml of this gas reduced to standard conditions weighs 1.0268 g. Derive its molecular formula.

8-19. A volume of an oxide of chlorine measuring 300 ml and reduced to standard conditions weighs 0.9035 g. The percentage composition is 52.56 per cent Cl and 47.43 per cent O. Derive the molecular formula of the oxide.

8-20. The percentage composition of a volatile nitrogen compound follows: C = 46.15 per cent; N = 53.85 per cent. At standard conditions of temperature and pressure, 47 ml of the vapor weighs 0.1092 g. Derive the molecular formula of this substance.

8-21. The percentage composition of an organic solvent is C = 62.029 per cent, H = 10.416 per cent, O = 27.555 per cent. At a temperature of 80°C and 740 mm Hg, 265.5 ml of the vapor of this compound weighs 0.5182 g. Determine the molecular formula of this substance.

8-22. An oxide of nitrogen has the following composition: N = 30.44 per cent; O = 69.56 per cent. At 140°C and 755 mm Hg, 228.5 ml of this gas weighs 0.308 g. What is its molecular formula?

8-23. An organic compound has the following percentage composition: C = 37.215 per cent; H = 7.815 per cent; Cl = 54.970 per cent. It was determined that 109 ml of the vapor of this compound, measured at 21°C and 750 mm Hg, weighed 0.2879 g. Determine the molecular formula of this volatile compound.

8-24. A volatile organic compound has the following composition: C = 24.259 per cent; H = 4.075 per cent; Cl = 71.665 per cent. It was found that 140.2 ml of the vapor of this compound, measured at 100°C and 740 mm Hg, weighed 0.4416 g. What is the molecular formula of this substance?

8-25. The percentage composition of a mineral was given as follows: lime (CaO) = 9.20 per cent; alumina (Al_2O_3) = 16.79 per cent; silica (SiO_2) = 59.21 per cent; water = 14.80 per cent. Derive the empirical formula of the mineral.

8-26. The gem stone emerald has the following theoretical composition: 5.06 per cent Be; 10.05 per cent Al; 31.48 per cent Si; 53.40 per cent O. Derive the theoretical empirical formula of the mineral.

Ans. $3BeO \cdot 6SiO_2 \cdot Al_2O_3$, or $Be_3Al_2Si_6O_{18}$.

8-27. The theoretical composition of kaolinite is 46.59 per cent SiO_2, 39.48 per cent Al_2O_3, 13.92 per cent H_2O. Derive the empirical formula of this mineral.

8-28. When 10 g of a salt of aluminum was heated, it was found to have lost 4.864 g of water of crystallization. The percentage composition of the crystalline salt is 8.13 per cent Al, 14.42 per cent S, 71.99 per cent O, 5.44 per cent H. Derive the empirical formula of the salt.

8-29. Upon heating, 5 g of washing soda was found to have lost water of crystallization which amounted to 3.147 g of its weight. The theoretical composition of the salt is 16.07 per cent Na, 4.19 per cent C, 72.68 per cent O, 7.04 per cent H. Derive the empirical formula of the substance.

8-30. A 1-g sample of a crystallized salt of iron lost 0.1279 g of water of crystallization upon dehydration. The theoretical percentage composition is 37.03 per cent K, 13.22 per cent Fe, 17.04 per cent C, 19.89 per cent N, 1.43 per cent H, 11.36 per cent O. Derive the empirical formula of the salt.

8-31. A phosphate of sodium contains 60.35 per cent water of crystallization. The theoretical composition of this salt is Na = 12.84 per cent, P = 8.66 per cent, H = 7.03 per cent, O = 71.47 per cent. (a) Determine the number of molecules of water of crystallization contained in this phosphate. (b) Derive the simplest formula of this compound.

8-32. It was found that a phosphate of sodium contained 23.09 per cent water of crystallization. The percentage composition was found to be as follows: Na = 14.74 per cent; P = 19.87 per cent; H = 3.87 per cent; O = 61.52 per cent. (a) Determine the number of molecules of water of crystallization contained in this phosphate. (b) What is the simplest formula of this compound?

8-33. The percentage composition of crystallized arsenate of magnesium is as follows: Mg = 8.37 per cent; As = 25.80 per cent; H = 5.21 per cent; O = 60.61 per cent. This compound contains 43.43 per cent water of crystallization. (a) How many molecules of water of crystallization are contained in this arsenate? (b) What is the simplest formula of this compound?

8-34. A compound has the following percentage composition: Zn = 28.5 per cent; S = 13.95 per cent; N = 24.4 per cent; O = 27.9 per cent; H = 5.22 per cent. It was found upon heating a sample of this compound that a loss of weight amounting to 29.6 per cent occurs, owing to the evolution of ammonia. (a) How many molecules of ammonia were originally present in the compound? (b) What is the empirical formula of the compound?

8-35. Cupric sulfate forms three hydrates containing, respectively, 10.141, 25.294, and 36.073 per cent of water of hydration. (a) Determine the number of molecules of water of hydration in each of these hydrates. (b) Write the formula of each hydrate.

8-36. A sample of crystallized cadmium sulfate weighing 10 g was heated until all the water of crystallization was driven off. The anhydrous cadmium sulfate weighed 6.25 g. What is the formula of the hydrated salt?

8-37. (a) A quantity of crystallized cupric sulfate weighing 13.5 g was heated at 260°C and all the water of crystallization was driven off. The anhydrous salt weighed 8.636 g. What is the formula of the hydrated salt? (b) It was found that if the crystallized cupric sulfate was heated at 110°C, it lost 80 per cent of its water of crystallization. What is the formula of this hydrated salt?

8-38. A crystallized sodium salt contains 39.72 per cent water of crystallization and has a molecular weight of 136.072. The theoretical composition of the salt is as follows: Na = 16.90 per cent; C = 17.64 per cent; H = 6.66 per cent; O = 58.80 per cent. What is the molecular formula of this crystallized salt?

8-39. A crystallized sodium salt has the following percentage composition: Na = 16.66 per cent; S = 23.19 per cent; H = 2.19 per cent; O = 57.96 per cent. The compound contains 13.05 per cent water of crystallization. The molecular weight of this substance is 138.024. Derive the molecular formula of this salt.

8-40. A crystallized organic acid contains 28.58 per cent water of crystallization. The theoretical composition of the compound is as follows: H = 4.80 per cent; C = 19.04 per cent; O = 76.16 per cent. The molecular weight of the compound is 126.048. Derive the molecular formula of this substance.

CHAPTER IX

CHEMICAL EQUATIONS, NONREDOX TYPE

OUTLINE

The chemical equation is a shorthand expression designed to represent chemical changes.

The correctly written (balanced) equation indicates (a) the number of molecules and atoms involved in the reaction, (b) the weight relationship of various molecules and atoms, and (c) the volume relationship when gases are involved in the reaction.

Chemical changes are classified under two distinct groups:

    I. Chemical reactions in which there are no changes in valence numbers (oxidation state) of any of the elements involved in the chemical reaction.

    II. Chemical reactions in which changes in valence numbers (oxidation state) of certain atoms or ions are involved. These are known as oxidation-reduction or redox-type reactions. Only Group I type of chemical reaction is considered in this chapter. The following chapter deals with Group II, Redox Type.

Balancing of chemical equations of Group I: (a) combination reactions and (b) double displacement (metathesis).

Equation writing calls for ability (a) to *predict the correct products* in a given chemical reaction and (b) to set down the *correct chemical formula of each of reacting substances and of products formed.*

Mole relations and weight relations as expressed by the balanced chemical equations as applied to solids, liquids, and gases.

Mole weight and gas-volume relations as expressed by equations involving reactions of gases.

A chemical change is one in which molecules of a substance or substances are altered and molecules of new substances are formed with different properties from those possessed by the original substances. Thus, when mercuric oxide is strongly heated, it suffers decomposition resulting in the formation of metallic mercury and oxygen, each of which, of course, has entirely different properties from those of the original mercuric oxide. In any chemical change the weights of the products formed are exactly equal to the weight of the original substances involved in a chemical reaction (law of conservation of mass). A chemical change or chemical experimental fact is conveniently represented by a **chemical equation** in which the terms of the expression are the symbols and formulas of the reacting substances and of the products formed by the chemical reaction.

Thus when calcium oxide (quicklime) is treated with water to form calcium hydroxide (slaked lime), the reaction is represented as follows: $CaO + H_2O \rightarrow Ca(OH)_2$. This equation states that 1 molecule of calcium oxide combines with 1 molecule of water to form 1 molecule of $Ca(OH)_2$. The chemical equation then is a shorthand expression designed to represent chemical changes. It not only tells what substances are reacting and what products are formed, but, when correctly written (balanced), the equation will give information pertaining to (a) the numbers of molecules and atoms involved in the reaction, (b) the weight relationship of various molecules and atoms, and (c) where gases are involved, the volume relationship will be indicated.

Chemical changes can be classified under two distinct groups. Group I consists of chemical reactions in which there are no changes in valence number (oxidation state) of any of the elements involved in the chemical reaction. Group II consists of chemical reactions in which changes in valence number (oxidation state) of certain atoms or ions are involved. These are known as oxidation-reduction reactions or simply redox-type reactions.

Group I. Simple Type
   A. Combination reactions
   B. Double displacement (metathesis)
Group II. Redox Type
   A. Combination of elements
   B. Simple decomposition
   C. Displacement reactions
   D. Complicated oxidation-reduction reactions

This chapter will be concerned with reactions classed as Group I, Simple Type. The next chapter will deal with reactions classed in the Group II, Redox Type.

BALANCING OF CHEMICAL EQUATIONS

The first exercise usually encountered in equation writing is one in which the student is given the chemical formulas of the reacting substances and of the products formed and is asked to *balance* the equation. In balancing a chemical equation it is necessary only to arrange for the *same numbers of atoms or ions* of the same element on either side of the equation. It may be necessary to use numbers as coefficients of molecules (as in an algebraic equation) to bring about this equality. This coefficient represents a multiple number of molecules of the substance. Thus, consider the following unbalanced equation:

$$SiO_2 + HF \rightarrow SiF_4 + H_2O$$

Inspection of this equation at once reveals there is 1 silicon atom on each side of the arrow, but there are 2 oxygen atoms on the left side and 1 oxygen on the right side of the equation. To balance the oxygen atom on the right, it becomes necessary to multiply the H_2O molecule by 2 as a coefficient, or $2H_2O$. Now there are 4 hydrogen atoms on the right and 1 hydrogen on the left side. To balance the hydrogen atoms, one multiplies the HF molecule by 4 as a coefficient, or 4HF, which in turn automatically balances the fluorine atoms. The balanced equation is then written as

$$SiO_2 + 4HF \rightarrow SiF_4 + 2H_2O$$

The student should verify that there are the same numbers of the same atoms on either side of the equation; this applies in the balancing of all equations.

Another example of balancing an equation follows. Consider the following unbalanced equation:

$$Bi_2(SO_4)_3 + NH_4OH \rightarrow Bi(OH)_3 + (NH_4)_2SO_4$$

Here one observes there are 2 Bi atoms on the left side and 1 Bi atom on the right side of the equation. To balance the Bi, it is required to multiply $Bi(OH)_3$ by 2 as a coefficient, or $2Bi(OH)_3$. This gives 6 OH radicals on the right, which necessitates multiplying NH_4OH by 6 as a coefficient, or $6NH_4OH$, to balance the OH radicals on the left side. Also, the 6 NH_4 radicals on the left side must be balanced by 3 $(NH_4)_2SO_4$ on the right side. Incidentally, this gives 3 SO_4 radicals on the right side which are balanced by the 3 SO_4, or $(SO_4)_3$, from $Bi_2(SO_4)_3$ on the left side of the equation. The balanced equation then becomes

$$Bi_2(SO_4)_3 + 6NH_4OH \rightarrow 2Bi(OH)_3\downarrow + 3(NH_4)_2SO_4$$

Again, the student should verify that there are exactly the same numbers of atoms of each element on each side of the equation.

NOTE. The arrow pointing downward ($\downarrow$) after a formula is here used to indicate an insoluble substance formed as a product of the reaction. It should be stated that in some instances the insoluble substance, or precipitate, is indicated by an underline with the color of the precipitate as in the equation

$$Bi_2(SO_4)_3 + 6NH_4OH \rightarrow \underline{2Bi(OH)_3} + 3(NH_4)_2SO_4$$
$$\text{white}$$

EQUATION WRITING

The ultimate goal in equation writing is to acquire the ability (a) to *predict the correct products* in a given chemical reaction and (b) to set down the *correct chemical formulas* of each reacting substance involved. Thorough knowledge of the symbols of elements and their valences is most essential and necessary for correct formula writing. In predicting products of a chemical reaction, considerable information is necessary, which is usually acquired through studies in the classroom, from the textbook, demonstration lectures, and personal experience in the chemical laboratory. A few fundamental principles are herewith presented to guide the student and to assist him in the prediction of the correct products of various types of chemical reactions herein classed as Group I.

One of the most fundamental differences between metals and nonmetals is that oxides of many metals react with water to form bases, and oxides of most nonmetals react with water to form acids. The metallic oxide is frequently called a *basic oxide* or basic anhydride, whereas the nonmetallic oxide is known as an *acidic oxide* or acid anhydride. Many chemical reactions take place with these two types of substances. The following are some generalizations.

A. Combination Reactions. 1. Combination of basic oxide with water to form a base.

$$BaO + H_2O \rightarrow Ba(OH)_2 \text{ (barium hydroxide)}$$
$$Na_2O + H_2O \rightarrow 2NaOH \text{ (sodium hydroxide)}$$

2. Combination of acidic oxide with water to form an acid.

$$SO_2 + H_2O \rightarrow H_2SO_3 \text{ (sulfurous acid)}$$
$$B_2O_3 + 3H_2O \rightarrow 2H_3BO_3 \text{ (boric acid)}$$
$$P_2O_5 + 3H_2O \rightarrow 2H_3PO_4 \text{ (phosphoric acid)}$$

3. Combination of basic oxide with an acidic oxide to form a salt.

$$CaO + SiO_2 \rightarrow CaSiO_3 \text{ (calcium silicate)}$$
$$MgO + CO_2 \rightarrow MgCO_3 \text{ (magnesium carbonate)}$$
$$3Li_2O + P_2O_5 \rightarrow 2Li_3PO_4 \text{ (lithium phosphate)}$$

In this type of reaction the salt formed is invariably the salt of the acid of which the nonmetallic oxide is the acid anhydride. Thus, CO_2 is the acid anhydride of carbonic acid; therefore this acidic oxide will react with basic oxides (or bases) to form carbonates. Similarly, P_2O_5 is the acid anhydride of phosphoric acid, and this acidic oxide will form phosphates when reacted with basic oxides or bases.

The student should familiarize himself with the acid anhydrides of the common acids as an aid in predicting products of this kind of chemical reaction.

4. Combination of acidic oxide with a base to form a salt and water, or acid salts.

$$SO_3 + 2KOH \rightarrow K_2SO_4 + H_2O$$
$$N_2O_5 + Ba(OH)_2 \rightarrow Ba(NO_3)_2 + H_2O$$
$$CO_2 + NaOH \rightarrow NaHCO_3$$
$$2SO_2 + Ca(OH)_2 \rightarrow Ca(HSO_3)_2$$

5. Combination of ammonia with any acid to form an ammonium salt of acid used.

$$NH_3 + HCl \rightarrow NH_4Cl$$
$$2NH_3 + H_2SO_4 \rightarrow (NH_4)_2SO_4$$
$$3NH_3 + H_3PO_4 \rightarrow (NH_4)_3PO_4$$

B. *Double Displacement Reactions.* 1. Simple neutralization. A reaction between *any acid* and *any base* to form a normal salt of the acid and to form water.

$$H_2SO_4 + Ba(OH)_2 \rightarrow BaSO_4\downarrow + 2H_2O$$
$$2H_3PO_4 + 3Ca(OH)_2 \rightarrow Ca_3(PO_4)_2\downarrow + 6H_2O$$

2. Reaction between *any acid* and *any basic oxide* to form a salt of the acid and to form water.

$$2HNO_3 + CaO \rightarrow Ca(NO_3)_2 + H_2O$$
$$2H_3PO_4 + 3Li_2O \rightarrow 2Li_3PO_4 + 3H_2O$$
$$2HC_2H_3O_2 + PbO \rightarrow Pb(C_2H_3O_2)_2 + H_2O$$

3. Double displacement involving a *salt with an acid* to form another salt (of acid used) and another acid (frequently a volatile acid).

$$Ba(NO_3)_2 + H_2SO_4 \rightarrow BaSO_4\downarrow + 2HNO_3\uparrow$$
$$FeS + 2HCl \rightarrow FeCl_2 + H_2S\uparrow$$
$$NaCl + H_2SO_4 \rightarrow NaHSO_4 + HCl\uparrow$$

NOTE. The arrow pointing upward ($\uparrow$) after a formula is used to indicate the product is a gas or volatile substance.

4. Double displacement involving the reaction between *two salts*, forming an insoluble product.

$$AgNO_3 + NaCl \rightarrow AgCl\downarrow + NaNO_3$$
$$Na_2SO_4 + Ba(NO_3)_2 \rightarrow BaSO_4\downarrow + 2NaNO_3$$
$$3CaCl_2 + 2K_3PO_4 \rightarrow Ca_3(PO_4)_2\downarrow + 6KCl$$
$$ZnCl_2 + (NH_4)_2S \rightarrow ZnS\downarrow + 2NH_4Cl$$
$$2CuSO_4 + K_4Fe(CN)_6 \rightarrow Cu_2Fe(CN)_6\downarrow + 2K_2SO_4$$

5. Double displacement involving the reaction of any acid on a carbonate to form a salt of the acid used and carbonic acid, which in turn decomposes into carbon dioxide and water.

$$2HCl + CaCO_3 \rightarrow CaCl_2 + CO_2\uparrow + H_2O$$
$$2H_3PO_4 + 3MgCO_3 \rightarrow Mg_3(PO_4)_2 + 3CO_2\uparrow + 3H_2O$$
$$2HC_2H_3O_2 + Li_2CO_3 \rightarrow 2LiC_2H_3O_2 + CO_2\uparrow + H_2O$$

6. Double displacement involving the reaction of any acid on a sulfite to form a salt of the acid used and sulfurous acid, which in turn decomposes into sulfur dioxide and water.

$$2HCl + Na_2SO_3 \rightarrow 2NaCl + SO_2\uparrow + H_2O$$
$$HCl + NaHSO_3 \rightarrow NaCl + SO_2\uparrow + H_2O$$
$$2HC_2H_3O_2 + CaSO_3 \rightarrow Ca(C_2H_3O_2)_2 + SO_2\uparrow + H_2O$$

7. Double displacement involving the reaction of an ammonium salt with a nonvolatile base to form a salt, and ammonium hydroxide which dissociates into ammonia and water.

$$(NH_4)_2SO_4 + Ca(OH)_2 \rightarrow CaSO_4 + 2NH_3\uparrow + 2H_2O$$
$$(NH_4)_3PO_4 + 3NaOH \rightarrow Na_3PO_4 + 3NH_3\uparrow + 3H_2O$$

8. Hydrolysis or hydrolytic action in which water plays the role of a chemical reagent.

$$BiCl_3 + H_2O \rightarrow \underset{\text{bismuth oxychloride}}{BiOCl\downarrow} + 2HCl$$
$$Al_2S_3 + 3H_2O \rightarrow 2Al(OH)_3\downarrow + 3H_2S\uparrow$$
$$PCl_3 + 3H_2O \rightarrow H_3PO_3 + 3HCl\uparrow$$

9. The action of hydrogen sulfide as a precipitant in analytical procedures.

$$PbCl_2 + H_2S \rightarrow PbS\downarrow + 2HCl$$
$$2BiCl_3 + 3H_2S \rightarrow Bi_2S_3\downarrow + 6HCl$$
$$SnCl_4 + 2H_2S \rightarrow SnS_2\downarrow + 4HCl$$
$$Ag_2SO_4 + H_2S \rightarrow Ag_2S\downarrow + H_2SO_4$$

Exercises in Balancing Equations

Set up the complete and balanced equation for each of the following sets of reactions, and state the type of each reaction.

9-1. Lead nitrate + cupric sulfate
Barium oxide + nitric acid
Mercurous nitrate + hydrogen sulfide
Ammonium carbonate + calcium oxide
9-2. Phosphorus tribromide + water
Magnesium chloride + silver nitrate

Manganous chloride + hydrogen sulfide

Lithium oxide + perchloric acid

9-3. Phosphorus pentoxide + potassium hydroxide

Strontium oxide + water

Iodic acid + calcium hydroxide

Barium carbonate + sulfuric acid

9-4. Magnesium oxide + ammonium chloride

Lithium carbonate + hypochlorous acid

Arsenious acid + hydrogen sulfide

Aluminum nitrate + barium hydroxide

9-5. Calcium sulfite + phosphoric acid

Manganous nitrate + ammonium sulfide

Phosphorus pentoxide + lithium hydroxide

Ammonium acetate + barium hydroxide

9-6. Magnesium oxide + ammonium phosphate

Antimony trichloride + hydrogen sulfide

Ammonia + acetic acid

Lithium oxide + water

9-7. Pyrophosphoric acid + potassium hydroxide

Arsenic trioxide + hydrogen sulfide

Calcium sulfide + water

Nitrogen pentoxide + lithium hydroxide

9-8. Ammonia + arsenic acid

Strontium oxide + phosphoric acid

Silver nitrate + potassium chromate

Cadmium chloride + hydrogen sulfide

9-9. Sulfur dioxide + aluminum hydroxide

Chromic sulfide + water

Zinc oxide + phosphoric acid

Arsenious acid + calcium hydroxide

9-10. Ammonium chromate + lead acetate

Calcium fluoride + phosphoric acid

Ammonium carbonate + acetic acid

Barium acetate + sodium chromate

9-11. Silver carbonate + sulfuric acid

Aluminum carbonate + water

Stannic chloride + hydrogen sulfide

Carbon dioxide + barium hydroxide

9-12. Calcium bicarbonate + calcium hydroxide

Ammonia solution + hydrogen sulfide

Nitrogen pentoxide + potassium hydroxide

Magnesium bicarbonate + acetic acid

9-13. Zinc sulfate + potassium chromate

Bismuth nitrate + potassium hydroxide

Arsenic trichloride + hydrogen sulfide

Phosphorus pentoxide + barium hydroxide

9-14. Aluminum hydroxide + acetic acid

Hydriodic acid + barium carbonate

Sodium oxide + iodic acid

Barium bromate + sulfuric acid

9-15. Aluminum sulfate + sodium carbonate
Potassium oxide + phosphoric acid
Magnesium hydroxide + perchloric acid
Phosphorus pentoxide + barium oxide

MOLE RELATIONS AND WEIGHT RELATIONS

From the foregoing examples it is seen that a complete and balanced chemical equation represents the numbers of molecules of substances that react and the numbers of molecules of the products formed in the reaction. It has been stated that actual weights of atoms are proportional to their atomic weights, and likewise the actual weights of molecules are proportional to molecular weights. It should be recalled that atomic weights and molecular weights are *relative weights*. The balanced equation will then indicate the relative weights of the reacting substances and the products formed. These relative weights can be expressed in any unit of weight: grams, kilograms, ounces, pounds, and tons. Thus, when sulfuric acid is completely neutralized by sodium hydroxide, the balanced equation is written

$$H_2SO_4 \quad + 2NaOH \quad \rightarrow Na_2SO_4 \quad + 2H_2O$$

1 mole	+ 2 moles	→ 1 mole	+ 2 moles	*mole relation*
1 g-mole	+ 2 g-moles	→ 1 g-mole	+ 2 g-moles	*g-mole relation*

or

98.1 g H_2SO_4	+ 2 × 40.0 g NaOH	→ 142.1 g Na_2SO_4	+ 2 × 18.0 g H_2O	*weight relation*
1 lb-mole	+ 2 lb-moles	→ 1 lb-mole	+ 2 lb-moles	*lb-mole relation*

or

98.1 lb H_2SO_4 + 2 × 40.0 lb NaOH → 142.1 lb Na_2SO_4 + 2 × 18.0 lb H_2O *weight relation*

Example 1. Given the following reacting substances:

(*a*) Lithium hydroxide + hydriodic acid

(*b*) Ferric oxide + sulfuric acid

(*c*) Magnesium oxide + phosphoric acid

(*d*) Nitrogen pentoxide + potassium hydroxide

(1) Write the balanced equation, and indicate the kind of reacting substances and of products formed in each reaction. (2) Express the gram-mole relation for each equation. (3) Express the weight relation in grams for each equation.

Note. Refer to the table of atomic weights on the inside cover of the book for weight relations, rounding off numbers to one digit to the right of the decimal place.

(*a*)

$$LiOH \quad + HI \quad \rightarrow LiI \quad + H_2O$$

base	acid	salt	water	
1 g-mole	1 g-mole	1 g-mole	1 g-mole	*g-mole relation*
23.9 g	127.9 g	133.8 g	18.0 g	*weight relations*

(b) Fe_2O_3 + $3H_2SO_4$ → $Fe_2(SO_4)_3$ + $3H_2O$
    basic oxide / acid / salt / water
    1 g-mole / 3 g-moles / 1 g-mole / 3 g-moles   *g-mole relation*
    159.6 g / 3 × 98.1 g / 399.9 g / 3 × 18.0 g

or

    159.6 g / 294.3 g / 399.9 g / 54.0 g   *weight relation*

(c) $3MgO$ + $2H_3PO_4$ → $Mg_3(PO_4)_2$ + $3H_2O$
    basic oxide / acid / salt / water
    3 g-moles / 2 g-moles / 1 g-mole / 3 g-moles   *g-mole relation*
    3 × 40.3 g / 2 × 98.0 g / 262.9 g / 3 × 18.0 g

or

    120.9 g / 196.0 g / 262.9 g / 54.0 g

(d) N_2O_5 + $2KOH$ → $2KNO_3$ + H_2O
    acidic oxide / base / salt / water
    1 g-mole / 2 g-moles / 2 g-moles / 1 g-mole   *g-mole relation*
    108.0 g / 2 × 56.1 g / 2 × 101.1 g / 18.0 g

or

    108.0 g / 112.2 g / 202.2 g / 18.0 g

MOLE-WEIGHT—GAS-VOLUME RELATIONS

In those chemical reactions which involve gases, the mole relations are expressed in terms of volume rather than weight of gases, since 1 g-mole of any gas occupies 22.4 l (STP), 1 kg-mole of any gas occupies 22.4 cu m (STP), 1 oz-mole of any gas occupies 22.4 cu ft (STP), and 1 lb-mole of any gas occupies 358 cu ft (STP).

Example 1. Given the following reacting substances:
(a) Ammonia + nitric acid
(b) Hydrogen sulfide + ammonium hydroxide
(c) Calcium hydroxide + sulfur dioxide
(d) Ammonium chloride + potassium hydroxide
Write the balanced equation for each reaction: Express (1) the gram-mole relations for each equation and (2) the weight relations in grams of solid substance and the volume relations in liters (STP) of the gaseous substances for each equation.

(a) NH_3 + HNO_3 → NH_4NO_3
    1 g-mole / 1 g-mole / 1 g-mole
    22.4 l (STP) / 63.0 g / 80.0 g

(b) H_2S + $2NH_4OH$ → $(NH_4)_2S$ + $2H_2O$
    1 g-mole / 2 g-moles / 1 g-mole / 2 g-moles
    22.4 l (STP) / 2 × 35.0 g / 68.1 g / 2 × 18.0 g

or

    22.4 l (STP) / 70.0 g / 68.1 g / 36.0 g

(c) $Ca(OH)_2$ $+ 2SO_2$ $\rightarrow Ca(HSO_3)_2$
    1 g-mole   2 g-moles   1 g-mole
    74.1 g   44.8 l (STP)   202.3 g

(d) NH_4Cl $+ KOH$ $\rightarrow KCl$ $+ NH_3\uparrow$ $+ H_2O$
    1 g-mole   1 g-mole   1 g-mole   1 g-mole   1 g-mole
    53.5 g   56.1 g   74.6 g   22.4 l (STP)   18.0 g

Example 2.   Given the following balanced equation for the composite reaction in the Solvay process for the manufacture of baking soda ($NaHCO_3$),

$$NaCl + H_2O + NH_3 + CO_2 \rightarrow NaHCO_3 + NH_4Cl$$
brine solution   gas   gas   baking soda   solution

express (a) the pound-mole relations and (b) the weight-volume (STP) relations in this equation.

	$NaCl$	$+ H_2O$	$+ NH_3$	$+ CO_2$	$\rightarrow NaHCO_3$
(a)	1 lb-mole	1 lb-mole	1 lb-mole	1 lb-mole	1 lb-mole
(b)	58.5 lb	18.0 lb	358 cu ft (STP)	358 cu ft (STP)	84.0 lb

                                                              $+ NH_4Cl$
                                                              1 lb-mole
                                                              53.5 lb

The following illustrative examples will show the application of the chemical equation in the solution of problems which may be classified under two distinct headings:

Class I.   Weight relations only, as applied to solids, liquids, and gases.

Class II.   Weight–gas-volume relations

It should be stated that these examples consist of chemical reactions of Group I, Simple Type, *i.e.*, no changes in valence of any atom or ion are involved.

CLASS I.   WEIGHT RELATIONS ONLY

Example 3.   Calculate (a) the number of grams of barium chloride needed to react completely with 10 g of sodium sulfate and (b) the weight in grams of barium sulfate formed.

Solution Method 1.   *Step* 1.   Write formulas for each of the reacting substances; then complete and balance the equation.

$$BaCl_2 + Na_2SO_4 \rightarrow BaSO_4\downarrow + 2NaCl$$

Step 2.   Express the gram-mole relations and the weight relations.

1 g-mole	1 g-mole	1 g-mole	2 g-moles	*g-mole relation*
208.4 g	142.1 g	233.5 g	117.0 g	*weight relation*

Step 3.   Convert 10 g Na₂SO₄ to gram-moles Na₂SO₄.

Let x = number of gram-moles in 10 g Na₂SO₄

$$= \frac{10 \text{ g}}{142.1 \text{ g/g-mole Na}_2\text{SO}_4} = 10 \text{ g} \times \frac{1 \text{ g-mole Na}_2\text{SO}_4}{142.1 \text{ g}}$$

$$= 0.07 \text{ g-mole Na}_2\text{SO}_4$$

(a) *Step* 4.   From the *balanced* equation, if 1 g-mole Na₂SO₄ reacts completely with 1 g-mole BaCl₂, then 0.07 g-mole Na₂SO₄ will react with 0.07 g-mole BaCl₂ and

$$0.07 \text{ g-mole BaCl}_2 \times \frac{208.4 \text{ g BaCl}_2}{1 \text{ g-mole BaCl}_2} = 14.6 \text{ g BaCl}_2$$

(b) *Step* 5.   From the *balanced* equation, if 1 g-mole Na₂SO₄ will produce 1 g-mole BaSO₄, then 0.07 g-mole Na₂SO₄ will produce 0.07 g-mole BaSO₄ and

$$0.07 \text{ g-mole BaSO}_4 \times \frac{233.5 \text{ g BaSO}_4}{1 \text{ g-mole}} = 16.3 \text{ g BaSO}_4$$

Alternate Solution Method 2.   By use of proportion

$$\begin{array}{cccc} x & 10 \text{ g} & y & \\ \text{BaCl}_2 & + \text{ Na}_2\text{SO}_4 & \rightarrow \text{BaSO}_4\downarrow & + 2\text{NaCl} \\ (208.4) & (142.1) & (233.5) & \\ 1 \text{ g-mole} & 1 \text{ g-mole} & 1 \text{ g-mole} & \\ 208.4 \text{ g} & 142.1 \text{ g} & 233.5 \text{ g} & \end{array}$$

(a) Let x = number of grams BaCl₂

$$\frac{x}{208.4 \text{ g BaCl}_2} = \frac{10 \text{ g Na}_2\text{SO}_4}{142.1 \text{ g Na}_2\text{SO}_4}$$

$$x = 208.4 \text{ g BaCl}_2 \times \frac{10}{142.1} = 14.6 \text{ g BaCl}_2$$

(b) Let y = number of grams BaSO₄

$$\frac{y}{233.5 \text{ g BaSO}_4} = \frac{10 \text{ g Na}_2\text{SO}_4}{142.1 \text{ g Na}_2\text{SO}_4}$$

$$y = 233.5 \text{ g BaSO}_4 \times \frac{10}{142.1} = 16.4 \text{ g BaSO}_4$$

Alternate Solution Method 3

$$\begin{array}{cccc} x & 10 \text{ g} & & \\ \text{BaCl}_2 & + \text{ Na}_2\text{SO}_4 & \rightarrow \text{BaSO}_4\downarrow & + 2\text{NaCl} \\ 1 \text{ g-mole} & 1 \text{ g-mole} & 1 \text{ g-mole} & \\ 208.4 \text{ g} & 142.1 \text{ g} & 233.5 \text{ g} & \end{array}$$

(a) From the equation, 1 g-mole Na₂SO₄ reacts with 1 g-mole BaCl₂, or 142.1 g Na_2SO_4 reacts with 208.4 g $BaCl_2$; 1 g Na_2SO_4 will react with $1/142.1 \times 208.4$ g $BaCl_2$, and 10 g Na_2SO_4 will react with $10 \times 208.4/142.1$ g $BaCl_2$ = 14.6 g $BaCl_2$.

(b) From the equation, 1 g-mole Na_2SO_4 will produce 1 g-mole $BaSO_4$, or 142.1 g Na_2SO_4 will produce 233.5 g $BaSO_4$; 1 g Na_2SO_4 will produce $1/142.1 \times 233.5$ g $BaSO_4$, and 10 g Na_2SO_4 will produce $10 \times 233.5/142.1$ g $BaSO_4$ = 16.4 g $BaSO_4$.

Example 4. Hydrogen chloride is made by the action of sulfuric acid on sodium chloride. The hydrogen chloride, being readily soluble in water, will form a solution of hydrochloric acid. Calculate (a) the weight in grams of hydrogen chloride formed by the action of excess sulfuric acid on 1 kg of salt which is 99.5 per cent pure NaCl, (b) the number of liters of hydrochloric acid solution (sp gr 1.2 and containing 40 per cent by weight pure HCl) that can be obtained from this reaction, and (c) the weight in kilograms of sodium sulfate produced.

(a) *Step* 1. Write the properly balanced equation for the chemical reaction involved.

$$2NaCl \qquad\qquad + H_2SO_4 \ \rightarrow Na_2SO_4 + 2HCl$$

Step 2. Express (a) the gram-mole relations and (b) the weight relations:

2 g-moles	1 g-mole	2 g-moles
2×58.5 g = 117.0 g	142.1 g	2×36.5 g = 73.0 g

Step 3. Determine the number of grams of pure NaCl in the salt.

1 kg salt = 1,000 g salt

$$99.5 \text{ per cent pure NaCl} = \frac{99.5 \text{ g pure NaCl}}{100 \text{ g salt}}$$

$$= 0.995 \text{ g pure NaCl/g salt}$$

1,000 g salt $\times$ 0.995 g NaCl/g salt = 995 g pure NaCl

Step 4. Calculate the number of gram-moles in 995 g pure NaCl.

Let x = number of gram-moles

$$= \frac{995 \text{ g pure NaCl}}{58.5 \text{ g pure NaCl/g-mole NaCl}} = 17.0 \text{ g-moles NaCl}$$

Step 5. From the equation, 2 g-moles NaCl produces 2 g-moles HCl, or 1 g-mole NaCl will produce 1 g-mole HCl; then 17.0 g-mole NaCl will produce 17.0 g-mole HCl, and

$$17.0 \text{ g-mole HCl} \times \frac{36.5 \text{ g pure HCl}}{1 \text{ g-mole HCl}} = 620.5 \text{ g pure HCl}$$

or 620.5 g hydrogen chloride is produced in the reaction.

(b) *Step* 6.   Determine the volume of hydrochloric acid (sp gr 1.2 and 40 per cent by weight pure HCl) in liters contained in 620.5 g pure HCl.

NOTE.   For convenience in expressing dimensional units only, hydrochloric acid solution is abbreviated *has*.

Specific gravity *has* = 1.2, or in density terms 1.2 kg *has*/l *has*.

$$\frac{1.2 \text{ kg } has}{1 \text{ l } has} \times \frac{0.40 \text{ kg pure HCl}}{1 \text{ kg } has} = 0.48 \text{ kg pure HCl/l } has$$

Since 620.5 g pure HCl = 0.620 kg pure HCl, then

$$\frac{0.620 \text{ kg pure HCl}}{0.48 \text{ kg pure HCl/l } has} = 1.29 \text{ l } has$$

or 1.29 l of hydrochloric solution (sp gr 1.2 and 40 per cent by weight pure HCl) is obtained by the reaction.

(c) *Step* 7.   Determine the weight of Na_2SO_4 produced.   From the equation, if 2 g-moles NaCl produces 1 g-mole Na_2SO_4, 1 g-mole NaCl will produce 0.5 g-mole Na_2SO_4 and 17.0 g-moles NaCl will produce 17.0 × 0.5 g-mole, or 8.5 g-moles Na_2SO_4; then

$$8.5 \text{ g-moles } Na_2SO_4 \times \frac{142.1 \text{ g } Na_2SO_4}{1 \text{ g-mole } Na_2SO_4} = 1{,}208 \text{ g } Na_2SO_4$$

or 1.21 kg Na_2SO_4.

Example 5.   A 10-g sample of marble containing 99 per cent pure $CaCO_3$ is treated with dilute sulfuric acid solution (sp gr 1.2 and containing 27.3 per cent by weight pure H_2SO_4).   Calculate (a) the number of milliliters of dilute sulfuric acid solution needed for complete chemical action, (b) the number of grams of calcium sulfate produced, and (c) the volume in liters at 20°C and 755 mm Hg of carbon dioxide liberated.

Step 1.   Write the properly balanced chemical equation representing the reaction.   Also express (a) the gram-mole relation and (b) the weight-volume relation.

$$CaCO_3 + H_2SO_4 \rightarrow CaSO_4 + CO_2 + H_2O$$

(a)	1 g-mole	1 g-mole	1 g-mole	1 g-mole	1 g-mole
(b)	100.1 g	98.1 g	136.2 g	22.4 l (STP)	18.0 g

Step 2.   Determine the weight of pure $CaCO_3$ in 10 g marble.

$$99 \text{ per cent pure } CaCO_3 = \frac{99 \text{ g pure } CaCO_3}{100 \text{ g marble}}$$
$$= 0.99 \text{ g pure } CaCO_3/\text{g marble}$$

10 g marble × 0.99 g pure $CaCO_3$/g marble = 9.9 g pure $CaCO_3$

Step 3. Calculate the number of gram-moles in 9.9 g pure $CaCO_3$.

Let x = number of gram-moles

$$= \frac{9.9 \text{ g pure } CaCO_3}{100.1 \text{ g pure } CaCO_3/\text{g-mole } CaCO_3} = 0.099 \text{ g-mole } CaCO_3$$

(a) *Step* 4. From the equation, if 1 g-mole $CaCO_3$ reacts with 1 g-mole H_2SO_4, then 0.099 g-mole $CaCO_3$ will react with 0.099 g-mole H_2SO_4, and

$$0.099 \text{ g-mole } H_2SO_4 \times \frac{98.1 \text{ g pure } H_2SO_4}{1 \text{ g-mole } H_2SO_4} = 9.71 \text{ g pure } H_2SO_4$$

Step 5. For convenience in expressing dimensional units only, dilute sulfuric acid is abbreviated *dsa* (sp gr *dsa* = 1.2, or in terms of density 1.2 g *dsa*/ml *dsa*).

$$\frac{1.2 \text{ g } dsa}{1 \text{ ml } dsa} \times \frac{0.273 \text{ g pure } H_2SO_4}{1 \text{ g } dsa} = 0.328 \text{ g pure } H_2SO_4/\text{ml } dsa$$

Step 6. Determine volume of dilute sulfuric acid in 9.71 g pure H_2SO_4.

$$\frac{9.71 \text{ g pure } H_2SO_4}{0.328 \text{ g pure } H_2SO_4/\text{ml } dsa} = 29.6 \text{ ml } dsa$$

or 29.6 ml dilute sulfuric acid (sp gr 1.2 and 27.3 per cent H_2SO_4) is required for complete reaction.

(b) *Step* 7. Determine the weight of $CaSO_4$ produced. From the equation, if 1 g-mole $CaCO_3$ produces 1 g-mole $CaSO_4$, then 0.099 g-mole $CaCO_3$ will produce 0.099 g $CaSO_4$, and

$$0.099 \text{ g-mole } CaSO_4 \times \frac{136.2 \text{ g } CaSO_4}{1 \text{ g-mole } CaSO_4} = 13.5 \text{ g } CaSO_4$$

(c) *Step* 8. Determine the volume in liters at standard conditions of CO_2 produced. From the equation, 1 g-mole $CaCO_3$ produces 22.4 l (STP) CO_2; then 0.099 g-mole $CaCO_3$ will produce 0.099 × 22.4 l (STP) CO_2, or 2.22 l (STP) CO_2 is produced.

Step 9. Convert 2.22 l (STP) CO_2 to 20°C and 755 mm Hg.

$$0°C = 273°K \qquad 20°C = 293°K$$
$$2.22 \text{ l} \times \frac{293°K}{273°K} \times \frac{760 \text{ mm}}{755 \text{ mm}} = 2.40 \text{ l}$$

or 2.40 l of CO_2 liberated at 20°C and 755 mm Hg.

Example 6. Ammonium sulfate is obtained as a by-product in the manufacture of illuminating gas, by removal of ammonia in the gas with sulfuric acid solution. (a) How many cubic feet of ammonia at

70°F and 29.5 in. Hg will be required in the preparation of 1 ton of ammonium sulfate which is 95 per cent pure $(NH_4)_2SO_4$? (b) How many gallons of sulfuric acid solution (sp gr 1.76 and 83 per cent by weight pure H_2SO_4) will be used up in this reaction?

(a) *Step* 1. Write the properly balanced equation representing the reaction together with gram-mole and volume-weight relations.

$$2NH_3 \qquad\qquad + H_2SO_4 \rightarrow (NH_4)_2SO_4$$

2 lb-moles	1 lb-mole	1 lb-mole
2 × 358 cu ft (STP)	98.1 lb	132.1 lb

Step 2. Determine the number of pounds pure $(NH_4)_2SO_4$ to be produced.

$$1 \text{ ton} = 2,000 \text{ lb}$$

$$2,000 \text{ lb ammonium sulfate} \times \frac{0.95 \text{ lb pure } (NH_4)_2SO_4}{1 \text{ lb ammonium sulfate}}$$
$$= 1,900 \text{ lb pure } (NH_4)_2SO_4$$

Step 3. Convert 1,900 lb pure $(NH_4)_2SO_4$ to pound-moles.

$$\frac{1,900 \text{ lb pure } (NH_4)_2SO_4}{132 \text{ lb pure } (NH_4)_2SO_4/\text{lb-mole } (NH_4)_2SO_4} = 14.4 \text{ lb-moles } (NH_4)_2SO_4$$

Step 4. Determine volume in cubic feet (STP) of ammonia. From the equation, 1 lb-mole $(NH_4)_2SO_4$ requires 2 lb-moles NH_3; then 14.4 lb-moles $(NH_4)_2SO_4$ will require 14.4 × 2 lb-moles NH_3, or

$$28.8 \text{ lb-moles } NH_3 \times \frac{358 \text{ cu ft (STP) } NH_3}{1 \text{ lb-mole } NH_3} = 10,310 \text{ cu ft } NH_3 \text{ (STP)}$$

Step 5. Convert 10,310 cu ft NH_3 (STP) to 70°F and 29.5 in. Hg. Standard conditions = 32°F and 29.92 in. Hg.

$$32°F = (32 + 460)°R = 492°R \qquad 70°F = (70 + 460)°R = 530°R$$
$$10,310 \text{ cu ft} \times \frac{530°R}{492°R} \times \frac{29.92 \text{ in.}}{29.5 \text{ in.}} = 11,264 \text{ cu ft}$$

Then 11,264 cu ft of NH_3 at 70°F and 29.5 in. Hg will be required in the preparation of 1 ton ammonium sulfate, 95 per cent pure $(NH_4)_2SO_4$.

(b) *Step* 6. Determine the number of pounds pure H_2SO_4 used. From the equation, 1 lb-mole $(NH_4)_2SO_4$ requires 1 lb-mole H_2SO_4 for complete reaction; then 14.4 lb-moles $(NH_4)_2SO_4$ will require 14.4 lb-moles H_2SO_4, or

$$14.4 \text{ lb-moles } H_2SO_4 \times \frac{98.1 \text{ lb pure } H_2SO_4}{1 \text{ lb-mole } H_2SO_4} = 1,413 \text{ lb pure } H_2SO_4$$

NOTE. For convenience in dealing with dimensional units, sulfuric acid solution is abbreviated *sas*. Sulfuric acid solution (*sas*) has a specific gravity of 1.76 and is 83 per cent by weight pure H_2SO_4.

Step 7. Since 1 gal water = 8.3 lb, the weight of 1 gal *sas* would be 1.76 × 8.3 lb/gal = 14.6 lb/gal, or 14.6 lb *sas*/gal *sas*.

$$\frac{14.6 \text{ lb } sas}{1 \text{ gal } sas} \times \frac{0.83 \text{ lb pure } H_2SO_4}{1 \text{ lb } sas} = 12.1 \text{ lb pure } H_2SO_4/\text{gal } sas$$

Step 8

$$\frac{1,413 \text{ lb pure } H_2SO_4}{12.1 \text{ lb pure } H_2SO_4/\text{gal } sas} = 1,413 \text{ lb pure } H_2SO_4$$

$$\times \frac{1 \text{ gal } sas}{12.1 \text{ lb pure } H_2SO_4} = 116.7 \text{ gal } sas$$

or 116.7 gal sulfuric acid solution (sp gr 1.76 and 83 per cent by weight pure H_2SO_4) will be used up in the preparation of 1 ton ammonium sulfate, 95 per cent pure $(NH_4)_2SO_4$.

Problems

A first requirement in the solution of these problems is the properly balanced chemical equation involved in the given reaction. To aid in solving some of the problems having unfamiliar chemical reactions, the unbalanced equation is given. However, this equation should be balanced by the student before making any calculations. Also the use of a slide rule to expedite arithmetical processes is to be encouraged.

9-16. (a) Calculate the number of gram-moles of ferric chloride and of sodium hydroxide required to react completely to produce 48.06 g of ferric hydroxide. (b) Convert the gram-moles obtained in (a) to grams of ferric chloride and sodium hydroxide, respectively.   *Ans.* (a) 0.45 g-mole; 1.35 g-moles.

9-17. (a) Determine the number of gram-moles of potassium iodide required to precipitate completely the lead iodide from a solution that contains 40.65 g of lead acetate [$Pb(C_2H_3O_2)_2$]. (b) Convert the gram-moles found in (a) to grams of potassium iodide. (c) How many grams of lead iodide are obtained in this reaction?   *Ans.* (a) 0.25 g-mole; (c) 57.6 g.

9-18. Given the unbalanced equation for the preparation of the blue pigment, ferric ferrocyanide [$Fe_4(Fe(CN)_6)_3$], from ferric chloride

$$FeCl_3 + K_4Fe(CN)_6 \rightarrow Fe_4(Fe(CN)_6)_3\downarrow + KCl$$

Determine (a) the number of pound-moles and (b) the number of pounds of pigment obtained from 584.3 lb of ferric chloride by the foregoing reaction.   *Ans.* (a) 2.7 lb-moles.

9-19. The unbalanced equation for the chemical reaction between silicon dioxide and hydrofluoric acid is

$$SiO_2 + HF \rightarrow SiF_4 + H_2O$$

Calculate the number of (a) gram-moles of hydrofluoric acid and (b) milliliters of hydrofluoric acid (sp. gr 1.16 and 50 per cent by weight pure HF) required for complete chemical reaction with 0.541 g of silicon dioxide.

Ans. 1.2 ml.

9-20. A sample of hard water contains 0.218 g $CaSO_4$ and 0.193 g $MgSO_4$ per gallon. Calculate the number of (a) gram-moles and (b) grams of Na_2CO_3 necessary to precipitate completely the calcium and magnesium salts from 5,000 gal of water. *Ans.* (a) 0.0032 g-mole.

9-21. Calculate the number of (a) ton-moles and (b) tons of quicklime (CaO) that can be produced from 7 tons of limestone which analyzed 96.5 per cent $CaCO_3$. (c) How many bags, each containing 50 lb of hydrated lime [$Ca(OH)_2$], can be obtained from the amount of quicklime produced in part (a)? *Ans.* (a) 0.0675 ton-mole; (c) 200 bags.

9-22. An excess of $NaNO_3$ is treated with 25 lb of sulfuric acid solution which contains 93.2 per cent by weight of pure H_2SO_4. Calculate (a) the number of pound-moles pure HNO_3, (b) the number of pounds of nitric acid containing 70 per cent by weight pure HNO_3, and (c) the number of pounds of Na_2SO_4 produced in this reaction.

Ans. (a) 0.476 lb-mole; (b) 42.8 lb; (c) 33.7 lb.

9-23. Calculate the weight in tons of sodium nitrate containing 89.5 per cent $NaNO_3$ necessary to produce 50 tons of nitric acid containing 65.3 per cent by weight of pure HNO_3 by reaction with sulfuric acid solution.

Ans. 49.2 tons.

9-24. How many milliliters of a silver nitrate solution (sp gr 1.14 and 15 per cent by weight pure $AgNO_3$) is necessary to react with 40 ml of hydrochloric acid solution having a specific gravity of 1.14 and containing 27.6 per cent by weight pure HCl? *Ans.* 343 ml.

9-25. Calculate (a) the number of ounce-moles of pure ferrous sulfide and (b) the weight in ounces of ferrous sulfide containing 95 per cent FeS that will be required to produce 2.5 cu ft of hydrogen sulfide at 21°C and 750 mm Hg by reaction with hydrochloric acid solution.

Ans. (a) 0.102 oz-mole; (b) 9.4 oz.

9-26. Calculate the number of milliliters (STP) of hydrogen sulfide needed to precipitate completely cupric sulfide from 100 ml of a solution that contains 0.75 g $CuCl_2$ in 1 l of solution. *Ans.* 12.4 ml.

9-27. Calculate the number of (a) pound-moles and (b) pounds of $Ca(OH)_2$ required to liberate all the ammonia from 1 ton $(NH_4)_2SO_4$. (c) How many cubic feet (STP) of NH_3 is liberated in the reaction?

Ans. (a) 15.14 lb-moles; (c) 10,840 cu ft.

9-28. (a) Calculate the number of gallons of sulfuric acid solution (sp gr 1.83 and 93 per cent by weight H_2SO_4) necessary to react completely with 100 lb of borax $(Na_2B_4O_7 \cdot 10 \ H_2O)$ to form boric acid. (b) How many pounds of boric acid will be produced? The unbalanced equation for this reaction is

$$Na_2B_4O_7 + H_2SO_4 + H_2O \rightarrow H_3BO_3 + Na_2SO_4$$

Ans. (a) 1.82 gal; (b) 64.8 lb.

9-29. Determine the number of (a) kilogram-moles and (b) kilograms of anhydrous aluminum sulfate obtained from 100 kg of a clay that is 51 per cent Al_2O_3 by reaction with sulfuric acid. (c) How many liters of aluminum sulfate solution [sp gr 1.23 and 20 per cent by weight $Al_2(SO_4)_3$] can be obtained from the foregoing weight of $Al_2(SO_4)_3$?

Ans. (a) 0.5 kg-mole; (c) 696 l.

9-30. Calculate the number of liters of ammonia solution (sp gr 0.92 and 20.5 per cent by weight NH_3) that can be prepared from a solution containing 0.05 kg-mole of ammonium sulfate by reaction with calcium hydroxide.

Ans. 9.0 l.

9-31. A hydrochloric acid solution containing 20.01 g of HCl is added to 20.01 g calcium carbonate. (a) Which substance is in excess, and by how many gram-moles? (b) How many grams of calcium chloride is produced? (c) How many liters of CO_2(STP) is liberated by this reaction?

Ans. (a) HCl in excess by 0.345 g-mole; (b) 222.2 g; (c) 4.48 l (STP).

9-32. A solution containing 30 g of silver nitrate is added to a solution containing 30 g of sodium chloride. (a) Which substance is in excess and by how many gram-moles? (b) What weight in grams of AgCl is produced?

Ans. (a) 0.336 g-mole NaCl; (b) 25.5 g.

9-33. When ammonia reacts with sulfuric acid, the following is the equation:

$$2NH_3 + H_2SO_4 \rightarrow (NH_4)_2SO_4$$

(a) If 716 cu ft NH_3(STP) reacts with 73.6 lb H_2SO_4, which substance is in excess and by how many pound-moles? (b) How many pounds of ammonium sulfate is produced?

Ans. (a) 0.5 lb-mole NH_3; (b) 100 lb $(NH_4)_2SO_4$.

9-34. (a) If 176.6 lb of NH_4Cl reacts with 185.2 lb of CaO in producing ammonia, which substance is in excess and by what amount in pounds? (b) How many cubic feet (STP) of ammonia is produced by this reaction?

Ans. (a) 92.6 lb CaO; (b) 1,181 cu ft (STP).

9-35. (a) Complete and balance each of the following equations:

$Ca(OH)_2 + HNO_3 \rightarrow$
$Li_2O + HI \rightarrow$
$Al(OH)_3 + HF \rightarrow$
$SrO + H_3PO_4 \rightarrow$
$CO_2 + LiOH \rightarrow$

(b) Express the gram-mole relations for each equation. (c) Express the weight relations in grams and the weight-volume (liters at STP) relations where gases are involved in the reaction.

9-36. (a) Complete and balance each of the following equations:

$BaCO_3 + HNO_3 \rightarrow$
$CaSO_3 + H_3PO_4 \rightarrow$
$AgNO_3 + K_2CrO_4 \rightarrow$
$(NH_4)_3PO_4 + CaO \rightarrow$
$Na_2O + H_4P_2O_7 \rightarrow$

(b) Express the ounce-mole relations for each equation. (c) Express the weight relations in ounces and the weight-volume (cubic feet at STP) relation where gases are involved.

9-37. What is the formula of the salt formed by the complete reaction of 1.653 g of RbOH with 1.581 g of H_2SO_4? Hint: Establish the mole ratio of reacting substances; then, using only this ratio, set up the balanced equation.

9-38. If 0.132 g of calcium hydroxide is allowed to react completely with 0.3488 g of orthophosphoric acid (H_3PO_4), what is the formula and name of the salt formed?

9-39. What is the formula and name of the salt formed when 0.5247 g of magnesium hydroxide reacts completely with 2.555 g of arsenic acid?

9-40. What is the formula and name of the salt produced when 2.688 l (STP) of SO_2 reacts completely with 4.446 g $Ca(OH)_2$?

9-41. How many (a) gram-moles and (b) grams of H_2O is obtained when 3.2938 g $Ca(OH)_2$ reacts completely with 8.712 g H_3PO_4?

9-42. (a) How many grams of quicklime, 90 per cent CaO, is necessary to react completely with 1 l of sodium carbonate solution (sp gr 1.12 and 11.8 per cent by weight Na_2CO_3)? (b) How many grams of caustic soda containing 85 per cent pure NaOH will be produced in this reaction?

9-43. Calculate the number of milliliters of sulfuric acid solution (sp gr 1.25 and 33.4 per cent by weight H_2SO_4) necessary to produce 10 g of $NaHSO_4$ by reaction with NaOH.

9-44. Determine the number of milliliters of sulfuric acid solution (sp gr 1.83 and 93 per cent H_2SO_4) that will react with 100 g of $Ca_3(PO_4)_2$ to form primary calcium orthophosphate [$Ca(H_2PO_4)_2$].

9-45. In the treatment of calcium phosphate with phosphoric acid the product formed is primary calcium orthophosphate [$Ca(H_2PO_4)_2$]. (a) How many gallons of phosphoric acid (sp gr 1.34 and 50 per cent by weight H_3PO_4) will be required for complete reaction with 56.9 tons of phosphate rock that contains 30 per cent $Ca_3(PO_4)_2$? (b) How many tons of primary calcium orthophosphate would be produced in this reaction?

9-46. If 0.35 g-mole of hydrochloric acid solution reacts with an excess of calcium carbonate, determine the number of (a) gram-moles and (b) liters (STP) of carbon dioxide produced in the reaction.

9-47. If ammonia reacts with an excess of sulfuric acid solution to produce 1.5 oz-moles of ammonium sulfate, determine the number of (a) ounce-moles and (b) cubic feet (STP) of ammonia required for this reaction.

9-48. Given the unbalanced equation,

$$H_3PO_4 + MgCO_3 \rightarrow Mg_3(PO_4)_2 + CO_2 + H_2O$$

From the balanced equation determine (1) the number of ounce-moles of magnesium carbonate required to react with 0.5 oz-mole of phosphoric acid and (2) the number of (a) ounce-moles and (b) cubic feet (STP) of carbon dioxide produced in this reaction.

CHAPTER X

OXIDATION—REDUCTION

OUTLINE

Oxidation is defined as a chemical reaction in which at least one element (atom or ion) has its valence number algebraically increased (involving a loss of electrons), while at least one other element (atom or ion) simultaneously has its valence number algebraically decreased (involving a gain of electrons). The latter process is termed "reduction."

Types of oxidation-reduction reactions:
1. Combination reactions.
2. Simple decomposition reactions.
3. Displacement reactions.
4. Complicated types.

Oxidizers: substances that readily gain or accept electrons.

Reducers: substances that readily give up or lose electrons.

List of common oxidizers and reducers.

Method of balancing oxidation-reduction equations by oxidation-number (valence-number) change and electron transfer. Summary of method. Several examples to illustrate method here used.

Ionic oxidation-reduction equations. The ionic equation used as a pattern for writing the molecular equation.

Ion-electron method of balancing oxidation-reduction equations.

In the preceding chapter chemical reactions were classified under two groupings. The last chapter dealt with Group I, in which there are no changes in valence of any elements involved in the reaction, and the problems were concerned with this type of reaction. This chapter will deal with chemical reactions of Group II, in which changes in valence numbers of certain elements are involved. These reactions in which one element (atom or ion) has its valence number algebraically increased (involving a loss of electrons) are called **oxidation reactions.** Simultaneously another element (atom or ion) has its valence number algebraically decreased (involving a gain of electrons); this process is termed **reduction.** The reactions are usually classed as **oxidation-reduction** or **redox type.**

OXIDATION NUMBER

It has been stated (Chap. III) that valence is expressed in terms of the number of electrons which an atom loses or gains and, also, the number of pairs of electrons which it shares with other atoms, or in terms of its state of oxidation. In an ionic or electrovalent compound the elements and radicals are held together by electrostatic forces. *Cations* always have a *positive valence number*, and *anions* have a *negative valence number*. In sodium sulfate (Na_2SO_4) each sodium atom has a valence number of $+1$ and the sulfate radical a valence of -2. In a covalent compound, electron pairs are shared and a valence number is assumed. Thus, when sulfur combines with oxygen to form sulfur dioxide (SO_2) it may be assumed that each oxygen atom takes 2 electrons from the sulfur atom, and the oxygen will have a valence number of -2, indicated by O^{-2}. In turn the sulfur atom in sulfur dioxide becomes $+4$, indicated by S^{+4}. Thus the sulfur will have a valence number of $+4$. This valence number is conveniently

TABLE XII. OXIDATION NUMBERS

Compound	Element	Oxidation number
PbO_2	Pb	$+4$
H_2SO_4	S	$+6$
$KClO_3$	Cl	$+5$
$KClO_4$	Cl	$+7$
$KMnO_4$	Mn	$+7$
$Ca(MnO_4)_2$	Mn	$+7$
K_2MnO_4	Mn	$+6$
K_2CrO_4	Cr	$+6$
$K_2Cr_2O_7$	Cr	$+6$

termed the **oxidation number.** To determine the oxidation number of sulfur in the sulfate radical (SO_4^{-2}), the 4 oxygens will give 8 negatives and in order that the radical will have a valence of -2, the sulfur atom must have an oxidation number of $+6$, indicated by S^{+6}. In any chemical compound, the sum of positive valence numbers must equal the sum of the negative valence numbers of the various elements in the compound, or otherwise stated, the sum of the valence numbers of elements in any compound must be zero. In nitric acid (HNO_3) the oxidation number of nitrogen may be determined as follows: the valence number of hydrogen is $+1$ and that of oxygen is -2; the 3 oxygen atoms will give 6 negatives, which requires that nitrogen have a valence number of $+5$, in order that the sum of the valence numbers be zero. The oxidation number of nitrogen is $+5$, indicated by N^{+5}. Since the oxidation number of N is $+5$ and there is a total of 6 negatives from 3 oxygens, the nitrate radical must have a valence number of -1, indicated by NO_3^-.

The student should verify the oxidation numbers of the elements in Table XII.

TYPES OF OXIDATION-REDUCTION REACTIONS WITH EQUATIONS

Combination Reactions. 1. Uncombined atoms (electrically neutral) have zero valence numbers, and combined atoms have non-zero valence numbers. Compound formation by combination of the elements is an oxidation-reduction reaction.

The burning of magnesium in air to form magnesium oxide is represented by

$$2Mg^0 + O_2^0 \rightarrow 2Mg^{+2}O^{-2}$$

When the magnesium atom (zero valence) combines with the oxygen atom (zero valence), the valence number of Mg is increased from 0 to +2 (oxidation), and the valence number of oxygen is decreased from 0 to −2 (reduction). These changes in valence numbers are brought about in the following manner: Each magnesium atom loses 2 electrons to become magnesium ion (Mg^{+2}, valence number +2); simultaneously each oxygen atom gains 2 electrons to become oxide ion (O^{-2}). However, the oxygen molecule (O_2) must gain 4 electrons; these are acquired from 2 magnesium atoms ($2Mg$). The combination of magnesium ions (Mg^{+2}) and oxide ions (O^{-2}) will form magnesium oxide (MgO).

The foregoing process can be conveniently expressed in the form of the following detailed equation:

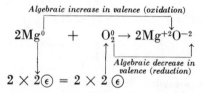

Algebraic increase in valence (oxidation)

$$2Mg^0 \quad + \quad O_2^0 \rightarrow 2Mg^{+2}O^{-2}$$

Algebraic decrease in valence (reduction)

$$2 \times 2\,\textcircled{\epsilon} = 2 \times 2\,\textcircled{\epsilon}$$

Note that the electron is symbolized as $\textcircled{\epsilon}$, and the arrow under the Mg atom pointing downward ($\downarrow$) over it designates a *loss of electrons* (*oxidation*). Also, the arrow over the electron pointing upward under the oxygen indicates a *gain of electrons* by the oxygen (*reduction*).

2. Combination of hydrogen and chlorine to form hydrogen chloride.

Oxidation

$$H_2^0 \quad + \quad Cl_2^0 \rightarrow 2H^+Cl^-$$

Reduction

$$2 \times 1\,\textcircled{\epsilon} = 2 \times 1\,\textcircled{\epsilon}$$

3. Combination of antimony and chlorine to form antimony trichloride.

$$\overset{\textit{Oxidation}}{2Sb^0 \quad + \quad 3Cl_2^0 \rightarrow 2Sb^{+3}Cl_3^-}$$

$$2 \times 3\,\textcircled{\epsilon} = 3 \times 2 \times 1\,\textcircled{\epsilon}$$

Reduction

4. When silver combines with sulfur, the product is silver sulfide.

$$\overset{\textit{Oxidation}}{2Ag^0 + S^0 \rightarrow Ag_2^+S^{-2}}$$

$$2 \times 1\,\textcircled{\epsilon} = 2\,\textcircled{\epsilon}$$

Reduction

5. The formation of phosphorus pentachloride by action of chlorine with phosphorus.

$$\overset{\textit{Oxidation}}{2P^0 \quad + \quad 5Cl_2^0 \rightarrow 2P^{+5}Cl_5^-}$$

$$2 \times 5\,\textcircled{\epsilon} = 5 \times 2 \times 1\,\textcircled{\epsilon}$$

Reduction

6. The oxidation of ferrous chloride to ferric chloride by chlorine is represented by the following equation:

$$\overset{\textit{Oxidation}}{2Fe^{+2}Cl_2 \quad + \quad Cl_2^0 \rightarrow 2Fe^{+3}Cl_3^-}$$

$$2 \times 1\,\textcircled{\epsilon} = 2 \times 1\,\textcircled{\epsilon}$$

Reduction

Simple Decomposition Reactions. 1. The decomposition of mercuric oxide by heat into mercury and oxygen.

$$\overset{\textit{Oxidation}}{2Hg^{+2}O^{-2} + heat \rightarrow 2Hg^0 + O_2^0}$$

$$2\,\textcircled{\epsilon} \quad 2\,\textcircled{\epsilon}$$

Reduction

In this equation it is to be noted the *valence number* of mercury is algebraically *decreased* from +2 to 0 (reduction) and the *valence number* of oxygen is algebraically *increased* from −2 to 0 (oxidation). These changes in valence numbers are brought about in the following manner:

The oxide ion gives up its 2 electrons to the mercuric ion, thereby neutralizing the positive charge ($+2$) on this ion and forming metallic mercury (*zero valence number*). At the same time neutral oxygen atoms (*zero valence number*) are formed. Then 2 oxygen atoms unite with each other, forming molecular oxygen, which escapes. In order to have 2 oxide ions for the formation of molecular oxygen (O_2), it is necessary to take 2 molecules of HgO, which also yields 2 atoms of free mercury, as indicated.

2. When potassium chlorate is decomposed by heat, the products are potassium chloride and oxygen.

Loss of 3 × 2 (ε) (Oxidation)

$$2KCl^{+5}O_3^{-2} + \text{heat} \rightarrow 2KCl^- + 3O_2^0$$

Gain of 6 (ε) (Reduction)

Simple decomposition reactions can usually be balanced by inspection.

Displacement Reactions. 1. Displacement of a metallic ion by a metal which is above that ion in the electrochemical series, as in the case of metallic zinc placed in a cupric sulfate solution. The cupric ion is displaced by the zinc, metallic copper (Cu^0) being formed, and zinc goes into solution as zinc ions (Zn^{+2}).

Oxidation

$$Zn^0 + Cu^{+2}SO_4 \rightarrow Cu^0 + Zn^{+2}SO_4$$

Reduction

$2(ε) = 2(ε)$

2. To prepare hydrogen one can react an active metal with a dilute acid.

Oxidation

$$Zn^0 + H_2^+SO_4 \rightarrow Zn^{+2}SO_4 + H_2^0$$

Reduction

$2(ε) = 2 \times 1(ε)$

Before dealing with more complicated types of oxidation-reduction reactions, it is well to note the following facts:

The equations exemplifying this type of reaction in reality consist of two parts, *viz.*, the partial equation representing *oxidation*, and the partial equation representing *reduction*, both taking place simultaneously. The oxidation part involves the *loss of electrons* by an element or ion, and this is accompanied by an algebraic *increase* in the *oxidation number* of that element or ion. The reduction part involves the *gain of electrons* by an element or ion, which brings about an algebraic *decrease in the oxidation* number of that element or ion. This is conveniently illustrated by the valence scale of Fig. 8.

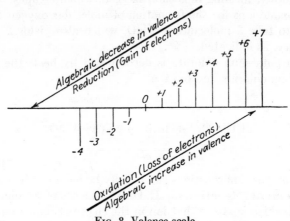

FIG. 8. Valence scale.

Those substances that readily gain or accept electrons are called **oxidizing agents** or **oxidizers.**

Those substances that readily give up or lose electrons are known as **reducing agents** or **reducers.**

TABLE XIII. OXIDIZERS

Oxidizer	→	Reducer
$2H^+ + 2\textcircled{\epsilon}$	→	H_2^0
$S^0 + 2H^+ + 2\textcircled{\epsilon}$	→	H_2S^{-2}
$S^{+6}O_4^{-2} + 4H^+ + 2\textcircled{\epsilon}$	→	$S^{+4}O_2 + 2H_2O$
concentrated H_2SO_4		
$I_2^0 + 2\textcircled{\epsilon}$	→	$2I^-$
$Fe^{+3} + 1\textcircled{\epsilon}$	→	Fe^{+2}
$N^{+5}O_3^- + 4H^+ + 2\textcircled{\epsilon}$	→	$N^{+4}O_2 + 2H_2O$
concentrated HNO_3		
$N^{+5}O_3^- + 4H^+ + 3\textcircled{\epsilon}$	→	$N^{+2}O + 2H_2O$
dilute HNO_3		
$Br_2^0 + 2\textcircled{\epsilon}$	→	$2Br^-$
$Mn^{+4}O_2 + 4H^+ + 2\textcircled{\epsilon}$	→	$Mn^{+2} + 2H_2O$
$Cl_2^0 + 2\textcircled{\epsilon}$	→	$2Cl^-$
$Cr_2^{+6}O_7^{-2} + 14H^+ + 6\textcircled{\epsilon}$	→	$2Cr^{+3} + 7H_2O$
dichromates in acid solution		
$Pb^{+4}O_2 + 4H^+ + 2\textcircled{\epsilon}$	→	$Pb^{+2} + 2H_2O$
$Mn^{+7}O_4^- + 8H^+ + 5\textcircled{\epsilon}$	→	$Mn^{+2} + 4H_2O$
permanganates in acid solution		
$H_2O_2 + 2H^+ + 2\textcircled{\epsilon}$	→	$2H_2O$
$Na_2O_2 + 2OH^- + 2\textcircled{\epsilon}$	→	$2NaOH + O_2^0$

Oxidizing power increases ↓

Reducing power decreases ↓

→ *Reduction*

Tables XIII and XIV are lists of the common oxidizers and reducers based on the electrochemical series. The relative oxidizing and reducing powers are indicated. Further considerations of the mechanism of oxidation-reduction reactions will be given in the study of electrochemical reactions (Chap. XVI).

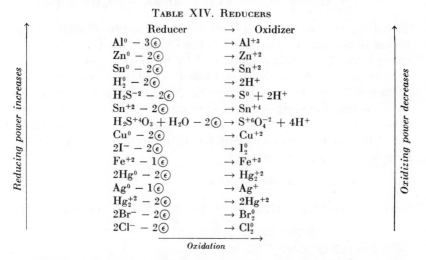

TABLE XIV. REDUCERS

Reducer $\rightarrow$ Oxidizer

$Al^0 - 3\,e \rightarrow Al^{+3}$

$Zn^0 - 2\,e \rightarrow Zn^{+2}$

$Sn^0 - 2\,e \rightarrow Sn^{+2}$

$H_2^0 - 2\,e \rightarrow 2H^+$

$H_2S^{-2} - 2\,e \rightarrow S^0 + 2H^+$

$Sn^{+2} - 2\,e \rightarrow Sn^{+4}$

$H_2S^{+4}O_3 + H_2O - 2\,e \rightarrow S^{+6}O_4^{-2} + 4H^+$

$Cu^0 - 2\,e \rightarrow Cu^{+2}$

$2I^- - 2\,e \rightarrow I_2^0$

$Fe^{+2} - 1\,e \rightarrow Fe^{+3}$

$2Hg^0 - 2\,e \rightarrow Hg_2^{+2}$

$Ag^0 - 1\,e \rightarrow Ag^+$

$Hg_2^{+2} - 2\,e \rightarrow 2Hg^{+2}$

$2Br^- - 2\,e \rightarrow Br_2^0$

$2Cl^- - 2\,e \rightarrow Cl_2^0$

Oxidation $\longrightarrow$

Reducing power increases — *Oxidizing power decreases*

METHOD OF BALANCING OXIDATION AND REDUCTION EQUATIONS BY OXIDATION-NUMBER CHANGE AND ELECTRON TRANSFER

In the study of the chemistry of chlorine, bromine, and iodine the student is confronted with a number of complicated equations, especially in the preparation of these halogens from their halides. The general statement is made at the outset that if one adds to a halide (fluorides excepted) a nonvolatile acid (sulfuric acid or phosphoric acid) and an oxidizer, the halogen will be liberated. As an example, consider the equation for the preparation of chlorine from sodium chloride.

$$NaCl + MnO_2 + \quad H_2SO_4 \rightarrow$$

halide   oxidizer   nonvolatile acid

The first step in predicting the products of this reaction is to determine which substance is the oxidizer and which is the reducer. Next note the reduction product and the oxidation product. Thus the essential part of this reaction is the oxidation of chloride ion (Cl^-) to free chlorine (Cl_2) by manganese dioxide in the presence of hydrogen ions. The Cl^- is the reducer and MnO_2 in the presence of H^+ (from H_2SO_4) is the oxidizer. The oxidation product is chlorine (Cl_2^0) and the reduction product is manganous ion (Mn^{+2}), and water is also formed. The sulfuric acid not only furnishes H^+ ions but supplies sulfate ions (SO_4^{-2}), thereby forming sulfates of all the metallic ions present in the reaction. The unbalanced equation becomes

$$NaCl + MnO_2 + H_2SO_4 \rightarrow Cl_2^0 + MnSO_4 + Na_2SO_4 + H_2O$$

To balance this equation, next note the changes in the oxidation numbers of both reducer and oxidizer. The Cl^- (oxidation number -1) is changed to Cl^0 (oxidation number 0) by the loss of 1 electron. But a molecule of chlorine (Cl_2) is formed, which requires $2Cl^-$. The coefficient 2 must be placed before the NaCl to provide for this. At the same time the oxidation number of manganese in MnO_2 is changed from $+4$ to $+2$, or Mn^{+2}, by the gain of 2 electrons. The final balancing of the equation can be completed by inspection. Then from the foregoing procedure one obtains

Oxidation (algebraic increase in valence)

$$2NaCl^- + Mn^{+4}O_2 + 2H_2SO_4 \rightarrow Cl_2^0 + Mn^{+2}SO_4 + Na_2SO_4 + 2H_2O$$

Reduction (algebraic decrease in valence)

$2 \times 1_{(e)} = 2_{(e)}$

It is convenient and helpful to the student in the beginning of this study if he draws an overhead bridge to indicate the algebraic *increase in valence number*, **oxidation**, and an underslung bridge to indicate the algebraic *decrease in valence number*, **reduction**, and uses the arrows under the reducer and oxidizer to show the number of electrons lost and gained, respectively. These numbers are determined by *noting the total change in oxidation numbers in each case*.

Further to illustrate this method of equation writing, consider the equation representing the oxidizing action of potassium permanganate ($KMnO_4$) on potassium bromide and sulfuric acid. It should first be noted that the permanganate ion (MnO_4^-, oxidizer) in the presence of hydrogen ions (H^+) oxidizes the bromide ion (Br^-, reducer), and that potassium ions (K^+) and sulfate ions (SO_4^{-2}) are incidental to the reaction. Employing the procedure outlined previously, the complete equation is set up, showing the reacting substance and the products. The changes in oxidation numbers are next noted and indicated together with the electron transfer. The *electron balance is then established by choosing the proper coefficients of oxidizer and reducer*. Finally, the balancing of the equation by inspection is undertaken.

Oxidation

$$5 \times 2KBr^- + 2KMn^{+7}O_4 + 8H_2SO_4 \rightarrow 5Br_2^0 + 2Mn^{+2}SO_4 +$$

Reduction

$$6K_2SO_4 + 8H_2O$$

$$5 \times 2 \times 1\textcircled{e} = 2 \times 5\textcircled{e}$$

From this equation one learns that the mole ratio of the reducer to the oxidizer is $10KBr:2KMnO_4$, or $5Br^-:1MnO_4^-$. That is to say, for every $5Br^-$ it requires $1MnO_4^-$ for complete oxidation-reduction.

Next consider the reaction of potassium dichromate ($K_2Cr_2O_7$) with an excess of concentrated hydrochloric acid. The essential part of the reaction is the oxidation of Cl^- by the dichromate ion $(Cr_2O_7^{-2}) + H^+$. From Table XIII of oxidizers, $Cr_2O_7^{-2} + H^+$ is reduced to chromic ion (Cr^{+3}). This represents a change in oxidation number for each chromium atom from $+6$ to $+3$. There are 2 chromium atoms in one $Cr_2O_7^{-2}$, and each of these 2 chromium atoms gains 3 electrons per atom, or a total gain of 6 electrons per $Cr_2O_7^{-2}$ ion, thereby forming 2 chromic ions ($2Cr^{+3}$). There is an excess of hydrochloric acid; it furnishes the H^+ ions necessary for the reaction to proceed. A part of the hydrochloric acid is oxidized to free chlorine, *i.e.*, Cl^- (oxidation number -1) is changed to 0 and Cl_2 is formed, while the remainder of the acid furnishes the necessary chloride ions (Cl^-) to form the salts KCl and $CrCl_3$. All this can be represented by the following molecular equation:

Oxidation

$$8HCl + 3 \times 2HCl^{-1} + K_2Cr_2^{+6}O_7 \rightarrow 3Cl_2^0 + 2Cr^{+3}Cl_3 + 2KCl + 7H_2O$$

Reduction

$$3 \times 2 \times 1\textcircled{e} = 2 \times 3\textcircled{e}$$

excess acid forms salts   reducer   oxidizer

Note that hydrochloric acid really plays a dual role in this equation. It acts as a reducer and as an ordinary acid to form salts. Also, a total of 14 moles of HCl is required for the reaction, and only 6 moles is oxidized, the remaining 8 moles furnishing the necessary $8Cl^-$ to form $2CrCl_3$ and $2KCl$.

The mole ratio of reducer:oxidizer in this equation is $6Cl^-:1Cr_2O_7^{-2}$.

SUMMARY OF METHOD FOR BALANCING OXIDATION-REDUCTION EQUATIONS

1. Determine the oxidizer and reducer. Then predict the products and set up the unbalanced equation.

2. Indicate the changes in oxidation numbers of the oxidizer and reducer, and the number of electrons involved in each change.

3. Establish the electron balance by multiplying each of these numbers (of electrons) so that the number of electrons lost by the reducer equals the number gained by the oxidizer. Then place these numbers as coefficients before the reducer and oxidizer and their reaction products, respectively.

4. By inspection supply the correct coefficients for the other formulas in order to balance the rest of the equation.

The application of the method of completing and balancing equations, just described, to other types of oxidation-reduction reactions will now be given consideration. Several of these equations will be required in the correct solution of problems given at the end of this presentation.

ACTION OF DILUTE NITRIC ACID AS AN OXIDIZER

The Reaction of Dilute Nitric Acid with Metals. Referring to Table XIII, we see that dilute nitric acid is an oxidizer. When dilute nitric acid acts on many metals, the nitrate ion, $(N^{+5}O_3)^-$, is reduced; the oxidation number of the nitrogen atom changes from $+5$ to $+2$ (by the gain of 3 electrons), resulting in the formation of nitric oxide ($N^{+2}O$). As a typical example, consider the reaction of dilute nitric acid with metallic copper. The copper, oxidation number 0, is oxidized to the cupric state, with oxidation number of $+2$, by the loss of 2 electrons, thereby forming cupric ions (Cu^{+2}).

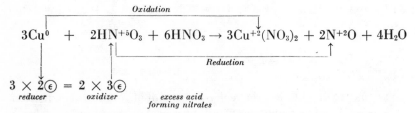

The Reaction of Dilute Nitric Acid with Metallic Sulfides. Reactions of this type can be exemplified in the case of the oxidation of cupric sulfide by dilute nitric acid. Reference to Table XIV gives the information that the sulfide ion (S^{-2}) is a reducer and when oxidized yields free sulfur (S^0) by the loss of 2 electrons per ion with the accompanying change in oxidation number from -2 to 0 (oxidation). The nitrate ion (NO_3^-) from the dilute nitric acid is simultaneously reduced to NO; the oxidation number of the nitrogen atom in the nitrate ion ($+5$) is decreased to $+2$ by the gain of 3 electrons (reduction). With this information at hand, the molecular equation can be written

Oxidation (algebraic increase in valence number of S)

$$3CuS^{-2} + 2HN^{+5}O_3 + 6HNO_3 \rightarrow 3Cu(NO_3)_2 + 3S^0 + 2N^{+2}O +$$

Reduction (algebraic decrease in valence number of N)

$$4H_2O$$

$3 \times 2\text{\textcircled{e}} = 2 \times 3\text{\textcircled{e}}$
reducer   *oxidizer*   *excess acid forming nitrates*

The Reaction of Dilute Nitric Acid with Nonmetals. When a nonmetal like phosphorus or arsenic is treated with dilute nitric acid, the products are phosphoric acid and arsenic acid, respectively, and nitric oxide. Thus

$$3As^0 + 5HN^{+5}O_3 + 2H_2O \rightarrow 3H_3As^{+5}O_4 + 5N^{+2}O\uparrow$$

$3 \times 5\text{\textcircled{e}} = 5 \times 3\text{\textcircled{e}}$

In this equation it should be observed that $2H_2O$ must be added to the left side in order to balance both hydrogen and oxygen.

Likewise, the action of concentrated nitric acid with arsenic sulfide will yield arsenic acid in addition to free sulfur and NO_2.

$$As_2S_5^{-2} + 10HN^{+5}O_3 \rightarrow 2H_3AsO_4 + 5S^0 + 10N^{+4}O_2\uparrow + 2H_2O$$

$5 \times 2\text{\textcircled{e}} = 10 \times 1\text{\textcircled{e}}$

The Reduction of Dichromates and Permanganates by Active Reducing Agents. When hydrogen sulfide is passed into a solution of potassium dichromate containing an excess of sulfuric acid, it will be noted the orange-red color of the dichromate ion $(Cr_2O_7^{-2})$ is changed to the green color of the chromic ion (Cr^{+3}) and also free sulfur is formed simultaneously. That is, the sulfide ion (S^{-2}) in being converted to free sulfur (S^0) represents a change in the oxidation number of sulfur from -2 to 0, by the loss of 2 electrons (reducer). The chromium atoms in $Cr_2O_7^{-2}$ gain 3 electrons per atom, or a total of 6 electrons for 2 chromium atoms to form $2Cr^{+3}$, representing a change in the oxidation number of chromium from $+6$ to $+3$ (oxidizer). The complete molecular equation for this reaction is

Oxidation

$$3H_2S^{-2} + K_2Cr_2^{+6}O_7 + 4H_2SO_4 \rightarrow 3S^0 + Cr_2^{+3}(SO_4)_3 + K_2SO_4 + 7H_2O$$

Reduction

$3 \times 2\text{\textcircled{e}} = 2 \times 3\text{\textcircled{e}}$
reducer   *oxidizer*   *forms sulfates*

The oxidation of ferrous sulfate by potassium permanganate in a solution containing an excess of sulfuric acid follows:

$$5 \times 2Fe^{+2}SO_4 + 2KMn^{+7}O_4 + 8H_2SO_4 \rightarrow 5Fe_2^{+3}(SO_4)_3 + 2Mn^{+2}SO_4$$

Oxidation

Reduction

$$+ K_2SO_4 + 8H_2O$$

$$5 \times 2 \times 1\textcircled{\scriptsize$\epsilon$} = 2 \times 5\textcircled{\scriptsize$\epsilon$}$$

Note the mole ratio $10FeSO_4:2KMnO_4$ or $5Fe^{+2}:1MnO_4^-$.

The Oxidizing Action of Hot, Concentrated Sulfuric Acid on (1) Metals and (2) Nonmetals

1. $Zn^0 + H_2S^{+6}O_4 + H_2SO_4 \rightarrow Zn^{+2}SO_4 + S^{+4}O_2\uparrow + 2H_2O$

$$2\textcircled{\scriptsize$\epsilon$} = 2\textcircled{\scriptsize$\epsilon$}$$

2. $C^0 + 2H_2S^{+6}O_4 \rightarrow C^{+4}O_2 + 2S^{+4}O_2\uparrow + 2H_2O$

$$4\textcircled{\scriptsize$\epsilon$} = 2 \times 2\textcircled{\scriptsize$\epsilon$}$$

Example of Internal Oxidation and Reduction. It is a well-known fact that when chlorine is passed into a cold dilute solution of a strong base, a hypochlorite and a chloride are obtained. This represents a change in the oxidation number of (*a*) one chlorine atom from zero to $+1$ in the hypochlorite ion and (*b*) a change in the oxidation number of another chlorine atom from 0 to -1 in the chloride ion. That is, chlorine is said to be internally oxidized and reduced. This type of equation is illustrated by the following:

Oxidation

$$2\{Cl^0 + Cl^0\} + 2Ba(OH)_2 \rightarrow Ba(Cl^+O)_2 + BaCl_2^- + 2H_2O$$

cold, dilute solution

Reduction

$$2 \times 1\textcircled{\scriptsize$\epsilon$} = 2 \times 1\textcircled{\scriptsize$\epsilon$}$$
$$\underbrace{\qquad\qquad}_{2Cl_2}$$

Likewise, if chlorine is passed into a hot concentrated solution of a strong base, a chlorate and a chloride are obtained. Thus

Oxidation

$$2\{Cl^0 + 5Cl^0\} + 6Ba(OH)_2 \rightarrow Ba(Cl^{+5}O_3)_2 + 5BaCl_2^-$$

hot, concentrated base

Reduction

$$+ 6H_2O$$

$$2 \times 5\textcircled{\scriptsize$\epsilon$} = 2 \times 5 \times 1\textcircled{\scriptsize$\epsilon$}$$
$$\underbrace{\qquad\qquad}_{6Cl_2}$$

The Oxidizing Action of (1) Hydrogen Peroxide and (2) Sodium Peroxide. 1. The two most common peroxides are hydrogen peroxide and sodium peroxide. These contain the peroxide radical (O_2^{-2}) in which each oxygen has an apparent oxidation number -1, and the radical will gain 2 electrons to become oxide ion (O^{-2}) with oxidation number -2.

H_2O_2 will oxidize black lead sulfide to the white lead sulfate.

$$PbS^{-2} + 4H_2O_2 \rightarrow PbS^{+6}O_4 + 4H_2O$$
$$8\epsilon = 4 \times 2\epsilon$$

Ferrous salts in acid solution are oxidized to ferric salts by H_2O_2.

$$2FeSO_4 + H_2O_2 + H_2SO_4 \rightarrow Fe_2(SO_4)_3 + 2H_2O$$
$$2 \times 1\epsilon = 2\epsilon$$

2. Sodium peroxide is a strong oxidizer in an alkaline medium. It will oxidize ferrous ion to ferric and forms ferric hydroxide, manganous ion to manganese dioxide, and chromic ion to chromate.

$$2Fe^{+2}Cl_2 + 3Na_2O_2 + 4H_2O \rightarrow 2Fe^{+3}(OH)_3\downarrow + 4NaCl$$
$$+ 2NaOH + O_2\uparrow$$
$$2 \times 1\epsilon = 2\epsilon$$

Note that $4H_2O$ must be added to the left side to balance the equation.

$$Mn^{+2}Cl_2 + Na_2O_2^- + H_2O \rightarrow Mn^{+4}O_2 \cdot H_2O\downarrow + 2NaCl$$
$$2\epsilon = 2\epsilon$$
$$2Cr^{+3}Cl_3 + 3Na_2O_2^- + 4NaOH \rightarrow 2Na_2Cr^{+6}O_4 + 6NaCl + 2H_2O$$
$$2 \times 3\epsilon = 3 \times 2\epsilon$$

Sodium peroxide readily reacts with water to form sodium hydroxide and oxygen.

$$\overset{\textit{Oxidation}}{Na_2O_2^- + Na_2O_2^- + 2H_2O \rightarrow 4NaO^{-2}H + O_2^0\uparrow}$$
$$\underset{\textit{Reduction}}{}$$
$$2 \times 1\epsilon = 2 \times 1\epsilon$$

This is another example of internal oxidation-reduction, in which the oxidation number -1 in peroxides changes to oxidation numbers -2 and 0.

IONIC OXIDATION-REDUCTION EQUATIONS

Thus far oxidation-reduction equations have been written in customary molecular form. However, the essential part of these reactions can be written using only the partial equations representing the combined actions of the oxidizers and the reducers. Consider the following molecular equation:

$$3CaBr_2^- \;+\; K_2Cr_2^{+6}O_7 + 7H_2SO_4 \rightarrow 3Br_2^0 + Cr_2^{+3}(SO_4)_3 + 3CaSO_4 + K_2SO_4 + 7H_2O$$

(Oxidation ... Reduction)

$3 \times 2 \times 1\,\text{\textcircled{e}} = 2 \times 3\,\text{\textcircled{e}}$

Using only the partial equations for the combined reaction between the reducer (Br^-) and the oxidizer ($Cr_2O_7^{-2} + H^+$) one can write

$$3 \times 2Br^- + Cr_2^{+6}O_7^{-2} + 14H^+ \rightarrow 3Br_2^0 + 2Cr^{+3} + 7H_2O$$

(Oxidation ... Reduction)

$3 \times 2 \times 1\,\text{\textcircled{e}} = 2 \times 3\,\text{\textcircled{e}}$

reducer   oxidizer   acid

In reality, this ionic equation is a pattern for writing the equation for the reaction between any bromide and any dichromate and a non-volatile acid to form bromine, chromic ions, salts of acid used, and water. It also shows the irrelevancy of the positive ions, Ca^{+2} and K^+, in the reaction. It expresses the ratio of $6Br^-:1Cr_2O_7^{-2}$, which will always be maintained irrespective of the positive ions associated with reducer and oxidizer.

The use of this pattern ionic equation to write the complete and balanced molecular equation can be illustrated by the following:

1. $NaBr + Na_2Cr_2O_7 + H_2SO_4 \rightarrow$

Ionic equation pattern:

$$6Br^- + Cr_2^{+6}O_7^{-2} + 14H^+ \rightarrow 3Br_2^0 + 2Cr^{+3} + 7H_2O$$

$6 \times 1\,\text{\textcircled{e}} \; 2 \times 3\,\text{\textcircled{e}}$

Molecular equation:

$$6NaBr + Na_2Cr_2O_7 + 7H_2SO_4 \rightarrow 3Br_2 + Cr_2(SO_4)_3 + 4Na_2SO_4 + 7H_2O$$

It will be noted the number of sulfate ions (SO_4^{-2}) is the same on both sides of the equation. This is a reliable check on the balancing of the equation.

2. $BaBr_2 + K_2Cr_2O_7 + H_3PO_4 \rightarrow$

Since phosphoric acid contains $3H^+$, to facilitate balancing the molecular equation, one multiplies the entire ionic equation pattern by a factor of 3.   Thus

Ionic equation:

$$18Br^- + 3Cr_2^{+6}O_7^{-2} + 42H^+ \rightarrow 9Br_2^0 + 6Cr^{+3} + 21H_2O$$

NOTE.   The ion ratios are still maintained as in the original pattern. Using this factored ionic equation and forming phosphates of positive ions present, one writes

$$9BaBr_2 + 3K_2Cr_2O_7 + 14H_3PO_4 \rightarrow 9Br_2 + 6CrPO_4 + 3Ba_3(PO_4)_2 \\ + 2K_3PO_4 + 21H_2O$$

A check on balancing will reveal there are the same number of phosphate radicals on both sides of the equation.

3. $AlBr_3 + CaCr_2O_7 + H_3PO_4 \rightarrow$

Using the same factored ionic equation as in Example 2, one can immediately write

$$6AlBr_3 + 3CaCr_2O_7 + 14H_3PO_4 \rightarrow 9Br_2 + 6CrPO_4 + Ca_3(PO_4)_2 \\ + 6AlPO_4 + 21H_2O$$

A great many oxidation-reduction reactions occur in an acid medium, and hydronium ions (H_3O^+) are present.   Since H_3O^+ is a hydrated hydrogen ion ($H^+ \cdot H_2O$), it is customary to abbreviate it to H^+, and it is with this understanding that it is used in writing ionic equations of the oxidation-reduction type.   It is also less confusing in balancing equations.

The following are some examples of ionic equations.

NOTE.   The sum of the ion charges on the left side of the arrow equals the sum of the ion charges on the right side of the arrow.

(a) $\quad 5 \times 2I^- \;+\; 2Mn^{+7}O_4^- + 16H^+ \rightarrow 5I_2^0 + 2Mn^{+2} + 8H_2O$

$\qquad 5 \times 2 \times 1_{(\epsilon)} = 2 \times 5_{(\epsilon)}$

(b) $\quad 5S^{-2} \;+\; 2Mn^{+7}O_4^- + 16H^+ \rightarrow 5S^0 + 2Mn^{+2} + 8H_2O$

$\qquad 5 \times 2_{(\epsilon)} = 2 \times 5_{(\epsilon)}$

(c) $\quad 6Fe^{+2} \;+\; Cr_2^{+6}O_7^{-2} + 14H^+ \rightarrow 6Fe^{+3} + 2Cr^{+3} + 7H_2O$

$\qquad 6 \times 1_{(\epsilon)} = 2 \times 3_{(\epsilon)}$

(d) $\quad 5S^{+4}O_3^{-2} + 2Mn^{+7}O_4^- + 6H^+ \rightarrow 5S^{+6}O_4^{-2} + 2Mn^{+2} + 3H_2O$

$\qquad 5 \times 2_{(\epsilon)} = 2 \times 5_{(\epsilon)}$

(e) $3HS^{+4}O_3^- + Cr_2^{+6}O_7^{-2} + 8H^+ \rightarrow 3HS^{+6}O_4^- + 2Cr^{+3} + 4H_2O$

$3 \times 2\text{\textcircled{e}} = 2 \times 3\text{\textcircled{e}}$

(f) $2Br^- + Pb^{+4}O_2 + 4H^+ \rightarrow Br_2^0 + Pb^{+2} + 2H_2O$

$2 \times 1\text{\textcircled{e}} = 2\text{\textcircled{e}}$

(g) $3Ag^0 + N^{+5}O_3^- + 4H^+ \rightarrow 3Ag^+ + N^{+2}O + 2H_2O$

dilute HNO₃

$3 \times 1\text{\textcircled{e}} = 3\text{\textcircled{e}}$

(h) $Cu^0 + 2N^{+5}O_3^- + 4H^+ \rightarrow Cu^{++} + 2N^{+4}O_2 + 2H_2O$

concentrated HNO₃

$2\text{\textcircled{e}} = 2 \times 1\text{\textcircled{e}}$

(i) $3S^{-2} + 2N^{+5}O_3^- + 8H^+ \rightarrow 3S^0 + 2N^{+2}O + 4H_2O$

dilute HNO₃

$3 \times 2\text{\textcircled{e}} = 2 \times 3\text{\textcircled{e}}$

(j) $\{Cl^0 + Cl^0\} + 2OH^- \rightarrow Cl^- + Cl^+O^- + H_2O$

cold, dilute base   *halide*   *hypohalite*

$1\text{\textcircled{e}} = 1\text{\textcircled{e}}$

Cl_2^0

(k) $Cl^0 + 5Cl^0 + 6OH^- \rightarrow 5Cl^- + Cl^{+5}O_3^- + 3H_2O$

hot, concentrated base   *halide*   *halate*

$5\text{\textcircled{e}} = 5 \times 1\text{\textcircled{e}}$

$3Cl_2^0$

Before proceeding with illustrative problems, it is apropos to give consideration to the method of balancing oxidation-reduction equations known as the **ion-electron method**, and it is hereby presented in very brief outline.

If potassium sulfite is added to a potassium permanganate solution acidified with sulfuric acid, one will observe that the original permanganate solution becomes completely decolorized and the acidity of the solution is increased. These facts can be represented by the unbalanced ionic equation

$$SO_3^{-2} + MnO_4^- + H^+ \rightleftharpoons SO_4^{-2} + Mn^{+2} + H_2O$$

The partial equation of the oxidizer which indicates the reducing action is

$$MnO_4^- + 8H^+ \rightleftharpoons Mn^{+2} + 4H_2O$$

It will be noted on the left side of this equation there are 1 negative and 8 positive charges, or a net charge of +7. On the right side there is a net charge of +2. To equalize the charges on the two sides of the equation requires the addition of 5 negatives or $5\text{\textcircled{e}}$ on the left side, represented by

$$MnO_4^- + 8H^+ + 5\text{\textcircled{e}} \rightleftharpoons Mn^{+2} + 4H_2O \qquad (1)$$

This partial equation is now electrically balanced.

The partial equation of the reducer to show the oxidizing action is

$$SO_3^{-2} + H_2O \rightleftharpoons SO_4^{-2} + 2H^+$$

The addition of water to the left side is necessary as a source of oxygen in the formation of SO_4^{-2}. To equalize the charges on the two sides of this equation necessitates the subtraction of 2 negatives or 2ϵ on the left side, or

$$SO_3^{-2} + H_2O - 2\epsilon \rightleftharpoons SO_4^{-2} + 2H^+ \qquad (2)$$

To complete the equation, these two partial equations are combined; but in order to cancel the electron charges, Equation (1) must be multiplied by a factor 2, and Equation (2) multiplied by a factor 5 as in solving two simultaneous equations in algebra. This gives

$$2MnO_4^- + 16H^+ + 10\epsilon \rightleftharpoons 2Mn^{+2} + 8H_2O \qquad \textit{reduction}$$
$$5SO_3^{-2} + 5H_2O - 10\epsilon \rightleftharpoons 5SO_4^{-2} + 10H^+ \qquad \textit{oxidation}$$

Adding,

$$5SO_3^{-2} + 2MnO_4^- + 6H^+ \rightleftharpoons 5SO_4^{-2} + 2Mn^{+2} + 3H_2$$

Molecular equation:

$$5K_2SO_3 + 2KMnO_4 + 3H_2SO_4 \rightleftharpoons 6K_2SO_4 + 2MnSO_4 + 3H_2O$$

In balancing the equation for the reaction between silver sulfide and concentrated nitric acid, one sets up the partial equation for the reduction and the partial equation for the oxidation in the following manner:

$$2 \times \{NO_3^- + 2H^+ + 1\epsilon \rightleftharpoons NO_2 + H_2O\} \qquad \textit{reduction}$$
$$Ag_2S - 2\epsilon \rightleftharpoons 2Ag^+ + S^0 \qquad \textit{oxidation}$$

Adding,

$$Ag_2S + 2NO_3^- + 4H^+ \rightleftharpoons 2Ag^+ + 2NO_2 + S + 2H_2O$$

Molecular equation:

$$Ag_2S + 4HNO_3 \rightleftharpoons 2AgNO_3 + 2NO_2 + S + 2H_2O$$

The reducing action by hydrogen sulfide of potassium dichromate acidified with sulfuric acid is represented by the following equations:

$$Cr_2O_7^{-2} + 14H^+ + 6\epsilon \rightleftharpoons 2Cr^{+3} + 7H_2O \qquad \textit{reduction}$$
$$3 \times \{H_2S \qquad - 2\epsilon \rightleftharpoons S^0 + 2H^+\} \qquad \textit{oxidation}$$

Adding,

$$3H_2S + Cr_2O_7^{-2} + 8H^+ \rightleftharpoons 3S^0 + 2Cr^{+3} + 7H_2O$$

Molecular equation:

$$3H_2S + K_2Cr_2O_7 + 4H_2SO_4 \rightleftharpoons 3S^0 + Cr_2(SO_4)_3 + K_2SO_4 + 7H_2O$$

Example. 1. (*a*) Complete and balance the following molecular equation:

$$H_2S + K_2Cr_2O_7 + H_3PO_4 \rightarrow$$

(*b*) Write the ionic equation which represents the facts.

(*a*) Using oxidation-number change and electron-transfer method,

$$3 \times 3H_2S^{-2} + 3K_2Cr_2^{+6}O_7 + 8H_3PO_4 \rightarrow 9S^0 + 6Cr^{+3}PO_4$$
$$+ 2K_3PO_4 + 21H_2O$$

$$3 \times 3 \times 2\text{\textcircled{e}} = 3 \times 2 \times 3\text{\textcircled{e}}$$

reducer   *oxidizer*   *salt former*

Using the ion-electron method,

$$Cr_2O_7^{-2} + 14H^+ + 6\text{\textcircled{e}} \rightleftharpoons 2Cr^{+3} + 7H_2O$$
$$3 \times \{H_2S \quad\quad - 2\text{\textcircled{e}} \rightleftharpoons S^0 + 2H^+\}$$

Ionic equation:

$$3H_2S + Cr_2O_7^{-2} + 8H^+ \rightleftharpoons 3S^0 + 2Cr^{+3} + 7H_2O$$

Since H_3PO_4 is the acid used in the reaction and $8H^+$ are required, it is necessary to multiply this complete ionic equation by 3 before the molecular equation can be written.

Molecular equation:

$$9H_2S + 3K_2Cr_2O_7 + 8H_3PO_4 \rightarrow 9S + 6CrPO_4 + 2K_3PO_4 + 21H_2O$$

(*b*) $3S^{-2} + Cr_2^{+6}O_7^{-2} + 14H^+ \rightarrow 3S^0 + 2Cr^{+3} + 7H_2O$

$$3 \times 2\text{\textcircled{e}} = 2 \times 3\text{\textcircled{e}}$$

Example. 2. Write (*a*) the complete molecular equation and (*b*) the ionic equation for the reaction of cadmium sulfide with dilute nitric acid.

(*a*) By oxidation-number change and electron-transfer method,

$$3CdS^{-2} + 2HN^{+5}O_3 + 6HNO_3 \rightarrow 3Cd(NO_3)_2 + 2N^{+2}O + 3S^0$$
$$+ 4H_2O$$

$$3 \times 2\text{\textcircled{e}} = 2 \times 3\text{\textcircled{e}}$$

By ion-electron method,

$$2 \times \{NO_3^- + 4H^+ + 3\text{\textcircled{e}} \rightleftharpoons NO + 2H_2O\}$$
$$3 \times \{CdS \quad\quad - 2\text{\textcircled{e}} \rightleftharpoons Cd^{+2} + S^0\}$$

Ionic equation:

$$3CdS + 2NO_3^- + 8H^+ \rightleftharpoons 3Cd^{+2} + 2NO + 3S^0 + 4H_2O$$

Molecular equation:

$$3CdS + 8HNO_3 \rightleftharpoons 3Cd(NO_3)_2 + 2NO + 3S + 4H_2O$$

(b) $3S^{-2} + 2N^{+5}O_3^- + 8H^+ \rightarrow 3S^0 + 2N^{+2}O + 4H_2O$

$$3 \times 2\text{ⓔ} = 2 \times 3\text{ⓔ}$$

Exercises in Balancing Oxidation-reduction Equations

10-1. For each of the following complete and balanced equations in tabular form, place in column A the symbol of the element oxidized, in column B the number of electrons lost, in column C the symbol of the element reduced, and in column D the number of electrons gained.

  1. $H_2 + Cl_2 \rightarrow 2HCl$
  2. $3Ca + N_2 \rightarrow Ca_3N_2$
  3. $2Sb + 3Cl_2 \rightarrow 2SbCl_3$
  4. $H_2S + Cl_2 \rightarrow S + 2HCl$
  5. $Zn + H_2SO_4 \text{ (dilute)} \rightarrow H_2 + ZnSO_4$
  6. $Zn + CuSO_4 \rightarrow Cu + ZnSO_4$
  7. $MnO_2 + 4HCl \rightarrow Cl_2 + MnCl_2 + 2H_2O$
  8. $BaCl_2 + PbO_2 + 2H_2SO_4 \rightarrow Cl_2 + PbSO_4\downarrow + BaSO_4\downarrow + 2H_2O$
  9. $2KBr + Cl_2 \rightarrow Br_2 + 2KCl$
  10. $Cl_2 + H_2O \rightarrow HCl + HClO$

10-2. Using the electron-transfer method, balance the equations for the following complete reactions:

  1. $Zn + N_2 \rightarrow Zn_3N_2$
  2. $HNO_3 + H_2S \rightarrow S + NO + H_2O$
  3. $NH_3 + O_2 \rightarrow NO + H_2O$
  4. $SnCl_2 + HgCl_2 \rightarrow SnCl_4 + Hg_2Cl_2$
  5. $PbO_2 + HCl \rightarrow Cl_2 + PbCl_2 + H_2O$
  6. $LiCl + KMnO_4 + H_2SO_4 \rightarrow Cl_2 + MnSO_4 + K_2SO_4 + Li_2SO_4 + H_2O$
  7. $K_2Cr_2O_7 + BaCl_2 + H_2SO_4 \rightarrow Cl_2 + Cr_2(SO_4)_3 + BaSO_4\downarrow$
       $+ K_2SO_4 + H_2O$
  8. $K_2Cr_2O_7 + HCl \rightarrow Cl_2 + CrCl_3 + KCl + H_2O$
  9. $MnO_2 + CaCl_2 + H_3PO_4 \rightarrow Cl_2 + Mn_3(PO_4)_2 + Ca_3(PO_4)_2 + H_2O$
  10. $SrCl_2 + KMnO_4 + H_3PO_4 \rightarrow Cl_2 + Mn_3(PO_4)_2 + Sr_3(PO_4)_2$
       $+ K_3PO_4 + H_2O$

10-3. Using the electron-transfer method, balance the equations for the following complete reactions:

  1. $FeCl_3 + SnCl_2 \rightarrow FeCl_2 + SnCl_4$
  2. $PbO_2 + HI \rightarrow I_2 + PbI_2 + H_2O$
  3. $MnO_2 + FeSO_4 + H_2SO_4 \rightarrow MnSO_4 + Fe_2(SO_4)_3 + H_2O$
  4. $KMnO_4 + BiBr_3 + H_2SO_4 \rightarrow Br_2 + MnSO_4 + Bi_2(SO_4)_3 + K_2SO_4$
       $+ H_2O$
  5. $K_2Cr_2O_7 + KI + H_3PO_4 \rightarrow I_2 + CrPO_4 + K_3PO_4 + H_2O$

10-4. Using the electron-transfer method, complete and balance the equations for the following reactions:

1. $K + O_2 \rightarrow$
2. $H_2S + I_2 \rightarrow$
3. $Al + H_2SO_4$ (dilute) $\rightarrow$
4. $FeCl_2 + Cl_2 \rightarrow$
5. $HgSO_4 + SnSO_4 \rightarrow$
6. $KMnO_4 + NaCl + H_2SO_4 \rightarrow$
7. $KCl + K_2Cr_2O_7 + H_2SO_4 \rightarrow$
8. $HCl + KMnO_4 \rightarrow$
9. $AlBr_3 + KMnO_4 + H_2SO_4 \rightarrow$
10. $KI + K_2Cr_2O_7 + H_3PO_4 \rightarrow$

10-5. Using the electron-transfer method, complete and balance the equations for the following reactions:

1. $HBr + KMnO_4 \rightarrow$
2. $Fe + Ag_2SO_4 \rightarrow$
3. $Sn + Cl_2$ (excess) $\rightarrow$
4. $Cl_2 + KOH$ (cold, dilute) $\rightarrow$
5. $Cl_2 + NaOH$ (hot, concentrated) $\rightarrow$
6. $Ba + H_2O \rightarrow$
7. $KBr + KMnO_4 + H_2SO_4 \rightarrow$
8. $AlBr_3 + K_2Cr_2O_7 + H_3PO_4 \rightarrow$
9. $Ag + HNO_3$ (concentrated) $\rightarrow$
10. $Cu + H_2SO_4$ (hot, concentrated) $\rightarrow$

10-6. Balance the following complete ionic equations by the electron-transfer method:

1. $Mg + H^+ \rightarrow Mg^{+2} + H_2$
2. $Sb + Sn^{+4} \rightarrow Sb^{+3} + Sn^{+2}$
3. $Cl_2 + OH^- \rightarrow Cl^- + ClO_3^- + H_2O$
4. $Cl^- + PbO_2 + H^+ \rightarrow Cl_2 + Pb^{+2} + H_2O$
5. $Cl^- + MnO_4^- + H^+ \rightarrow Cl_2 + Mn^{+2} + H_2O$

10-7. Balance the following complete ionic equations by the electron-transfer method:

1. $H_2S + Cr_2O_7^{-2} + H^+ \rightarrow S^0 + Cr^{+3} + H_2O$
2. $Al + H^+ \rightarrow Al^{+3} + H_2$
3. $Zn + Ag^+ \rightarrow Zn^{+2} + Ag$
4. $Br_2 + OH^- \rightarrow Br^- + BrO_3^- + H_2O$
5. $Ag + NO_3^- + H^+ \rightarrow Ag^+ + NO + H_2O$

10-8. Balance the following complete ionic equations by the electron-transfer method:

1. $I^- + Cr_2O_7^{-2} + H^+ \rightarrow I_2 + Cr^{+3} + H_2O$
2. $S^{-2} + MnO_4^- + H^+ \rightarrow S + Mn^{+2} + H_2O$
3. $Fe^{+2} + Cr_2O_7^{-2} + H^+ \rightarrow Fe^{+3} + Cr^{+3} + H_2O$
4. $Pb + NO_3^- + H^+ \rightarrow Pb^{+2} + NO_2 + H_2O$
5. $CuS + NO_3^- + H^+ \rightarrow Cu^{+2} + S + NO + H_2O$

10-9. Complete and balance the following ionic equations by the electron-transfer method:

1. $Bi + NO_3^- + H^+$ (dilute HNO_3) →
2. $S^{-2} + NO_3^- + H^+$ (dilute HNO_3) →
3. $Br^- + Cr_2O_7^{-2} + H^+$ →
4. $Fe^{+2} + MnO_4^-] + H^+$ →
5. $Cl_2 + OH^-$ (hot, concentrated base) →

10-10. Complete and balance the following ionic equations by the electron-transfer method:

1. $Ag + NO_3^- + H^+$ (concentrated HNO_3) →
2. $Ag_2S + NO_3^- + H^+$ (dilute HNO_3) →
3. $I^- + MnO_4^- + H^+$ →
4. $HSO_3^- + MnO_4^- + H^+ → HSO_4^- +$
5. $Sn^{+2} + MnO_4^- + H^+$ →

The remainder of this chapter is devoted to problems involving oxidation-reduction reactions. The fundamental principles presented in previous chapters with respect to weight relations, weight, and gas-volume relations will, of course, pertain to the solution of these problems. The following example is designed to illustrate the foregoing relations.

Example. Copper sulfate is prepared by treating metallic copper with hot concentrated sulfuric acid. Blue vitriol ($CuSO_4 \cdot 5H_2O$) is obtained by crystallization of copper sulfate from aqueous solution. (a) Calculate the number of gallons of sulfuric acid (sp gr = 1.835 and 93.2 per cent by weight of pure H_2SO_4) required to prepare 1 ton of blue vitriol. (b) How many cubic feet of SO_2, measured at 75°F and 29.8 in. Hg, will be obtained by this reaction?

The chemical equation representing the foregoing reaction must first be written

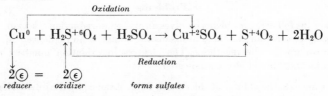

From the equation, 1 lb-mole Cu requires 2 lb-moles active H_2SO_4 to form 1 lb-mole $CuSO_4$, and 1 lb-mole or 358 cu ft at STP of SO_2.

(a) Molecular weight $CuSO_4 \cdot 5H_2O$ = 249.7.

$$1 \text{ ton blue vitriol} = 2{,}000 \text{ lb } CuSO_4 \cdot 5H_2O$$

$$\frac{2{,}000 \text{ lb } CuSO_4 \cdot 5H_2O}{249.7 \text{ lb } CuSO_4 \cdot 5H_2O/\text{lb-mole } CuSO_4 \cdot 5H_2O}$$

$$= 8.0 \text{ lb-moles } CuSO_4 \cdot 5H_2O$$

8.0 lb-moles $CuSO_4 \cdot 5H_2O$ contains 8.0 lb-moles $CuSO_4$.

Since 1 lb-mole $CuSO_4$ requires 2 lb-moles pure H_2SO_4, 8.0 lb-moles $CuSO_4$ will require 8.0 × 2 lb-moles pure H_2SO_4 = 16.0 lb-moles pure H_2SO_4. Since 1 lb-mole pure H_2SO_4 = 98.0 lb pure H_2SO_4, then 16.0 lb-moles pure H_2SO_4 × 98.0 lb pure H_2SO_4/lb-mole pure H_2SO_4 = 1,568 lb pure H_2SO_4.

The specific gravity of H_2SO_4 is 1.835, and it is 93.2 per cent by weight pure H_2SO_4; 1 gal water = 8.3 lb.

NOTE. For convenience in expressing dimensional units, sulfuric acid solution is abbreviated *sas*.

$$1.835 \times 8.3 \text{ lb/gal} = 15.23 \text{ lb } sas/\text{gal } sas$$
$$15.23 \text{ lb } sas/\text{gal } sas \times 0.932 \text{ lb pure } H_2SO_4/\text{lb } sas$$
$$= 14.2 \text{ lb pure } H_2SO_4/\text{gal } sas$$
$$\frac{1,568 \text{ lb pure } H_2SO_4}{14.2 \text{ lb pure } H_2SO_4/\text{gal } sas} = 111 \text{ gal } sas$$

or 111 gal sulfuric acid (sp gr 1.835 and 93.2 per cent pure H_2SO_4) will be required in the preparation of 1 ton blue vitriol ($CuSO_4 \cdot 5H_2O$).

(*b*) From part (*a*), for every 1 lb-mole $CuSO_4$ formed, 1 lb-mole or 358 cu ft at STP of SO_2 is formed at the same time. Then for 8.0 lb-moles $CuSO_4$ produced there will be 8.0 lb-moles SO_2, or 8 lb-moles × 358 cu ft of (STP) SO_2/lb-mole = 2,864 cu ft (STP) SO_2 formed.

$$STP = 32°F \text{ and } 29.92 \text{ in. Hg}$$
$$32°F + 460 = 492°R \qquad 75°F + 460 = 535°R$$
$$2,864 \text{ cu ft} \times \frac{535°R}{492°R} \times \frac{29.92 \text{ in.}}{29.8 \text{ in.}} = 3,133 \text{ cu ft}$$

or 3,133 cu ft SO_2 at 75°F and 29.8 in. Hg will be produced.

Problems

Each of the following problems involves an oxidation-reduction reaction. Before attempting to solve any of these problems the complete and balanced equation is first drawn up for the reaction. The changes in oxidation numbers and the electron balance should also be indicated.

10-11. Calculate the volume of chlorine, at STP, obtained by the interaction of 25 g of lead dioxide and excess concentrated hydrochloric acid. *Ans.* 2.34 l.

10-12. Calculate the volume of chlorine, at standard conditions, liberated by the action of excess $KMnO_4$ with 100 ml of hydrochloric acid, which has a specific gravity of 1.2 and contains 39.8 per cent by weight of pure HCl. *Ans.* 9.17 l.

10-13. Calculate the volume of H_2S, at standard conditions, required to reduce 1 g of $K_2Cr_2O_7$ to chromic chloride, in a solution acidified with hydrochloric acid. *Ans.* 228 ml.

10-14. A solution containing 10 g of ferrous sulfate is treated with the requisite amounts of $KMnO_4$ and H_2SO_4 for complete chemical action. Calculate the weight of ferric sulfate obtained by this reaction. *Ans.* 13.2 g.

10-15. (*a*) How many milliliters of sulfuric acid (sp gr 1.84 and containing 97.5

per cent by weight of pure H_2SO_4) will be necessary to produce 2 l of SO_2, at standard conditions, by heating with copper turnings? (b) If the resultant solution is evaporated to dryness, what weight of crystalline $CuSO_4 \cdot 5H_2O$ could be obtained from the residue?

Ans. (a) 9.7 ml; (b) 22.3 g.

10-16. A sample of silver weighing 10 g is dissolved in nitric acid, which has a specific gravity of 1.26 and contains 41.3 per cent by weight of pure HNO_3. (a) Calculate the number of milliliters of nitric acid necessary to dissolve the Ag. (b) How many milliliters of nitric acid is used for oxidizing purposes? *Ans.* (a) 15 ml.

10-17. A sample of brass (70 per cent Cu and 30 per cent Zn) weighing 5 g is dissolved by nitric acid which has a specific gravity of 1.2 and contains 33.0 per cent by weight of pure HNO_3. Calculate the number of milliliters of this nitric acid solution required to dissolve the brass. *Ans.* 32 ml.

10-18. Calculate (a) the weight of sodium hypochlorite obtained by passing excess chlorine into a cold solution of caustic soda containing 100 g of NaOH and (b) the volume of chlorine, at standard conditions, required to convert the NaOH to NaClO. *Ans.* (a) 93 g; (b) 28 l.

10-19. Chlorine is passed into a hot solution of caustic potash, thus forming potassium chlorate. Calculate the weight of potassium chlorate formed by action of excess chlorine on a solution that contains 50 g of KOH.

Ans. 18 g.

10-20. Chlorine is passed into a hot solution of barium hydroxide which contains 30 g of $Ba(OH)_2$ in 1 l solution. Calculate (a) the volume of chlorine, at standard conditions, required for the complete reaction and (b) the weight of barium chlorate obtained as a product of this reaction.

Ans. (a) 3.9 l; (b) 8.9 g.

10-21. Calculate (a) the weight of $K_2Cr_2O_7$ required to react completely with 20 ml of hydriodic acid (sp gr 1.7 and containing 57 per cent by weight of pure HI) and (b) the weight of sublimed iodine obtained from this reaction.

Ans. (a) 3.18 g; (b) 8.24 g.

10-22. A solution containing 20 g of ferrous sulfate acidified with sulfuric acid is treated with excess nitric acid. Calculate (a) the weight of ferric sulfate produced in the reaction and (b) the volume of NO liberated at standard conditions. *Ans.* (a) 26.4 g; (b) 985 ml.

10-23. What volume of ammonia at standard conditions will reduce 100 g of cupric oxide?

10-24. Calculate the weight of metallic silver obtained by the action of 1.5 g of ferrous sulfate with a silver nitrate solution.

10-25. Calculate the volume of chlorine at 70°F and 28.5 in. Hg that is required to oxidize 10 g of ferrous chloride.

10-26. What volume of hydrogen sulfide at 25°C and 750 mm Hg will be required to bring about the reduction of 10 g of $KMnO_4$ in a solution acidified with sulfuric acid?

10-27. What volume of hydrogen sulfide at 22°C and 755 mm Hg will be required to reduce 10 g of ferric sulfate in a solution acidified with sulfuric acid?

10-28. Calculate the volume of hydrogen sulfide at 21°C and 750 mm Hg that will be required to reduce 15 g of ferric chloride to ferrous chloride.

10-29. A mixture of KCl and $KMnO_4$ is treated with concentrated sulfuric acid. Calculate (a) the weight of $KMnO_4$ required to oxidize 10 g of KCl and (b) the volume of chlorine produced at standard conditions.

10-30. A mixture of KBr and $K_2Cr_2O_7$ is treated with concentrated sulfuric acid. (a) Calculate the weight of $K_2Cr_2O_7$ required to oxidize 25 g of KBr. (b) If the bromine liberated is allowed to react with phosphorus, what weight of phosphorus tribromide could be obtained?

10-31. A laboratory method for making bromine consists of treating a mixture of NaBr and $K_2Cr_2O_7$ with concentrated sulfuric acid. Determine the weights of (a) NaBr and (b) $K_2Cr_2O_7$ required to obtain 100 ml of bromine (sp gr 3.12).

10-32. Calculate the volume of chlorine, collected at 20°C and 755 mm Hg, that is obtained by the interaction of 500 ml of hydrochloric acid solution (sp gr 1.2 and containing 39 per cent by weight of pure HCl) and excess potassium dichromate.

10-33. What volume of bromine at 70°F and 30.3 in. Hg is obtained by complete reaction between excess manganese dioxide and 100 ml of hydrobromic acid (sp gr 1.49 and containing 47.8 per cent by weight pure HBr)?

10-34. What volume of chlorine collected at 23°C and 758 mm Hg can be obtained from the interaction of 10 g of $K_2Cr_2O_7$ and excess concentrated hydrochloric acid?

10-35. Determine the weight of iodine obtained by complete reaction between 100 ml of hydriodic acid (sp gr 1.67 and containing 57 per cent by weight pure HI) and excess lead dioxide.

10-36. How many milliliters of hydrobromic acid (sp gr 1.49 and containing 47.8 per cent by weight pure HBr) is required to react completely with 25 g of $KMnO_4$?

10-37. Determine the number of milliliters of hydriodic acid (sp gr 1.67 and containing 57 per cent by weight pure HI) required to react completely with 25 g of $K_2Cr_2O_7$.

10-38. Manganese dioxide is treated with an excess of concentrated hydrochloric acid. The chlorine liberated by this action is absorbed in cold KOH solution. Calculate the amount of MnO_2 required to prepare 100 g of potassium hypochlorite.

10-39. Lead dioxide is treated with an excess of concentrated hydrochloric acid. The chlorine liberated by this action is absorbed in hot KOH solution. Calculate the amount of PbO_2 required in the preparation of 100 lb of potassium chlorate.

10-40. (a) Calculate the number of milliliters of nitric acid (sp gr 1.41 and containing 67.5 per cent by weight of pure HNO_3) that will react completely with 10 g of metallic Cu. (b) What volume of NO_2, collected at 23°C and 745 mm Hg, will be liberated by this action?

10-41. A sample of sterling silver (92.5 per cent Ag, 7.5 per cent Cu) weighing 2.488 g is dissolved in nitric acid which has a sp gr of 1.22 and contains 40.6 per cent by weight of pure HNO_3. Calculate the actual number of milliliters of acid that will be required to dissolve the sample completely.

10-42. (a) How many milliliters of nitric acid (sp gr 1.2 and containing 32.3 per cent by weight of pure HNO_3) will be required to interact completely with 10 g of phosphorus? (b) How many grams of phosphoric acid will be produced by this reaction?

10-43. (a) How many milliliters of nitric acid (sp gr 1.2 and containing 32.3 per cent by weight of pure HNO_3) will be required to interact completely with 100 g of iodine? (b) How many grams of iodic acid will be produced by this reaction?

CHAPTER XI

GRAM-EQUIVALENT WEIGHT

OUTLINE

Gram-equivalent weight of an element may be defined as that quantity of the element which reacts with or displaces 1 g-atom of hydrogen (1.008 g).

Gram-equivalent weight of an element is equal to the gram-atomic weight of that element divided by its valence number.   To find the number of gram-equivalents in any given weight of an element, divide the given number of grams of the element by the number of grams per gram-equivalent weight of that element.

Gram-equivalent weight of compounds:

1. Gram-equivalent weight of an acid is that quantity of acid which contains 1 g-equiv of H^+, or 1.008 g of H^+.
2. Gram-equivalent weight of a base is that quantity of base which contains 1 g-equiv of OH^-, or 17.008 g of OH^-.
3. Gram-equivalent weight of normal salts (nonoxidizers and nonreducers) is that quantity of salt which contains 1 g-eq of the positive ion.
4. Gram-equivalent weight of oxidizer and/or reducer

$$= \frac{\text{gram-mole}}{\text{total algebraic change in oxidation number in 1 molecule}}$$

Gram-equivalent volume of gases.   The liter-equivalent of a gas may be determined by dividing 22.4 l (STP) of gas by the positive polar valence of the compound formed when the gas dissolves in water, or when it chemically reacts with other substances.

GRAM-EQUIVALENT OF ELEMENTS

When hydrogen and oxygen combine chemically, the reaction is represented by

$$2H_2 \quad + O_2 \quad \rightarrow 2H_2O$$

2 g-moles + 1 g-mole → 2 g-moles
1 g-mole + ½ g-mole → 1 g-mole

or

2 g-atoms + 1 g-atom → 1 g-mole

or

1 g-atom + ½ g-atom → ½ g-mole
1.008 g + ½ × 16 g → ½ × 18.016 g

or

1.008 g + 8 g   → 9.008 g

That is to say, 1.008 g of hydrogen (1 g-atom H) combines with 8 g of oxygen (½ g-atom O).   Thus 1.008 g of hydrogen (1 g-atom H) is said to be chemically *equivalent to* 8 g of oxygen ($\frac{1}{2}$ g-atom O), and the weights, H = 1.008 g and O = 8 g, are known as combining weights, or **gram-equivalent weights,** of these elements.

Since a great many elements combine with oxygen, and with hydrogen, and also several elements displace hydrogen from many dilute acids, on this basis, the gram-equivalent weight of an element is that quantity of the element which reacts with 8 g of oxygen or 1.008 g of hydrogen, or displaces 1 g-atom of hydrogen (1.008 g).

There is a direct relationship between the gram-atom and the gram-equivalent weight (g-eq wt) of an element. Thus

$$\frac{1 \text{ g-atom H}}{1 \text{ g-eq wt H}} = \frac{1.008 \text{ g}}{1.008 \text{ g}} = \frac{1}{1}$$

$$\frac{1 \text{ g-atom O}}{1 \text{ g-eq wt O}} = \frac{16.00 \text{ g}}{8.00 \text{ g}} = \frac{2}{1}$$

$$\frac{1 \text{ g-atom Al}}{1 \text{ g-eq wt Al}} = \frac{27.0 \text{ g}}{9.0 \text{ g}} = \frac{3}{1}$$

$$\frac{1 \text{ g-atom Zn}}{1 \text{ g-eq wt Zn}} = \frac{65.4 \text{ g}}{32.7 \text{ g}} = \frac{2}{1}$$

From these relations it can be said the gram-atom of an element is a whole-number multiple of the gram-equivalent weight of that element. These whole numbers represent the valence numbers of the elements. Then

$$\frac{1 \text{ gram-atomic weight of element}}{1 \text{ gram-equivalent weight of element}} = \text{valence number}$$

Rearranging this expression,

$$1 \text{ gram-equivalent weight} = \frac{1 \text{ gram-atomic weight of element}}{\text{valence number}}$$

Thus for those elements having +1 or −1 valence numbers, 1 g-eq wt is numerically the same as 1 g-atomic wt. For those elements with +2 or −2 valence numbers, 1 g-eq wt = $\frac{1}{2}$ g-atomic wt, and for those with +3 or −3 valence numbers, 1 g-eq wt = $\frac{1}{3}$ g-atomic wt, and so on.

Example 1. How many grams are contained in 1 gram-equivalent weight (1 g-eq wt) of each of the following elements: potassium, calcium, aluminum. Atomic weights: K = 39.1; Ca = 40.1; Al = 27.0. Since 1 g-eq wt of element = 1 g-atomic weight of element/valence number, then 1 g-eq wt K = 39.1 g K/1 = 39.1 g K, or 39.1 g K/g-eq wt; 1 g-eq wt Ca = 40.1 g Ca/2 = 20.0 g Ca, or 20.0 g Ca/g-eq wt; 1 g-eq wt Al = 27.0 g Al/3 = 9.0 g Al, or 9.0 g Al/g-eq wt.

An element with more than one valence number will have variable equivalent weights. The element iron (atomic weight = 55.8), with valence numbers $+2$ in ferrous compounds and $+3$ in ferric compounds, will have two different equivalent weights. Thus

$$1 \text{ g-eq wt } Fe^{+2} = \frac{55.8 \text{ g } Fe^{+2}}{2} = 27.9 \text{ g } Fe^{+2}$$

or 27.9 g Fe^{+2}/g-eq wt.

$$1 \text{ g-eq wt } Fe^{+3} = \frac{55.8 \text{ g } Fe^{+3}}{3} = 18.6 \text{ g } Fe^{+3}$$

or 18.6 g Fe^{+3}/g-eq wt.

Example 2. Determine the gram-equivalent weight of arsenic in (*a*) arsenic trioxide and (*b*) arsenic pentoxide.

To determine the gram-equivalent weight of any element in a compound, one can deal with only the atomic weight and the valence numbers irrespective of the numbers of atoms of the element in the compound.

(*a*) Since atomic weight As = 74.9, or 1 g-atomic weight As = 74.9 g, the valence number of arsenic in arsenic trioxide (As_2O_3) is $+3$. Then

$$1 \text{ g-eq wt } As^{+3} = \frac{74.9 \text{ g } As^{+3}}{3} = 25.0 \text{ g } As^{+3}$$

or 25.0 g As^{+3}/g-eq wt.

(*b*) The valence number of arsenic in arsenic pentoxide (As_2O_5) is $+5$. Then

$$1 \text{ g-eq wt } As^{+5} = \frac{74.9 \text{ g } As^{+5}}{5} = 15.0 \text{ g } As^{+5}$$

or 15.0 g As^{+5}/g-eq wt.

To find the *number* of gram-equivalents in any given weight of an element, it is necessary to divide the given number of grams of the element by the number of grams in 1 gram-equivalent weight of that element or

$$\text{No. of g-eq} = \frac{G}{\text{no. of g/g-eq wt}}$$

where G = given number of grams of the element and no. of g/g-eq wt = number of grams in 1 g-eq wt of that element.

Example 3. Determine the number of gram-equivalents (*a*) in 171.75 g of barium and (*b*) of Fe in 6.52 g of ferric iron.

$$\text{No. of g-eq} = \frac{G}{\text{no. of g/g-eq wt}}$$

Atomic weight Ba = 137.4.

$$1 \text{ g-eq wt Ba} = \frac{137.4 \text{ g Ba}}{2} = 68.7 \text{ g Ba}$$

or 68.7 g Ba/g-eq wt.

Let x = number of gram-equivalents Ba

$$= \frac{171.75 \text{ g Ba}}{68.7 \text{ g Ba/g-eq wt}} = 171.75 \text{ g Ba} \times \frac{1 \text{ g-eq wt}}{68.7 \text{ g Ba}}$$

$$= 2.5 \text{ g-eq}$$

(b) Atomic weight Fe = 55.8.

$$1 \text{ g-eq wt Fe}^{+3} = \frac{55.8 \text{ g Fe}^{+3}}{3} = 18.6 \text{ g Fe}^{+3}$$

or 18.6 g Fe^{+3}/g-eq wt.

Let y = number of gram-equivalents Fe^{+3}

$$= \frac{6.52 \text{ g Fe}^{+3}}{18.6 \text{ g Fe}^{+3}/\text{g-eq wt}} = 6.52 \text{ g Fe}^{+3} \times \frac{1 \text{ g-eq wt}}{18.6 \text{ g Fe}^{+3}}$$

$$= 0.35 \text{ g-eq}$$

Example 4. A lead oxide contains 59.412 g Pb combined with 4.588 g O. Determine (a) the gram-equivalent weight and (b) the valence number of lead in this oxide.

(a) If 4.588 g O combines with 59.412 g Pb,

$$1 \text{ g O combines with } \frac{1}{4.588} \times 59.412 \text{ g Pb}$$

$$8 \text{ g O combines with } 8 \times \frac{59.412}{4.588} \text{ g Pb} = 103.6 \text{ g Pb}$$

or 1 g-eq wt Pb = 103.6 g.

(b) Atomic weight Pb = 207.2.

$$\text{Valence number} = \frac{1 \text{ g-atomic wt}}{1 \text{ g-eq wt}}$$

$$\text{Valence number Pb} = \frac{207.2 \text{ g}}{103.6 \text{ g}} = 2$$

A most useful application of the gram-equivalent follows from the fact that 1 gram-equivalent weight of an element will combine with or replace 1 gram-equivalent weight of another element. As examples of these facts:

1. When sodium combines with oxygen to form sodium oxide (Na_2O), 1 g-eq wt Na combines with 1 g-eq wt O, or 23.0 g Na combines with 8.0 g O.

2. In the formation of aluminum oxide (Al_2O_3), 1 g-eq wt of combines with 1 g-eq wt O, or 9.0 g Al combines with 8.0 g O.

3. When sodium displaces hydrogen from a dilute acid, 1 g-eq wt Na will displace 1 g-eq wt H, or 23.0 g Na will displace 1.0 g H or 11.2 l (STP) H.

4. Also 1 g-eq wt Al will displace 1 g-eq wt H, or 9.0 g Al will displace 1.0 g H or 11.2 l (STP) H

5. Furthermore, 1 g-eq wt Zn will displace 1 g-eq wt Cu^{+2} from cupric sulfate solution, or 32.7 g Zn will displace 31.8 g Cu.

Example 5. A quantity of an oxide of copper weighing 21.47 g was reduced with hydrogen and 19.07 g of copper was obtained by this reaction. What is (a) the gram-equivalent weight of copper and (b) the formula of this oxide of copper?

(a) 21.47 g oxide of copper
    19.07 g copper
    2.40 g oxygen

or 2.40 g O is combined with 19.07 g Cu.

$$8 \text{ g O is combined with } 8 \times \frac{19.07}{2.4} \text{ g Cu} = 63.6 \text{ g Cu}$$

or 63.6 g Cu = gram-equivalent weight of Cu.

(b) Atomic weight of Cu = 63.6, or gram-atom Cu = 63.6 g Cu. Since the gram-equivalent weight is identical with the gram-atom, the valence number of Cu in this oxide is +1. The formula is then Cu_2O or cuprous oxide.

Example 6. It was determined that 1.52 g of a metal displaced 1.4 l at STP of hydrogen from an acid. What is the gram-equivalent weight of the metal?

By definition, *the gram-equivalent weight of a metal is that weight of metal which displaces 1.008 g, or 11.2 l at STP of H from an acid.*

Since 1.4 l at STP of H is displaced by 1.52 g of metal, 1 l at STP of H is displaced by 1.52/1.4 g of metal, and

$$11.2 \text{ l at STP of H is displaced by } 11.2 \times \frac{1.52}{1.4} \text{ g of metal} = 12.16 \text{ g}$$

The gram-equivalent weight of metal = 12.16 g.

Example 7. A quantity of zinc weighing 0.254 g, when treated with excess hydrochloric acid, yielded 96.4 ml of hydrogen, collected over water at 21°C and 758 mm Hg. From these data calculate the gram-equivalent weight of zinc.

$$21°C + 273 = 294°K \qquad 0°C = 273°K$$

Pressure of gas plus vapor pressure of water........ 758   mm Hg
Vapor pressure of H_2O at 21°C.................   18.5 mm Hg
Actual pressure of dry gas......................   739.5 mm Hg

$$96.4 \text{ ml} \times \frac{273°K}{294°K} \times \frac{740 \text{ mm}}{760 \text{ mm}} = 87 \text{ ml at STP}$$

87 ml at STP = 0.087 l at STP of H

0.087 l at STP of H liberated by 0.254 g Zn

$$11.2 \text{ l at STP of H liberated by } 11.2 \times \frac{0.254 \cdot g}{0.087} = 32.7 \text{ g}$$

or gram-equivalent weight of Zn = 32.7 g of Zn.

Problems

11-1. Calculate the gram-equivalent weight of each metal in the following oxides: ZrO_2; TiO_2; UO_2. *Ans.* 22.6 g; 12.0 g; 59.5 g.

11-2. Calculate the gram-equivalent weight of (a) lithium in lithium oxide, (b) bismuth in bismuth oxide, and (c) magnesium in magnesium nitride.
Ans. (a) 6.9 g; (b) 69.7 g; (c) 12.2 g.

11-3. Calculate the gram-equivalent weight of (1) iron in (a) ferrous chloride and (b) ferric chloride; (2) copper in (a) cuprous oxide and (b) cupric oxide.
Ans. (1) Fe (a) 27.9 g; (b) 18.6 g; (2) Cu (a) 63.5 g; (b) 31.8 g.

11-4. Calculate the gram-equivalent weight of (1) arsenic in (a) arsenic trichloride and (b) arsenic pentachloride and (2) chromium in (a) chromic oxide and (b) chromium trioxide.
Ans. (1) As (a) 25.0 g; (b) 15.0 g; (2) Cr (a) 17.3 g; (b) 8.7 g.

11-5. Determine the number of gram-equivalents in (a) 7.34 g of nickel and (b) 104.55 g of bismuth. *Ans.* (a) 0.25 g-eq Ni; (b) 1.5 g-eq Bi.

11-6. Determine the number of gram-equivalents (a) in 24.55 g of silicon and (b) of Fe in 5.92 g of ferrous ion.
Ans. (a) 3.5 g-eq Si; (b) 0.212 g-eq Fe.

11-7. Find the number of gram-equivalents (a) of Sn in 13.18 g of stannous ion and (b) of Sn in 65.89 g of stannic ion.
Ans. (a) 0.222 g-eq Sn; (b) 2.22 g-eq Sn.

11-8. It is found that 15.2151 g of silver combines with bromine to form 26.487 g of silver bromide. The gram-equivalent weight of Ag is 107.9 g. Calculate the gram-equivalent weight of bromine from these data. *Ans.* 79.9 g.

11-9. By analysis 1.25 g of an iron oxide was found to contain 0.8742 g of Fe. From these data determine (a) the gram-equivalent weight of iron and (b) the valence number of iron in this oxide. *Ans.* (a) 18.6 g.

11-10. There are two oxides of antimony; (a) contains 83.356 per cent Sb; (b) contains 75.031 per cent Sb. What are (1) the gram-equivalent weights, and (2) the valence number of Sb in each of these oxides? *Ans.* (a) (1) 40.6 g; (b) (1) 24.4 g.

11-11. When 2.5 g of zinc is treated with excess hydrochloric acid, 0.857 l at STP of hydrogen is evolved. From these data determine the gram-equivalent weight of zinc. *Ans.* 32.6 g.

11-12. A quantity of aluminum weighing 0.125 g is acted upon by excess dilute sulfuric acid; 155 ml at STP of hydrogen is evolved. From these data calculate the gram-equivalent weight of aluminum. *Ans.* 9.0 g.

11-13. A quantity of iron weighing 5 g is heated to a red heat and steam passed over it. Hydrogen is evolved which measures 2.67 l at STP. Calculate the gram-equivalent weight of Fe. *Ans.* 20.9 g.

11-14. It was found that 2.5 g of aluminum acted upon by a dilute solution of sodium hydroxide and heated evolved 3.39 l of hydrogen at 20°C and 745 mm Hg, collected over mercury. From these data calculate the gram-equivalent weight of aluminum. *Ans.* 9.0 g.

11-15. A sample of zinc weighing 0.2023 g was treated with excess hydrochloric acid, the hydrogen liberated being collected over water at 26.5°C and pressure of 1 atm. The gram-equivalent weight of zinc is 32.7 g. Calculate the theoretical volume of dry hydrogen obtainable at the given temperature and pressure. *Ans.* 78.7 ml.

11-16. A quantity of zinc weighing 5 g was added to a mercuric chloride solution. It was found that zinc displaced 15.343 g of Hg. The gram-equivalent weight of zinc is 32.68 g. Calculate the gram-equivalent weight of mercury from these data. *Ans.* 100.3 g.

11-17. A piece of zinc is placed in a solution containing 1.896 g of stannous chloride. After the action had ceased, the tin precipitated was found to weigh 1.187 g and the zinc was found to have lost 0.6537 g. The gram-equivalent weight of zinc is 32.68. From these data calculate the gram-equivalent weights of (a) tin and (b) chlorine. *Ans.* (a) 59.34.

11-18. Calculate the gram-equivalent weight of each metal in the following binary compounds: (a) Cu_2S, (b) Ca_3N_2, and (c) CrI_3.

11-19. Calculate the gram-equivalent weight of each metal in the following binary compounds: (a) MoS_2, (b) Co_2O_3, and (c) CrF_3.

11-20. Find the gram-equivalent weight of (a) cadmium in cadmium iodide, (b) calcium in calcium phosphide, and (c) chromium in chromic nitride.

11-21. Calculate the number of gram-equivalents (a) in 6.81 g of magnesium and (b) in 9.71 g of chromic ion.

11-22. Determine the number of gram-equivalents (a) in 14.9 g of strontium and (b) in 22.10 g of cobaltous ion.

11-23. Iron forms two chlorides in which (a) contains 34.42 per cent Fe and (b) contains 44.05 per cent Fe. The gram-equivalent weight of chlorine is 35.5 g. Determine (1) the gram-equivalent weights and (2) the valence numbers of iron in these chlorides.

11-24. Calculate the gram-equivalent weight of (a) mercury in the oxide that contains 92.6 per cent Hg and (b) manganese in the oxide that contains 77.44 per cent Mn.

11-25. Calculate the gram-equivalent weight of a metal, 0.329 g of which yielded 0.472 l of hydrogen, collected over water at 22°C and 750 mm Hg.

11-26. The gram-equivalent weight of a metal is 23.0 g. Calculate the volume of hydrogen, measured over water at 22°C and 750 mm Hg, that will be liberated by 3.0 g of this metal when treated with excess of acid.

11-27. The gram-equivalent weight of a metal is 9.0 g. Calculate the volume of hydrogen, measured over water at 21°C and 753 Hg, that will be displaced by 1.25 g of this metal when treated with an excess of hydrochloric acid.

11-28. The gram-equivalent weight of a metal is 32.5 g.   Determine the volume of hydrogen liberated when collected over water at 28°C and 748 mm Hg, by action of an acid on 2.03 g of the metal.

11-29. A piece of iron weighing 25 g was immersed for some time in a solution of $CuSO_4$.   Removed, it was found to have lost 3.15 g.   By the action, 3.586 g of copper was displaced.   The gram-equivalent weight of Fe is 27.9 g.   Calculate the gram-equivalent weight of Cu.

11-30. When phosphorus trichloride comes in contact with water, it is completely hydrolyzed, forming phosphorous acid and hydrochloric acid.   It was found that when 2.35 g of phosphorus trichloride was decomposed by water, and when $AgNO_3$ had been added to this solution, the precipitate of AgCl obtained weighed 7.353 g.   The gram-equivalent weight of Ag is 107.9 g and that of Cl is 35.5.   From these data calculate the gram-equivalent weight of phosphorus.

GRAM-EQUIVALENT WEIGHTS OF COMPOUNDS

The principle of gram-equivalents may be extended to compounds.

1. Gram-equivalent Weights of Acids.   Since all acids contain the replaceable hydrogen, the *gram-equivalent weight of an acid is that quantity of acid which contains 1 g-atom or 1 g-ion of replaceable hydrogen,* or 1 g-eq H^+ = 1.008 g of H^+.   Thus (a) 1 g-mole HCl contains 1 g-eq H^+, or 36.5 g HCl = 1 g-eq wt HCl.   (b) Since 1 g-mole H_2SO_4 contains 2 g-eq H^+, or $\frac{1}{2}$ g-mole H_2SO_4 contains 1 g-eq H^+, then $\frac{1}{2} \times$ 98.1 g H_2SO_4, or 49.0 g H_2SO_4 = 1 g-eq wt H_2SO_4.   (c) Since 1 g-mole H_3PO_4 contains 3 g-eq H^+, or $\frac{1}{3}$ g-mole H_3PO_4 contains 1 g-eq H^+, then $\frac{1}{3} \times$ 98.0 g H_3PO_4 or 32.7 g H_3PO_4 = 1 g-eq wt H_3PO_4.

2. Gram-equivalent Weights of Bases.   All bases contain the hydroxyl ion OH^-.   From the fact that $H_2O \rightleftharpoons H^+ + OH^-$, it can be stated that 1 g-eq H^+ is equivalent to 1 g-eq OH^-.   The *gram-equivalent weight of a base is that quantity of base which contains 1 g-eq OH^-,* or 17.008 g of OH^-.   Thus (a) 1 g-mole NaOH contains 1 g-eq OH^-, or 40.0 g NaOH = 1 g-eq wt NaOH.   (b) Since 1 g-mole $Ba(OH)_2$ contains 2 g-eq OH^-, or $\frac{1}{2}$ g-mole $Ba(OH)_2$ contains 1 g-eq OH^-, then $\frac{1}{2} \times$ 171.4 g $Ba(OH)_2$ = 85.7 g $Ba(OH)_2$ = 1 g-eq wt $Ba(OH)_2$.   (c) Since 1 g-mole $Fe(OH)_3$ contains 3 g-eq OH^-, then $\frac{1}{3} \times$ 106.9 g $Fe(OH)_3$ or 35.6 g $Fe(OH)_3$ = 1 g-eq wt $Fe(OH)_3$.

3. Gram-equivalent Weights of Normal Salts (Nonoxidizers and Nonreducers).   Salts are formed by replacement of H^+ of an acid by a positive ion.   The *gram-equivalent weight of a normal salt is that quantity of salt which contains 1 g-eq of the positive ion.*   Thus (a) 1 g-mole NaCl contains 1 g-eq Na^+, or 58.5 g NaCl = 1 g-eq wt NaCl.   (b) Since 1 g-mole Na_2CO_3 contains 2 g-eq Na^+, or $\frac{1}{2}$ g-mole Na_2CO_3 contains 1 g-eq Na^+, then $\frac{1}{2} \times$ 106.0 g Na_2CO_3 = 53.0 g Na_2CO_3 = 1 g-eq wt Na_2CO_3.   (c) Since 1 g-mole $Cr_2(SO_4)_3$ contains

6 g-eq Cr^{+3}, or $\frac{1}{6}$ g-mole $Cr_2(SO_4)_3$ contains 1 g-eq Cr^{+3}, then $\frac{1}{6} \times$
392.3 g $Cr_2(SO_4)_3$ = 65.4 g $Cr_2(SO_4)_3$ = 1 g-eq wt $Cr_2(SO_4)_3$.

As in the case of elements, there is a direct relationship between
the gram-mole weight and the gram-equivalent weight of any compound. Thus

$$\frac{1 \text{ g-mole HCl}}{1 \text{ g-eq wt HCl}} = \frac{36.5 \text{ g}}{36.5 \text{ g}} = \frac{1}{1}$$

$$\frac{1 \text{ g-mole Ba(OH)}_2}{1 \text{ g-eq wt Ba(OH)}_2} = \frac{171.4 \text{ g}}{85.7 \text{ g}} = \frac{2}{1}$$

$$\frac{1 \text{ g-mole Cr}_2(SO_4)_3}{1 \text{ g-eq wt Cr}_2(SO_4)_3} = \frac{392.3 \text{ g}}{65.4 \text{ g}} = \frac{6}{1}$$

The numerators 1, 2, 6, respectively, are actually equal to the total
positive ion valence (or total negative ion valence) in each compound.
*Also these numbers represent the number of gram-equivalents in 1 g-mole
of each of these compounds.* A simple rule to follow in order to determine the gram-equivalent weight of a compound is to divide the gram-
molecular weight of compound by its total positive ion valence (or
total negative ion valence). Thus

$$1 \text{ g-eq wt compound} = \frac{\text{gram-molecular weight}}{\text{total} + \text{or} - \text{ion valence}}$$

$$= \frac{\text{no. of g/g-mole}}{\text{no. of g-eq/g-mole}}$$

NOTE. This rule or formulation applies only to acids, bases, and
salts (nonreducers and nonoxidizers).

Example. Calculate the gram-equivalent weight of each of the
following: (a) K_2SO_4; (b) $CsOH$; (c) $H_4P_2O_7$.

$$1 \text{ g-eq wt compound} = \frac{\text{no. of g/g-mole}}{\text{no. of g-eq/g-mole}}$$

(a) Molecular weight K_2SO_4 = 135; total positive ion valence number = 2.

Let x = number of grams in 1 g-eq wt K_2SO_4

$$= \frac{135 \text{ g/g-mole}}{2 \text{ g-eq/g-mole}} = \frac{135 \text{ g}}{1 \text{ g-mole}} \times \frac{1 \text{ g-mole}}{2 \text{ g-eq}}$$

$$= 67.5 \text{ g/g-eq wt}$$

(b) Molecular weight $CsOH$ = 149.9; total positive ion valence
number = 1.

Let y = number of grams in 1 g-eq wt CsOH

$$= \frac{149.9 \text{ g/g-mole}}{1 \text{ g-eq/g-mole}} = 149.9 \text{ g/g-eq wt}$$

(c) Molecular weight $H_4P_2O_7$ = 178.0; total positive ion valence number = 4.

Let z = number of grams in 1 g-eq wt $H_4P_2O_7$

$$= \frac{178.0 \text{ g/g-mole}}{4 \text{ g-eq/g-mole}} = 44.5 \text{ g/g-eq wt}$$

4. Gram-equivalent Weight of Oxidizers and Reducers. Oxidizers are substances containing an atom or ion capable of gaining electrons and thus effecting a decrease in the oxidation number of that atom or ion. Reducers are substances containing an atom or ion capable of losing electrons, a process resulting in an increase in the oxidation number of that atom or ion. The gram-equivalent weight of an oxidizer is that quantity obtained by dividing the gram-molecular weight (1 g-mole) of oxidizer by the total number of electrons gained per molecule of oxidizer (or by the total change in oxidation number in 1 molecule of oxidizer). Likewise the gram-equivalent weight of a reducer is that quantity obtained by dividing the gram-molecular weight (1 g-mole) of reducer by the total number of electrons lost per molecule of reducer (or the total change in oxidation number in 1 molecule of reducer). Thus

1 g-eq wt of oxidizer and/or reducer

$$= \frac{1 \text{ gram-molecular weight}}{\text{total change in oxidation number per molecule}}$$

For changes in oxidation numbers in oxidizers and reducers, consult Table XIII, page 136, and Table XIV, page 137.

Example 1.   Determine the gram-equivalent weights of (a) lead dioxide as an oxidizer and (b) ferrous sulfate as a reducer.

(a) Molecular weight PbO_2 = 239.2; total oxidation-number change = 2.

Let x = number of grams in 1 g-eq wt PbO_2 as an oxidizer

$$= \frac{239.2 \text{ g}}{2} = 119.6 \text{ g}$$

or 119.6 g PbO_2 = 1 g-eq wt PbO_2 as an oxidizer.

(b) Molecular weight $FeSO_4$ = 151.9; total oxidation-number change = 1.

Let y = number of grams in 1 g-eq wt $FeSO_4$ as a reducer

$$= \frac{151.9 \text{ g}}{1} = 151.9 \text{ g}$$

or 151.9 g $FeSO_4$ = 1 g-eq wt $FeSO_4$ as a reducer.

To find the *number of gram-equivalents* in any given weight of any compound, it is necessary to divide the given number of grams of the compound by the number of grams per gram-equivalent weight of that substance.

$$\text{No. of g-eq compound} = \frac{G}{\text{no. of g/g-eq wt}}$$

where G = any given number of grams of compound and no. of g/g-eq wt = number of grams in 1 g-eq wt of compound.

Example 2. Calculate the number of gram-equivalents in (*a*) 49.76 g $Zr(OH)_4$ and (*b*) 712.75 g $Al_2(SO_4)_3$.

(*a*) Molecular weight $Zr(OH)_4$ = 159.2. There are 4 g-eq in 1 g-mole $Zr(OH)_4$; then

$$1 \text{ g-eq wt } Zr(OH)_4 = \frac{159.2 \text{ g/g-mole}}{4 \text{ g-eq wt/g-mole}} = 39.8 \text{ g/g-eq wt}$$

Let x = number of gram-equivalents of $Zr(OH)_4$

$$= \frac{49.76 \text{ g}}{39.8 \text{ g/g-eq wt}} = 49.76 \text{ g} \times \frac{1 \text{ g-eq wt}}{39.8 \text{ g}} = 1.25 \text{ g-eq}$$

Alternate Solution. Since

$$\text{No. of g-eq} = \text{no. of g-moles} \times \frac{\text{no. of g-eq wts}}{1 \text{ g-mole}}$$

then 1 g-mole $Zr(OH)_4$ contains 4 g-eq, or 4 g-eq/g-mole.

Let x = number of gram-equivalents of $Zr(OH)_4$

$$= \frac{49.76 \text{ g}}{159 \text{ g/g-mole}} \times \frac{4 \text{ g-eq}}{1 \text{ g-mole}}$$

$$= 0.313 \text{ g-mole} \times \frac{4 \text{ g-eq}}{1 \text{ g-mole}}$$

$$= 1.25 \text{ g-eq}$$

(*b*) Molecular weight $Al_2(SO_4)_3$ = 342. There are 6 g-eq in 1 g-mole $Al_2(SO_4)_3$; then

$$1 \text{ g-eq wt } Al_2(SO_4)_3 = \frac{342 \text{ g/g-mole}}{6 \text{ g-eq wts/g-mole}} = 57 \text{ g/g-eq wt}$$

Let y = number of gram-equivalents of $Al_2(SO_4)_3$

$$= \frac{712.75 \text{ g}}{57 \text{ g/g-eq wt}} = 712.75 \text{ g} \times \frac{1 \text{ g-eq wt}}{57 \text{ g}} = 12.5 \text{ g-eq}$$

Alternate Solution

$$y = \frac{712.75 \text{ g}}{342 \text{ g/g-mole}} \times \frac{6 \text{ g-eq}}{1 \text{ g-mole}} = 2.08 \text{ g-moles} \times \frac{6 \text{ g-eq}}{1 \text{ g-mole}}$$
$$= 12.5 \text{ g-eq}$$

The importance of the concept of the gram-equivalent weight cannot be overestimated. The next two chapters will deal with (1) the use of the gram-equivalent weight in preparing standard solutions and (2) the principle of equivalency.

VOLUME-EQUIVALENT OF GASES

Since gases are involved in many types of chemical reactions, they too have gram-equivalent weights which can be expressed in terms of volume-equivalents. Since 1 g-mole H = 2.016 g H = 22.4 l (STP) H and 1 g-eq wt H = 1.008 g H = 11.2 l (STP) H, the volume 11.2 l (STP) of H may be called the volume-equivalent of H, or 1 liter-equivalent H (1 l-eq H). Also 1 g-mole O = 32.0 g O = 22.4 l (STP) O, 1 g-atom O = 16.0 g O = 11.2 l (STP) O, and 1 g-eq wt O = 8.0 g O = 5.6 l (STP) O. The volume 5.6 l (STP) of O = 1 l-eq O.

Consider the reaction

$$\underset{\text{1 g-mole}}{CO_2} + NaOH \rightarrow \underset{\text{1 g-mole}}{NaHCO_3}$$

22.4 l (STP) CO_2 produces 1 g-mole, or 1 g-eq wt $NaHCO_3$; then 22.4 l (STP) CO_2 = 1 l-eq CO_2, since it produces 1 g-eq wt $NaHCO_3$. Also

$$\underset{\text{1 g-mole}}{CO_2} + 2NaOH \rightarrow \underset{\text{1 g-mole}}{Na_2CO_3} + H_2O$$

22.4 l (STP) CO_2 produces 1 g-mole, or 2 g-eq wt Na_2CO_3; then 11.2 l (STP) CO_2 = 1 l-eq CO_2, since it produces 1 g-eq wt Na_2CO_3. Thus CO_2 has two volume-equivalents, depending on the type of compound formation.

In general, the liter-equivalent of a gas may be determined by dividing 22.4 l (STP) of gas by the positive ion valence of the compound formed when the gas dissolves in water or when it chemically reacts with other substances.

Problems

11-31. Calculate the gram-equivalent weight of (a) Li_2SO_4, (b) $Al(OH)_3$, and (c) K_3PO_4.   *Ans.*   (a) 55.0 g; (b) 26.0 g; (c) 70.8 g.

11-32. Calculate the gram-equivalent weight of (a) $BaCl_2$, (b) $Fe(OH)_3$, and (c) $Ca_3(PO_4)_2$.   *Ans.*   (a) 104.2 g; (b) 35.6 g; (c) 51.7 g.

11-33. Calculate the gram-equivalent weight of (a) $Fe_2(SO_4)_3$, (b) $Ba_3(PO_4)_2$, and (c) SnF_4.   *Ans.*   (a) 66.6 g; (b) 100.4 g; (c) 48.7 g.

11-34. Determine the gram-equivalent weights of the following oxidizers when used in solutions acidified with sulfuric acid: (a) MnO_2; (b) $KMnO_4$.
                    Ans.   (a) 43.4 g; (b) 31.6 g.

11-35. Determine the gram-equivalent weights of the following: (a) $K_2Cr_2O_7$ as an oxidizer in acid medium; (b) $FeCl_2$ as a reducer.
                    Ans.   (a) 49.0 g; (b) 126.8 g.

11-36. Calculate the number of gram-equivalents in (a) 3.5 g-moles $Ba(OH)_2$, (b) 6 g-moles H_3PO_4, and (c) 5.5 g-moles $Al_2(SO_4)_3$.
                    Ans.   (a) 7 g-eq; (b) 18 g-eq; (c) 33 g-eq.

11-37. Calculate the number of gram-equivalents in (a) 4.5 g-moles $SnCl_4$, (b) 3.5 g-moles Na_3PO_4, and (c) 6.5 g-moles $Fe_2(SO_4)_3$.
                    Ans.   (a) 18.0 g-eq; (b) 10.5 g-eq; (c) 39 g-eq.

11-38. Determine the number of grams in (a) 2.5 g-eq $Ba(OH)_2$, (b) 0.5 g-eq $FeCl_3$, and (c) 1.5 g-eq H_3PO_4.   *Ans.*   (a) 214.2 g; (b) 27.05 g; (c) 49.0 g.

11-39. Calculate the number of grams in (a) 3.5 g-eq $Pb(NO_3)_2$, (b) 1.5 g-eq $Cr(OH)_3$, and (c) 2.5 g-eq $Bi_2(SO_4)_3$.
                    Ans.   (a) 579.6 g; (b) 51.4 g; (c) 294.2 g.

11-40. Calculate the number of gram-equivalents in (a) 26.56 g Cr_2O_3, (b) 18.74 g CsOH, and (c) 66.0 g H_3AsO_4.
                    Ans.   (a) 1.05 g-eq; (b) 0.125 g-eq; (c) 1.4 g-eq.

11-41. Determine the number of gram-equivalents in (a) 120.0 g $Fe(OH)_3$, (b) 311.0 g K_2CO_3, and (c) 401 g $Cr_2(SO_4)_3 \cdot 18H_2O$.
                    Ans.   (a) 3.4 g-eq; (b) 4.5 g-eq; (c) 3.4 g-eq.

11-42. Determine the number of gram-equivalents in (a) 43.4 g $Pb(OH)_2$, (b) 15.4 g $Al_2(SO_4)_3$, and (c) 312.0 g $CuSO_4 \cdot 5H_2O$.
                    Ans.   (a) 0.36 g-eq; (b) 0.27 g-eq; (c) 2.5 g-eq.

11-43. Determine the number of liter-equivalents (a) in 0.35 g-mole NH_3 and (b) in 224 ml (STP) HCl.   *Ans.*   (a) 0.35 l-eq; (b) 0.01 l-eq.

11-44. Determine (a) the number of liters (STP) O_2 in 0.25 g-eq O_2 and (b) the number of liter-equivalents Cl_2 in 3.36 l (STP) Cl_2.
                    Ans.   (a) 1.4 l (STP); (b) 0.3 l-eq.

11-45. Calculate (a) the gram-equivalent weight of anhydrous stannous chloride when used as a reducer and (b) the weight in grams of $SnCl_2 \cdot 2H_2O$ required for this weight of anhydrous stannous chloride.
                    Ans.   (a) 94.8 g $SnCl_2$; (b) 112.8 g $SnCl_2 \cdot 2H_2O$.

11-46. Calculate (a) the gram-equivalent weight of anhydrous potassium sulfite when used as a reducer and (b) the weight in grams of $K_2SO_3 \cdot 2H_2O$ required for this weight of anhydrous potassium sulfite.
                    Ans.   (a) 59.6 g K_2SO_3; (b) 97.14 g $K_2SO_3 \cdot 2H_2O$.

11-47. Determine (a) the gram-equivalent weight of anhydrous sodium permanganate when used as an oxidizer ·in an acid medium and (b) the weight in grams of $NaMnO_4 \cdot 3H_2O$ required for this weight of sodium permanganate.
                    Ans.   (a) 28.4 g $NaMnO_4$; (b) 39.2 $NaMnO_4 \cdot 3H_2O$.

11-48. Calculate the gram-equivalent weight of (a) $CdCl_2$, (b) $Ca(OH)_2$, and (c) K_2CO_3.

11-49. Calculate the gram-equivalent weight of (a) $AlCl_3$, (b) $Cr(OH)_3$, and (c) $Sr_3(PO_4)_2$.

11-50. Calculate the number of gram-equivalents in (a) 2.5 g-moles $Pb(OH)_2$, (b) 0.125 g-mole $Co_3(PO_4)_2$, and (c) 3.5 g-moles H_3PO_4.

11-51. Calculate the number of gram-equivalents in (a) 0.75 g-mole Na_2SO_4, (b) 0.35 g-mole $Zn_3(PO_4)_2$, and (c) 0.56 g-mole $Bi(OH)_3$.

11-52. Determine the number of grams in (a) 0.75 g-eq Na_2CO_3, (b) 3.5 g-eq $Fe(OH)_3$, and (c) 2.5 g-eq H_3AsO_4.

11-53. Determine the number of grams in (a) 3.6 g-eq K_3PO_4, (b) 0.25 g-eq $Ba(OH)_2$, and (c) 1.5 g-eq $Cr_2(SO_4)_3$.

11-54. Calculate the number of gram-equivalents in (a) 17.2 g H_2SO_4, (b) 23.0 g $Sr(OH)_2$, and (c) 20.0 g $Al_2(SO_4)_3$.

11-55. Calculate the number of gram-equivalents in (a) 14.7 g H_3PO_4, (b) 15.4 g $Cr(OH)_3$, and (c) 29.0 g $Zn_3(PO_4)_2$.

11-56. Find the following: (a) the number of liter-equivalents SO_2 in 3.5 g-moles SO_2, used in formation of bisulfite; (b) the number of liters (STP) H_2S in 1.25 g-eq H_2S used in forming normal sulfide; (c) the number of liter-equivalents O_2 in 25 l (STP) O_2.

11-57. Determine the following: (a) the number of cubic-foot-equivalents H_2 in 1.5 oz-moles H_2; (b) the number of cubic feet (STP) CO_2 in 7.5 oz-eq CO_2, used in formation of normal carbonate; (c) the number of cubic-foot-equivalents NH_3 (on a basis of ounce-equivalents) in 1,000 cu ft (STP) NH_3.

CHAPTER XII

MOLAR AND NORMAL CONCENTRATION

OUTLINE

Solutions.

Concentration.

Physical units: (a) percentage or weight concentration; (b) volume concentration.

Chemical units: (c) molar concentration; (d) normal concentration.

Molar concentration: the number of gram-moles of solute per liter of solution, or number of liters of solution multiplied by the molarity of solution equals the number of gram-moles of solute.

Normal concentration: the number of gram-equivalent weights of solute per liter of solution, or number of liters of solution multiplied by the normality of solution equals the number of gram-equivalents of solute.

A solution may be defined in general terms, as a homogeneous molecular mixture of two or more substances. Thus, if a solid, like sugar, is added to water, sugar crystals disappear and the molecules of sugar become uniformly dispersed in the water. It is customary to think of the dissolved substance (usually present in the smaller quantity) as the **solute,** and the medium in which the substance is dissolved (the more abundant constituent) as the **solvent.**

CONCENTRATION

The quantity of solute per unit of solvent is known as the **concentration** of the solution and may be expressed in various ways. The most commonly used methods are (1) *physical units* [(a) percentage of weight concentration; (b) volume concentration, grams of solute per liter of solution (g/l)] and (2) *chemical units* [(c) molar concentration; (d) normal concentration].

PERCENTAGE CONCENTRATION

Percentage concentration is the weight of solute contained in 100 parts by weight of solution. Thus a 20 per cent sodium hydroxide solution (abbreviated *shs*) means that in 100 unit weights of sodium hydroxide solution there will be 20 unit weights of pure NaOH. On a gram basis this would mean 20 g pure NaOH in 100 g *shs*, or 20 g

169

of pure NaOH with 80 g H_2O. However, in preparing a given volume, say 1 l of 20 per cent sodium hydroxide solution (*shs*), it is necessary to know the total weight of this solution. This is obtained from specific-gravity tables. Thus, it is found that a 20 per cent sodium hydroxide solution has a specific gravity of 1.22. On a density basis there is 1.22 g *shs*/ml *shs*, or 1.22 kg *shs*/l *shs*, or 1,220 g *shs*/l *shs*. Then

1,220 g *shs*/l *shs* $\times$ 0.2 g pure NaOH/g *shs* = 244 g pure NaOH/l *shs*

In preparing a 20 per cent sodium hydroxide solution, it is required that 244 g of pure NaOH be dissolved in sufficient water to make 1 l of solution. The amount of water needed in this solution will be

1,220 g (NaOH + water) − 244 g (pure NaOH) = 976 g water

This type of problem has been given consideration in Chap. II, Example 2, page 24, and this principle will be utilized in other types of examples that follow.

MOLAR SOLUTIONS

Molar concentration may be defined as the number of gram-moles of solute per liter of solution. Then a *one molar solution* (M) contains 1 g-mole of solute per liter of solution, or 1 l of a M solution contains 1 g-mole of solute. Also 1 l of a 2 M solution contains 2 g-moles of solute, 1 l of a 0.5 M solution contains 0.5 g-mole of solute, 2 l of a 1.5 M solution contains 3 g-moles of solute, and 0.5 l of a 0.2 M solution contains 0.1 g-mole of solute, or

Number of liters of solution $\times$ molarity of solution

= number of gram-moles of solute

or

$$\text{No. of l solution} \times M = \text{no. of g-moles solute} \qquad (1)$$

then

$$M = \frac{\text{no. of g-moles solute}}{\text{no. of l solution}} \qquad (2)$$

or the molarity of a solution expresses *the number of gram-moles of solute per liter of solution.*

In Chap. IV it was shown that for *any given weight* of substance

$$\text{No. of g-moles} = \frac{G}{\text{no. of g/g-mole}} \qquad (3)$$

where G = given number of grams of substance and no. of g/g-mole = number of grams of substance in 1 gram-molecular weight.

From Equations (1) and (3), it follows that

$$\text{No. of l solution} \times M = \frac{G}{\text{no. of g/g-mole}} \qquad (4)$$

On the basis of milliliters of solution, one needs only to express the number of grams per mole as the number of grams per millimole; then

$$\text{No. of ml solution} \times M = \text{no. of millimoles solute}$$

then

$$M = \frac{\text{no. of millimoles solute}}{\text{no. of ml solution}}$$

and

$$\text{No. of ml solution} \times M = \frac{G}{\text{no. of g/millimole}}$$

Example 1. Determine the number of gram-moles of solute contained in each of the following solutions: (a) 2.5 l of 2 M H_2SO_4; (b) 5 l of 0.525 M $Ba(OH)_2$.

Since no. of g-moles solute = no. of l solution $\times$ M and M = no. of g-moles of solute/l solution, then

(a) Let x = number of gram-moles of solute

$$= 2.5 \text{ l} \times \frac{2 \text{ g-moles solute}}{1 \text{ l}} = 5.0 \text{ g-moles solute}$$

(b) Let y = number of gram-moles of solute

$$= 5 \text{ l} \times \frac{0.525 \text{ g-moles solute}}{1 \text{ l}} = 2.62 \text{ g-moles solute}$$

Example 2. Determine the number of millimoles of solute contained in each of the following solutions: (a) 10 ml of 0.125 M $Pb(NO_3)_2$; (b) 25 ml of 9 M H_2SO_4.

Since no. of millimoles solute = no. of ml solution $\times$ M and M = no. of millimoles solute/no. of ml solution, then

(a) Let x = number of millimoles of solute

$$= 10 \text{ ml} \times \frac{0.125 \text{ millimole solute}}{1 \text{ ml}} = 1.25 \text{ millimoles solute}$$

(b) Let y = number of millimoles of solute

$$= 25 \text{ ml} \times \frac{9 \text{ millimoles solute}}{1 \text{ ml}} = 225 \text{ millimoles solute}$$

Example 3. Determine the molarity of following solutions which contain (a) 41.65 g $MgCl_2$ in 3.5 l of solution and (b) 4.9 g $Cr_2(SO_4)_3$ in 25 ml of solution.

(*a*) Molecular weight $MgCl_2$ = 95.3, or 95.3 g $MgCl_2$/g-mole.

$$\text{No. of l} \times M = \frac{G}{\text{no. of g/g-mole}}$$

Let x = molarity of $MgCl_2$ solution

$$3.5 \text{ l} \times x = \frac{41.65 \text{ g } MgCl_2}{95.3 \text{ g } MgCl_2/\text{g-mole}}$$

$$x = \frac{41.65 \text{ g } MgCl_2}{3.5 \text{ l}} \times \frac{1 \text{ g-mole}}{95.3 \text{ g } MgCl_2} = 1.25 \text{ g-moles/l}$$

or 1.25 g-moles/l = 1.25 M = molarity of $MgCl_2$ solution.

(*b*) Molecular weight $Cr_2(SO_4)_3$ = 392.3, or 392.3 g $Cr_2(SO_4)_3$/g-mole, or 0.392 g $Cr_2(SO_4)_3$/millimole.

$$\text{No. of ml} \times M = \frac{G}{\text{no. of g/millimole}}$$

Let y = molarity of $Cr_2(SO_4)_3$ solution

$$25 \text{ ml} \times y = \frac{4.9 \text{ g } Cr_2(SO_4)_3}{0.392 \text{ g } Cr_2(SO_4)_3/\text{millimole}}$$

$$y = \frac{4.9 \text{ g } Cr_2(SO_4)_3}{25 \text{ ml}} \times \frac{1 \text{ millimole}}{0.392 \text{ g } Cr_2(SO_4)_3}$$

$$= 0.5 \text{ millimole/ml}$$

or 0.5 millimole/ml = 0.5 M = molarity of $Cr_2(SO_4)_3$ solution.

Example 4. How many grams of $Cd(NO_3)_2 \cdot 4H_2O$ is required to prepare 250 ml of 2.5 M $Cd(NO_3)_2$ solution?

Since 1 g-mole $Cd(NO_3)_2$ is contained in 1 g-mole $Cd(NO_3)_2 \cdot 4H_2O$, then 2.5 g-mole $Cd(NO_3)_2$ is contained in 2.5 g-mole $Cd(NO_3)_2 \cdot 4H_2O$.

Molecular weight = $Cd(NO_3)_2 \cdot 4H_2O$ = 308.5, or 308.5 g/g-mole.

$$250 \text{ ml} = 0.25 \text{ l}$$

$$\text{No. of l} \times M = \frac{G}{\text{no. of g/g-mole}} \quad \text{and} \quad M = \text{no. of g-moles/l}$$

$$2.5 \ M = 2.5 \text{ g-moles/l}$$

Let x = number of grams $Cd(NO_3)_2 \cdot 4H_2O$

$$0.25 \text{ l} \times \frac{2.5 \text{ g-moles}}{1 \text{ l}} = \frac{x}{308.5 \text{ g/g-mole}}$$

$$x = 0.25 \text{ l} \times \frac{2.5 \text{ g-moles}}{1 \text{ l}} \times \frac{308.5 \text{ g}}{1 \text{ g-mole}} = 193 \text{ g}$$

Alternate Solution on a Milliliter and Millimole Basis.

$$\text{No. of ml} \times M = \frac{G}{\text{no. of g/millimole}}$$
$$2.5 \ M = 2.5 \text{ millimoles/ml}$$

and

$$\text{No. of g/millimole} = 0.3085 \text{ g/millimole}$$

Let x = number of grams $Cd(NO_3)_2 \cdot 4H_2O$

$$250 \text{ ml} \times \frac{2.5 \text{ millimoles}}{1 \text{ ml}} = \frac{x}{0.3085 \text{ g/millimole}}$$
$$x = 250 \text{ ml} \times \frac{2.5 \text{ millimoles}}{1 \text{ ml}} \times \frac{0.3085 \text{ g}}{1 \text{ millimole}} = 193 \text{ g}$$

or 193 g of $Cd(NO_3)_2 \cdot 4H_2O$.

Example 5. What is the molarity of a concentrated sulfuric acid solution (sp gr 1.836 and containing 97 per cent by weight H_2SO_4)?

NOTE. For convenience in dealing with dimensional units, sulfuric acid solution is abbreviated *sas*.

Step 1. Determine the number of grams of pure H_2SO_4 in 1 l of acid solution.

$$\frac{1.836 \text{ g } sas}{1 \text{ ml } sas} \times \frac{0.97 \text{ g } H_2SO_4}{1 \text{ g } sas} = \frac{1.781 \text{ g pure } H_2SO_4}{1 \text{ ml } sas}$$

or 1,781 g pure H_2SO_4 in 1 l *sas*.

Molecular weight H_2SO_4 = 98.1, or 98.1 g H_2SO_4/g-mole.

$$\text{No. of l} \times M = \frac{G}{\text{no. of g/g-mole}}$$

Let x = molarity (no. of g-moles/l) of sulfuric acid solution

$$1 \text{ l} \times x = \frac{1{,}781 \text{ g } H_2SO_4}{98.1 \text{ g } H_2SO_4/\text{g-mole}}$$
$$x = \frac{1{,}781 \text{ g } H_2SO_4}{1 \text{ l}} \times \frac{1 \text{ g-mole}}{98.1 \text{ g } H_2SO_4} = 18.2 \text{ g-moles/l}$$

or 18.2 g-moles/l = 18.2 M = molarity of concentrated sulfuric acid solution.

Alternate Solution on Milliliter and Millimole Basis.

$$1 \text{ ml} \times x = \frac{1.781 \text{ g } H_2SO_4}{0.0981 \text{ g } H_2SO_4/\text{millimole}}$$
$$x = \frac{1.781 \text{ g } H_2SO_4}{1 \text{ ml}} \times \frac{1 \text{ millimole}}{0.0981 \text{ g } H_2SO_4} = 18.2 \text{ millimoles/ml}$$
$$= 18.2 \ M$$

Example 6. Calculate the molarity of a dilute phosphoric acid solution made by diluting 100 ml of phosphoric acid solution (sp gr 1.426 and containing 60 per cent by weight pure H_3PO_4) to 500 ml.

NOTE. For convenience only in dealing with dimensional units, phosphoric acid solution is abbreviated *pas*.

$$\frac{1.426 \text{ g } pas}{1 \text{ ml } pas} \times \frac{0.6 \text{ g pure } H_3PO_4}{1 \text{ g } pas} \times 100 \text{ ml } pas = 85.56 \text{ g pure } H_3PO_4$$

then 85.56 g pure H_3PO_4 is contained in 500 ml of dilute phosphoric acid solution.

Molecular weight $H_3PO_4 = 98.0$, or 98.0 g H_3PO_4/g-mole.

$$500 \text{ ml} = 0.5 \text{ l}$$

$$\text{No. of l} \times M = \frac{G}{\text{no. of g/g-mole}}$$

Let x = molarity of dilute phosphoric acid solution

$$0.5 \text{ l} \times x = \frac{85.56 \text{ g } H_3PO_4}{98.0 \text{ g } H_3PO_4/\text{g-mole}}$$

$$x = \frac{85.56 \text{ g } H_3PO_4}{0.5 \text{ l}} \times \frac{1 \text{ g-mole}}{98 \text{ g } H_3PO_4} = 1.75 \text{ g-mole/l}$$

$$= 1.75 \text{ } M$$

then 1.75 M = molarity of dilute phosphoric acid solution.

Alternate Solution on Milliliter and Millimole Basis.

$$500 \text{ ml} \times x = \frac{85.56 \text{ g } H_3PO_4}{0.098 \text{ g } H_3PO_4/\text{millimole}}$$

$$x = \frac{85.56 \text{ g } H_3PO_4}{500 \text{ ml}} \times \frac{1 \text{ millimole}}{0.098 \text{ g } H_3PO_4} = 1.75 \text{ millimoles/ml}$$

$$= 1.75 \text{ } M.$$

Problems (Molar Concentration)

12-1. Determine the number of gram-moles of solute contained in each of the following: (a) 1.5 l of 2.5 M KOH solution; (b) 2.5 l of 0.1 M $(NH_4)_2SO_4$ solution; (c) 2.2 l of 3 M H_3PO_4 solution.

      Ans. (a) 3.75 g-moles; (b) 0.25 g-mole; (c) 6.6 g-moles.

12-2. Determine the number of gram-moles of solute contained in each of the following: (a) 250 ml of 2.5 M $MgSO_4$ solution; (b) 350 ml of 0.5 M H_2SO_4 solution; (c) 500 ml of 5 M NaOH solution.

      Ans. (a) 0.625 g-mole; (b) 0.175 g-mole; (c) 2.5 g-moles.

12-3. Determine the number of millimoles of solute contained in each of the following: (a) 25 ml of 0.25 M $Pb(NO_3)_2$ solution; (b) 5 ml of 5 M NH_4OH solution (ammonia in water); (c) 17.5 ml of 3 M H_3PO_4 solution.

      Ans. (a) 6.25 millimoles; (b) 25 millimoles; (c) 52.5 millimoles.

12-4. Determine the number of millimoles of solute contained in each of the following: (a) 100 ml of 0.6 M H_2SO_4 solution; (b) 15 ml of 1.5 M $Ba(OH)_2$ solution; (c) 50 ml of 6 M $Al_2(SO_4)_3$ solution.

Ans. (a) 60 millimoles; (b) 22.5 millimoles; (c) 300 millimoles.

12-5. Determine the molarity of the following solutions which contain (a) 6.88 g Li_2SO_4 in 250 ml of solution; (b) 14.7 g H_3PO_4 in 1 l of solution; (c) 140 g NaOH in 350 ml of solution. *Ans.* (a) 0.25 M; (b) 0.15 M; (c) 10 M.

12-6. Calculate the molarity of the following solutions which contain (a) 1.962 g H_3PO_4 in 20 ml of solution, (b) 2.549 g $AgNO_3$ in 30 ml of solution, and (c) 0.429 g $Ba(OH)_2$ in 25 ml of solution.

Ans. (a) 1 M; (b) 0.5 M; (c) 0.1 M.

12-7. The solubilities of several slightly soluble lead salts are as follows: (a) $PbCl_2 = 4.7$ g/l; (b) $PbI_2 = 5.98 \times 10^{-1}$ g/l; (c) $PbSO_4 = 4.06 \times 10^{-2}$ g/l. Determine the molar concentration or molarity of each.

Ans. (a) 1.6×10^{-2} M; (b) 1.3×10^{-3} M; (c) 1.34×10^{-4} M.

12-8. The molar solubility of several slightly soluble hydroxides is as follows: (a) $Pb(OH)_2 = 4.1 \times 10^{-6}$ g-mole/l; (b) $Sn(OH)_2 = 2.3 \times 10^{-9}$ g-mole/l; (c) $Al(OH)_3 = 2.9 \times 10^{-9}$ g-mole/l. Determine the solubility of each in grams per liter.

Ans. (a) 9.9×10^{-4} g/l; (b) 2.3×10^{-9} g/l; (c) 2.26×10^{-7} g/l.

12-9. Determine the number of grams of solute required to prepare each of the following: (a) 2 l of 6 M $NH_4C_2H_3O_2$ solution; (b) 500 ml $M/6$ $CrCl_3$ solution, using $CrCl_3 \cdot 6H_2O$ as solute; (c) 100 ml 0.25 M $BaCl_2$ solution, using $BaCl_2 \cdot 2H_2O$ as solute. *Ans.* (a) 924 g; (b) 22.5 g; (c) 6.1 g.

12-10. Find the molarity of (a) ferric chloride solution of specific gravity 1.29 and containing 30 per cent by weight pure $FeCl_3$ and (b) of nitric acid solution of specific gravity 1.31 and containing 50 per cent by weight pure HNO_3. *Ans.* (a) 2.4 M; (b) 10.4 M.

12-11. Determine the molarity of (a) 30 per cent potassium hydroxide solution of specific gravity 1.29 and (b) sodium carbonate solution of specific gravity 1.103 and containing 27 per cent by weight $Na_2CO_3 \cdot 10H_2O$.

Ans. (a) 6.9 M; (b) 1.04 M.

12-12. (a) How many milliliters of sulfuric acid solution (sp gr 1.835 and containing 93.2 per cent by weight pure H_2SO_4) is required in the preparation of 2 l of 9 M H_2SO_4 solution? (b) How many milliliters of 9 M H_2SO_4 contains 22.05 g pure H_2SO_4? *Ans.* (a) 1,030 ml; (b) 250 ml.

12-13. Determine (a) the number of liters of phosphoric acid solution (sp gr 1.18 and 30 per cent by weight pure H_3PO_4) necessary to prepare 2 l of 3 M H_3PO_4 solution and (b) the number of milliliters of 3 M H_3PO_4 that will contain 34.3 g pure H_3PO_4. *Ans.* (a) 1.66 l; (b) 117 ml.

12-14. Calculate (a) the number of liters of nitric acid solution (sp gr 1.31 and 50 per cent by weight pure HNO_3) required in the preparation of 2 l of 6 M HNO_3 and (b) the number of milliliters of 6 M HNO_3 that will contain 47.25 g pure HNO_3. *Ans.* (a) 1.15 l; (b) 125 ml.

NORMAL SOLUTION

Normal concentration may be defined as the number of gram-equivalent weights of solute per liter of solution. Then a *one normal* solution (N) contains 1 g-eq wt of solute per liter of solution, or

1 l of a N solution contains 1 g-eq wt of solute. Also 1 l of a $2N$ solution contains 2 g-eq wt of solute, and 1 l of a $0.5N$ solution contains 0.5 g-eq wt of solute, and 2 l of a $1.5N$ solution contains 3 g-eq wt of solute, and 0.5 l of a $0.2N$ solution contains 0.1 g-eq wt of solute, or

Number of liters of solution × normality of solution
$$= \text{number of gram-equivalent weights of solute}$$

or

$$\text{No. of l solution} \times N = \text{no. of g-eq wts solute} \tag{1}$$

then

$$N = \frac{\text{no. of g-eq wts solute}}{\text{no. of l solution}} \tag{2}$$

or the *normality* of a solution expresses the *number* of *gram-equivalent* weights of solute per liter of solution.

In Chap. XI it was shown that for any given weight of solute

$$\text{No. of g-eq} = \frac{G}{\text{no. of g/g-eq wt}} \tag{3}$$

where G = given number of grams of substance and no. of g/g-eq wt = number of grams in 1 g-eq wt of substance.

From Equations (1) and (3), it follows that

$$\text{No. of l solution} \times N = \frac{G}{\text{no. of g/g-eq wt}} \tag{4}$$

In volumetric chemical analysis it is necessary to deal with milliliters of solution rather than liters of solution. This requires the number of gram-equivalent weights of solute to be expressed in terms of **gram-milliequivalent weights (g-meq wts)**:

$$1 \text{ g-meq wt} = 1 \text{ g-eq wt} \times 0.001$$

Then the number of milliliters of solution times the normality equals the number of gram-milliequivalent weights of solute, **or**

$$\text{No. of ml solution} \times N = \text{no. of g-meq wts solute} \tag{5}$$

and

$$N = \frac{\text{no. of g-meq wts solute}}{\text{no. of ml solution}} \tag{6}$$

For any given weight of solute in grams,

$$\text{No. of g-meq solute} = \frac{G}{\text{no. of g/g-meq wt}} \tag{7}$$

where G = given number of grams of substance and no. of g/g-meq wt = number of grams of substance in 1 g-meq wt.

Equating (5) and (7), one obtains

$$\text{No. of ml} \times N = \frac{G}{\text{no. of g/g-meq wt}} \qquad (8)$$

Example 1.   Determine the number of gram-equivalents of solute in (a) 500 ml of 6 N H_2SO_4 solution and (b) 350 ml of 0.5 N $Al_2(SO_4)_3$ solution.

Since no. of g-eq wts solute = no. of l solution $\times$ N and N = no. of g-eq wts solute/l of solution, then

$$\text{No. of g-eq solute} = \text{no. of l solution} \times \frac{\text{no. of g-eq wts solute}}{1\ \text{l solution}}$$

$$500\ \text{ml} = 0.5\ \text{l}$$

(a) Let x = number of gram-equivalents of H_2SO_4

$$= 0.5\ \text{l} \times \frac{6\ \text{g-eq wt}}{1\ \text{l}} = 3\ \text{g-eq wt}$$

or 3 g-eq H_2SO_4.

$$350\ \text{ml} = 0.35\ \text{l}$$

(b) Let y = number of gram-equivalents of $Al_2(SO_4)_3$

$$= 0.35\ \text{l} \times \frac{0.5\ \text{g-eq wt}}{1\ \text{l}} = 0.175\ \text{g-eq wt}$$

or 0.175 g-eq $Al_2(SO_4)_3$.

Example 2.   Determine the number of gram-milliequivalents of solute in (a) 10 ml of 0.125 N HCl solution and (b) 25 ml of 0.5 N $Ba(OH)_2$ solution.

Since no. of g-meq wts solute = no. of ml solution $\times$ N and N = no. of g-meq wts solute/ml solution, then

$$\text{No. of g-meq solute} = \text{no. of ml solution} \times \frac{\text{no. of g-meq wts solute}}{1\ \text{ml solution}}$$

(a) Let x = number of gram-milliequivalents of HCl

$$= 10\ \text{ml} \times \frac{0.125\ \text{g-meq wt}}{1\ \text{ml}} = 1.25\ \text{g-meq wt}$$

or 1.25 g-meq HCl.

(b) Let y = number of gram-milliequivalents of $Ba(OH)_2$

$$= 25\ \text{ml} \times \frac{0.5\ \text{g-meq wt}}{1\ \text{ml}} = 12.5\ \text{g-meq wt}$$

or 12.5 g-meq $Ba(OH)_2$.

Example 3.   Calculate the number of grams of solute required for the preparation of (a) 500 ml of 3 N H_3PO_4 solution, (b) 200 ml of 0.25 N $Ba(OH)_2$ solution, (c) 250 ml of 0.5 N $KMnO_4$ solution as oxidizer in acid medium, and (*d*) 350 ml of 0.4 *N* $FeSO_4$ solution as reducer.

$$\text{No. of } l \times N = \frac{G}{\text{no. of g/g-eq wt}}$$

Also recall that

$$N = \frac{\text{no. of g-eq wts solute}}{1 \text{ l solution}}$$

(*a*) Molecular weight H_3PO_4 = 98, or 98 g H_3PO_4/g-mole.

$$1 \text{ g-eq wt } H_3PO_4 = \frac{98 \text{ g } H_3PO_4/\text{g-mole}}{3 \text{ g-eq wt/g-mole}} = \frac{32.7 \text{ g } H_3PO_4}{1 \text{ g-eq wt}}$$

$$500 \text{ ml} = 0.5 \text{ l}$$

$$3 \ N = \frac{3 \text{ g-eq wt}}{1 \text{ l}}$$

Let x = number of grams H_3PO_4

$$0.5 \text{ l} \times \frac{3 \text{ g-eq wt}}{1 \text{ l}} = \frac{x}{32.7 \text{ g } H_3PO_4/\text{g-eq wt}}$$

$$x = 0.5 \text{ l} \times \frac{3 \text{ g-eq wt}}{1 \text{ l}} \times \frac{32.7 \text{ g } H_3PO_4}{1 \text{ g-eq wt}} = 49 \text{ g } H_3PO_4$$

Therefore, 49 g H_3PO_4 is required for 500 ml of 3 *N* H_3PO_4 solution.

(*b*) Molecular weight $Ba(OH)_2$ = 171.4, or 171.4 g $Ba(OH)_2$/g-mole.

$$1 \text{ g-eq wt } Ba(OH)_2 = \frac{171.4 \text{ g } Ba(OH)_2/\text{g-mole}}{2 \text{ g-eq wt/g-mole}}$$

$$= \frac{85.7 \text{ g } Ba(OH)_2}{1 \text{ g-eq wt}}$$

$$200 \text{ ml} = 0.2 \text{ l}$$

$$0.25 \ N = \frac{0.25 \text{ g-eq wt}}{1 \text{ l}}$$

Let y = number of grams $Ba(OH)_2$

$$0.2 \text{ l} \times \frac{0.25 \text{ g-eq wt}}{1 \text{ l}} = \frac{y}{85.7 \text{ g } Ba(OH)_2/\text{g-eq wt}}$$

$$y = 0.2 \text{ l} \times \frac{0.25 \text{ g-eq wt}}{1 \text{ l}} \times \frac{85.7 \text{ g } Ba(OH)_2}{1 \text{ g-eq wt}}$$

$$= 4.28 \text{ g } Ba(OH)_2$$

or 4.28 g $Ba(OH)_2$ is required for 200 ml of 0.25 *N* $Ba(OH)_2$ solution.

(*c*) Molecular weight $KMnO_4$ = 158, or 158 g $KMnO_4$/g-mole.

$$1 \text{ g-eq wt } KMnO_4 \text{ (oxidizer)} = \frac{158 \text{ g } KMnO_4/\text{g-mole}}{5 \text{ g-eq wt/g-mole}}$$

$$= \frac{31.6 \text{ g } KMnO_4}{1 \text{ g-eq wt}}$$

The foregoing expression arises from the fact that the total change in oxidation number in 1 molecule of $KMnO_4$ acting as an oxidizer in acid medium is 5.

$$250 \text{ ml} = 0.25 \text{ l}$$

$$0.5 \ N = \frac{0.5 \text{ g-eq wt}}{1 \text{ l}}$$

Let z = number of grams $KMnO_4$

$$0.25 \text{ l} \times \frac{0.5 \text{ g-eq wt}}{1 \text{ l}} = \frac{z}{31.6 \text{ g } KMnO_4/\text{g-eq wt}}$$

$$z = 0.25 \text{ l} \times \frac{0.5 \text{ g-eq wt}}{1 \text{ l}} \times \frac{31.6 \text{ g } KMnO_4}{1 \text{ g-eq wt}} = 3.95 \text{ g } KMnO_4$$

or 3.95 g $KMnO_4$ is required for 250 ml of 0.5 N $KMnO_4$ as oxidizer.

(d) Molecular weight $FeSO_4$ = 151.9, or 151.9 g $FeSO_4$/g-mole.

$$1 \text{ g-eq wt } FeSO_4 \text{ (reducer)} = \frac{151.9 \text{ g } FeSO_4/\text{g-mole}}{1 \text{ g-eq wt/g-mole}}$$

$$= \frac{151.9 \text{ g } FeSO_4}{1 \text{ g-eq wt}}$$

Note that this expression arises from the fact that the total change in oxidation number in 1 molecule of $FeSO_4$ acting as a reducer is 1.

$$350 \text{ ml} = 0.35 \text{ l}$$

$$0.4 \ N = \frac{0.4 \text{ g-eq wt}}{1 \text{ l}}$$

Let v = number of grams $FeSO_4$

$$0.35 \text{ l} \times \frac{0.4 \text{ g-eq wt}}{1 \text{ l}} = \frac{v}{151.9 \text{ g } FeSO_4/\text{g-eq wt}}$$

$$v = 0.35 \text{ l} \times \frac{0.4 \text{ g-eq wt}}{1 \text{ l}} \times \frac{151.9 \text{ g } FeSO_4}{1 \text{ g-eq wt}} = 21.27 \text{ g } FeSO_4$$

or 21.27 g $FeSO_4$ is required for 350 ml of 0.4 N $FeSO_4$ as reducer.

Example 4. Determine the normality of the following solutions which contain (a) 19.62 g H_3PO_4 in 2 l of solution, (b) 5.7 g $Al_2(SO_4)_3$ in 200 ml of solution, (c) 15.75 g $(NH_4)_2Cr_2O_7$ in 500 ml of solution as oxidizer (acid medium), and (d) 11.3 g $SnCl_2 \cdot 2H_2O$ in 250 ml of solution as reducer.

$$\text{No. of l} \times N = \frac{G}{\text{no. of g/g-eq wt}}$$

(a) Molecular weight H_3PO_4 = 98, or 98 g H_3PO_4/g-mole.

$$1 \text{ g-eq wt } H_3PO_4 = \frac{98 \text{ g } H_3PO_4/\text{g-mole}}{3 \text{ g-eq wt/g-mole}} = \frac{32.7 \text{ g } H_3PO_4}{1 \text{ g-eq wt}}$$

Let x = normality of H_3PO_4 solution

$$2 \text{ l} \times x = \frac{19.62 \text{ g } H_3PO_4}{32.7 \text{ g } H_3PO_4/\text{g-eq wt}}$$

$$x = \frac{19.62 \text{ g } H_3PO_4}{2 \text{ l}} \times \frac{1 \text{ g-eq wt}}{32.7 \text{ g } H_3PO_4} = \frac{0.3 \text{ g-eq wt}}{1 \text{ l}}$$

or 0.3 g-eq wt/l = 0.3 N = normality of H_3PO_4 solution.

(b) Molecular weight $Al_2(SO_4)_3$ = 342, or 342 g $Al_2(SO_4)_3$/g-mole.

$$1 \text{ g-eq wt } Al_2(SO_4)_3 = \frac{342 \text{ g } Al_2(SO_4)_3/\text{g-mole}}{6 \text{ g-eq wt/g-mole}}$$

$$= \frac{57 \text{ g } Al_2(SO_4)_3}{1 \text{ g-eq wt}}$$

$$200 \text{ ml} = 0.2 \text{ l}$$

Let y = normality of $Al_2(SO_4)_3$ solution

$$0.2 \text{ l} \times y = \frac{5.7 \text{ g } Al_2(SO_4)_3}{57 \text{ g } Al_2(SO_4)_3/\text{g-eq wt}}$$

$$y = \frac{5.7 \text{ g } Al_2(SO_4)_3}{0.2 \text{ l}} \times \frac{1 \text{ g-eq wt}}{57 \text{ g } Al_2(SO_4)_3} = \frac{0.5 \text{ g-eq wt}}{1 \text{ l}}$$

or 0.5 g-eq wt/l = 0.5 N = normality of $Al_2(SO_4)_3$ solution.

(c) Molecular weight $(NH_4)_2Cr_2O_7$ = 252, or 252 g $(NH_4)_2Cr_2O_7$/g-mole.

$$1 \text{ g-eq wt } (NH_4)_2Cr_2O_7 \text{ (oxidizer)} = \frac{252 \text{ g } (NH_4)_2Cr_2O_7/\text{g-mole}}{6 \text{ g-eq wt/g-mole}}$$

$$= \frac{42 \text{ g } (NH_4)_2Cr_2O_7}{1 \text{ g-eq wt}} \text{ as oxidizer}$$

since total change in oxidation number in 1 molecule $(NH_4)_2Cr_2O_7$ is 6.

$$500 \text{ ml} = 0.5 \text{ l}$$

Let z = normality of $(NH_4)_2Cr_2O_7$ solution as oxidizer (acid medium)

$$0.5 \text{ l} \times z = \frac{15.75 \text{ g } (NH_4)_2Cr_2O_7}{42 \text{ g } (NH_4)_2Cr_2O_7/\text{g-eq wt}}$$

$$z = \frac{15.75 \text{ g } (NH_4)_2Cr_2O_7}{0.5 \text{ l}} \times \frac{1 \text{ g-eq wt}}{42 \text{ g } (NH_4)_2Cr_2O_7}$$

$$= \frac{0.75 \text{ g-eq wt}}{1 \text{ l}}$$

or 0.75 g-eq wt/l = 0.75 N = normality of $(NH_4)_2Cr_2O_7$ solution as oxidizer.

(d) Molecular weight $SnCl_2 \cdot 2H_2O$ = 226, or 226 g $SnCl_2 \cdot 2H_2O$/g-mole.

$$1 \text{ g-eq wt SnCl}_2 \cdot 2\text{H}_2\text{O (reducer)} = \frac{226 \text{ g SnCl}_2 \cdot 2\text{H}_2\text{O/g-mole}}{2 \text{ g-eq wts/g-mole}}$$

$$= \frac{113 \text{ g SnCl}_2 \cdot 2\text{H}_2\text{O}}{1 \text{ g-eq wt}} \text{ as reducer}$$

since total change in oxidation number in 1 molecule $SnCl_2 \cdot 2H_2O$ is 2.

$$250 \text{ ml} = 0.25 \text{ l}$$

Let v = normality of $SnCl_2$ solution as reducer

$$0.25 \text{ l} \times v = \frac{11.3 \text{ g SnCl}_2 \cdot 2\text{H}_2\text{O}}{113 \text{ g SnCl}_2 \cdot 2\text{H}_2\text{O/g-eq wt}}$$

$$v = \frac{11.3 \text{ g SnCl}_2 \cdot 2\text{H}_2\text{O}}{0.25 \text{ l}} \times \frac{1 \text{ g-eq wt}}{113 \text{ g SnCl}_2 \cdot 2\text{H}_2\text{O}} = \frac{0.4 \text{ g-eq wt}}{1 \text{ l}}$$

or 0.4 g-eq wt/l = 0.4 N = normality of $SnCl_2$ solution as reducer.

Example 5. Calculate the number of grams of solute required for the preparation of 100 ml of N Li_2SO_4 solution on the basis of milliequivalents.

$$\text{No. of ml} \times N = \frac{G}{\text{no. of g/g-meq wt}} \quad \text{and} \quad N = \frac{\text{no. of g-meq wts}}{\text{no. of ml}}$$

Molecular weight Li_2SO_4 = 110, or 110 g Li_2SO_4/g-mole.

$$1 \text{ g-eq wt Li}_2\text{SO}_4 = \frac{110 \text{ g Li}_2\text{SO}_4\text{/g-mole}}{2 \text{ g-eq wt/g-mole}} = \frac{55 \text{ g Li}_2\text{SO}_4}{1 \text{ g-eq wt}}$$

or on a gram-milliequivalent weight basis 0.055 g Li_2SO_4/g-meq wt.

Let x = number of grams Li_2SO_4

$$100 \text{ ml} \times \frac{1 \text{ g-meq wt}}{1 \text{ ml}} = \frac{x}{0.055 \text{ g Li}_2\text{SO}_4\text{/g-meq wt}}$$

$$x = 100 \text{ ml} \times \frac{1 \text{ g-meq wt}}{1 \text{ ml}} \times \frac{0.055 \text{ g Li}_2\text{SO}_4}{1 \text{ g-meq wt}} = 5.5 \text{ g Li}_2\text{SO}_4$$

or 5.5 g Li_2SO_4 is required in preparation of 100 ml of N Li_2SO_4 solution.

Example 6. Determine the number of gram-milliequivalent weights per milliliter (normality) of a solution that contains 3.2 g $Ba(OH)_2$ in 30 ml.

$$\text{No. of ml} \times N = \frac{G}{\text{no. of g/g-meq wt}}$$

Molecular weight $Ba(OH)_2$ = 171.4, or 0.1714 g $Ba(OH)_2$/millimole.

$$1 \text{ g-meq wt Ba(OH)}_2 = \frac{0.1714 \text{ g Ba(OH)}_2}{2 \text{ g-meq wt}} = \frac{0.0857 \text{ g Ba(OH)}_2}{1 \text{ g-meq wt}}$$

Let x = number of gram-milliequivalent weights per milliliter, or normality of $Ba(OH)_2$ solution

$$30 \text{ ml} \times x = \frac{3.2 \text{ g } Ba(OH)_2}{0.0857 \text{ g } Ba(OH)_2/\text{g-meq wt}}$$

$$x = \frac{3.2 \text{ g } Ba(OH)_2}{30 \text{ ml}} \times \frac{1 \text{ g-meq wt}}{0.0857 \text{ g } Ba(OH)_2} = \frac{1.24 \text{ g-meq wt}}{1 \text{ ml}}$$

or 1.24 g-meq wt/ml = 1.24 N = normality of $Ba(OH)_2$ solution.

Example 7. A sodium hydroxide solution containing 40 per cent by weight pure NaOH has a specific gravity of 1.43. How many milliliters of this solution will be required in the preparation of 500 ml of 0.5 N NaOH solution?

Step 1.   Determine the number of grams pure NaOH in 500 ml of 0.5 N NaOH solution.

$$\text{No. of ml} \times N = \frac{G}{\text{no. of g/g-meq wt}}$$

Molecular weight NaOH = 40, or 40 g NaOH/g-mole.

$$1 \text{ g-eq wt NaOH} = \frac{40 \text{ g NaOH/g-mole}}{1 \text{ g-eq wt/g-mole}} = 40 \text{ g NaOH/g-eq wt}$$

On a gram-milliequivalent basis, this becomes 0.040 g NaOH/g-meq wt.

Let x = number of grams NaOH in 500 ml of 0.5 N NaOH solution

$$500 \text{ ml} \times \frac{0.5 \text{ g-meq wt}}{1 \text{ ml}} = \frac{x}{0.040 \text{ g NaOH/g-meq wt}}$$

$$x = 500 \text{ ml} \times \frac{0.5 \text{ g-meq wt}}{1 \text{ ml}} \times \frac{0.040 \text{ g NaOH}}{1 \text{ g-meq wt}} = 10.0 \text{ g NaOH}$$

or 10.0 g pure NaOH is required for 500 ml of 0.5 N NaOH solution.

Step 2.   Determine the number of grams of pure NaOH in 1 ml of sodium hydroxide solution.

NOTE.   For convenience in expressing dimensional units, sodium hydroxide solution is abbreviated *shs*.

Specific gravity of *shs* = 1.43, or in density terms 1.43 g *shs*/ml *shs*.

$$\frac{1.43 \text{ g } shs}{1 \text{ ml } shs} \times \frac{0.4 \text{ g pure NaOH}}{1 \text{ g } shs} = \frac{0.572 \text{ g pure NaOH}}{1 \text{ ml } shs}$$

Step 3.   Find the number of milliliters sodium hydroxide solution which will contain 10.0 g pure NaOH.

$$\frac{10.0 \text{ g pure NaOH}}{0.572 \text{ g pure NaOH/ml } shs}$$

$$= 10.0 \text{ g pure NaOH} \times \frac{1 \text{ ml } shs}{0.572 \text{ g pure NaOH}}$$

$$= 17.5 \text{ ml } shs$$

Then 17.5 ml sodium hydroxide solution (sp gr 1.43 and containing 40 per cent by weight pure NaOH) must be diluted with sufficient water to make 500 ml in the preparation of 500 ml of 0.5 N NaOH solution.

The relationship between *molarity* and *normality* of solutions (non-oxidizers) can be shown by the following: Recall that M = no. of g-moles solute/l and N = no. of g-eq wts solute/l.

To convert molarity to normality, and vice versa, for various types of solutions the following identities are useful: 1 M NaOH $\equiv$ 1 g-mole NaOH/l $\equiv$ 1 g-eq wt NaOH/l $\equiv$ 1 N NaOH, or 1 M NaOH $\equiv$ 1 N NaOH, *i.e.*, a one *molar* NaOH solution is identical with a one *normal* NaOH solution since each contains the same quantity of solute in 1 l of solution. Thus 1 M H_2SO_4 $\equiv$ 1 g-mole H_2SO_4/l $\equiv$ 2 g-eq wt H_2SO_4/l $\equiv$ 2 N H_2SO_4, or 1 M H_2SO_4 $\equiv$ 2 N H_2SO_4, and 1 N H_2SO_4 $\equiv$ 0.5 M H_2SO_4; then 3 M H_2SO_4 $\equiv$ 6 N H_2SO_4, and 3 N H_2SO_4 $\equiv$ 1.5 M H_2SO_4. Also, 1 M H_3PO_4 $\equiv$ 3 N H_3PO_4, and 1 N H_3PO_4 $\equiv$ ⅓ M H_3PO_4; then 5 M H_3PO_4 $\equiv$ 15 N H_3PO_4, and 6 N H_3PO_4 $\equiv$ 2 M H_3PO_4. Also, 1 M $Al_2(SO_4)_3$ $\equiv$ 6 N $Al_2(SO_4)_3$, and 1 N $Al_2(SO_4)_3$ $\equiv$ ⅙ M $Al_2(SO_4)_3$; then 1.5 M $Al_2(SO_4)_3$ $\equiv$ 9 N $Al_2(SO_4)_3$, and 3 N $Al_2(SO_4)_3$ $\equiv$ 0.5 M $Al_2(SO_4)_3$.

From the foregoing statements the *normality* of a given solution is either numerically equal to or numerically greater than the molarity of the given solution, or $N \gtreqless M$.

In dealing with oxidizers and reducers the student should bear in mind that the number of gram-equivalent weights per gram-mole of an oxidizer (or reducer) is represented by the total change in oxidation number in 1 molecule of that oxidizer (or reducer). Thus, if 1 N $KMnO_4$ $\equiv$ ⅕ M $KMnO_4$ as oxidizer (acid medium), then 3 N $KMnO_4$ $\equiv$ (3 × ⅕) M $KMnO_4$ $\equiv$ 0.6 M $KMnO_4$; also if 1 M $KMnO_4$ $\equiv$ 5 N $KMnO_4$ as oxidizer (acid medium), then 0.3 M $KMnO_4$ $\equiv$ (0.3 × 5) N $KMnO_4$ $\equiv$ 1.5 N $KMnO_4$ as oxidizer.

Example 8. Convert molarity to normality of following solutions: (*a*) 3.5 M $Ba(OH)_2$; (*b*) 0.125 M $SnCl_4$.

(*a*) If 1 M $Ba(OH)_2$ $\equiv$ 2 N $Ba(OH)_2$, then

$$3.5 \ M \ Ba(OH)_2 \equiv (3.5 \times 2) \ N \ Ba(OH)_2 \equiv 7 \ N \ Ba(OH)_2$$

(*b*) If 1 M $SnCl_4$ $\equiv$ 4 N $SnCl_4$, then

$$0.125 \ M \ SnCl_4 \equiv (0.125 \times 4) \ N \ SnCl_4 \equiv 0.5 \ N \ SnCl_4$$

Example 9. Convert normality to molarity of following solutions: (*a*) 1.26 N H_3PO_4; (*b*) 1.8 N $Cr_2(SO_4)_3$; (*c*) 2.5 N $KMnO_4$ as oxidizer (acid medium).

(a) If $1\ N\ H_3PO_4 \equiv \frac{1}{3}\ M\ H_3PO_4$, then

$$1.26\ N\ H_3PO_4 \equiv (1.26 \times \tfrac{1}{3})\ M\ H_3PO_4 \equiv 0.42\ M\ H_3PO_4$$

(b) If $1\ N\ Cr_2(SO_4)_3 \equiv \frac{1}{6}\ M\ Cr_2(SO_4)_3$, then

$$1.8\ N\ Cr_2(SO_4)_3 \equiv (1.8 \times \tfrac{1}{6})\ M\ Cr_2(SO_4)_3$$
$$\equiv 0.3\ M\ Cr_2(SO_4)_3$$

(c) If $1\ N\ KMnO_4 \equiv \frac{1}{5}\ M\ KMnO_4$ as oxidizer (acid medium), then

$$2.5\ N\ KMnO_4 \equiv (2.5 \times \tfrac{1}{5})\ M\ KMnO_4$$
$$\equiv 0.5\ M\ KMnO_4 \text{ as oxidizer (acid medium)}$$

Problems (Normal Concentration)

12-15. Find the number of gram-equivalents of solute in (a) 2.5 l of 6 N H_2SO_4 solution, (b) 1.5 l of 0.5 N KOH solution, and (c) 300 ml of 1.25 N Na_2CO_3 solution. *Ans.* (a) 15 g-eq; (b) 0.75 g-eq; (c) 0.375 g-eq.

12-16. Determine the number of gram-equivalents of solute in (a) 100 ml of 2.5 N $BaCl_2$ solution, (b) 1.5 l of 15 N NH_4OH solution, and (c) 200 ml of 16 N HNO_3 solution. *Ans.* (a) 0.25 g-eq; (b) 22.5 g-eq; (c) 3.2 g-eq.

12-17. Determine the number of gram-milliequivalents of solute in (a) 25 ml of 12 N HCl solution, (b) 50 ml of 0.5 N $Pb(NO_3)_2$ solution, and (c) 20 ml of 5 N NH_4OH solution.

Ans. (a) 300 g-meq; (b) 25 g-meq; (c) 100 g-meq.

12-18. Determine the number of gram-milliequivalents of solute in (a) 30 ml of 6 N Na_2CO_3 solution, (b) 20 ml of 18 N H_2SO_4 solution, and (c) 25 ml of 15 N NH_4OH solution.

Ans. (a) 180 g-meq; (b) 360 g-meq; (c) 375 g-meq.

12-19. Find the number of grams of solute required for the preparation of (a) 1 l of 2 N KOH solution, (b) 500 ml of 9 N H_2SO_4 solution, (c) 250 ml of 0.5 N $AgNO_3$ solution, and (d) 2 l of 0.5 N $KMnO_4$ solution as oxidizer in acid medium. *Ans.* (a) 112.2 g; (b) 220.5 g; (c) 21.2 g; (d) 31.6 g.

12-20. Find the number of grams of solute required for the preparation of (a) 1.5 l of 0.2 N $Ba(OH)_2$ solution, (b) 5 l of 6 N HNO_3 solution, (c) 2 l of 1.5 N Na_2CO_3 solution, and (d) 500 ml of 5 N $K_2Cr_2O_7$ solution as oxidizer in acid medium. *Ans.* (a) 25.7 g; (b) 1890 g; (c) 159 g; (d) 122.5 g.

12-21. How many grams of solute are contained in each of the following: (a) 25 ml of 6 N H_2SO_4 solution; (b) 50 ml of 5 N $AgNO_3$ solution; (c) 15 ml of 0.5 N $Ba(OH)_2$ solution; (d) 25 ml of 0.1 N $KMnO_4$ solution as oxidizer in acid medium. *Ans.* (a) 7.4 g; (b) 42.5 g; (c) 0.643 g; (d) 0.079 g.

12-22. Determine the normality of the following: (a) 21 g KOH in 2.5 l of solution; (b) 220 g H_2SO_4 in 5 l of solution; (c) 3.06 g $K_2Cr_2O_7$ in 250 ml of solution as oxidizer. *Ans.* (a) 0.15 N; (b) 0.9N; (c) 0.25 N.

12-23. Determine the normality of the following: (a) 8.33 g $AlCl_3$ in 250 ml of solution; (b) 5.35 g $Ba(OH)_2$ in 500 ml of solution; (c) 19.75 g $KMnO_4$ in 500 ml of solution. *Ans.* (a) 0.75 N; (b) 0.125 N; (c) 1.25 N.

12-24. (a) How many grams of pure H_2SO_4 is contained in 25 ml of 0.4 N H_2SO_4 solution? (b) How many milliliters of sulfuric acid solution (sp gr 1.835 and containing 93.2 per cent by weight H_2SO_4) is necessary to prepare 1 l of 0.4 N H_2SO_4 solution? *Ans.* (a) 0.49 g; (b) 11.5 ml.

12-25. Calculate (a) the number of grams of pure Na_2CO_3 contained in 100 ml of 0.5 N Na_2CO_3 solution and (b) the number of milliliters of sodium carbonate solution (sp gr 1.19 and containing 17.9 per cent by weight Na_2CO_3) required to prepare 250 ml of 0.5 N Na_2CO_3 solution.

Ans. (a) 2.65 g; (b) 31.1 ml.

12-26. Calculate the number of milliliters of 0.4 N $AgNO_3$ solution that can be obtained by dissolving 13.59 g of silver nitrate in water.   *Ans.* 200 ml.

12-27. How many milliliters of N/10 Na_3PO_4 solution can be obtained by dissolving 0.684 g of sodium orthophosphate in water?   *Ans.* 125 ml.

12-28. Calculate the number of milliliters of 0.05 N $KMnO_4$ solution, as oxidizer in acid medium, that can be made by dissolving 0.3950 g of potassium permanganate in water.   *Ans.* 250 ml.

12-29. Determine the number of milliliters of 0.4 N $K_2Cr_2O_7$ solution, as oxidizer in acid medium, that can be obtained by dissolving 3.9226 g of potassium dichromate in water.   *Ans.* 200 ml.

12-30. Determine (1) the number of gram-moles and (2) the number of grams of solute in each of the following: (a) 500 ml of 0.5 M $AgNO_3$ solution; (b) 2 l of 3 M NH_4Cl solution; (c) 250 ml of 6 M $NH_4C_2H_3O_2$ solution.

12-31. Determine (1) the number of gram-moles and (2) the number of grams of solute in each of the following: (a) 300 ml of 0.5 M $Cd(NO_3)_2$ solution; (b) 10 l of 6 M HNO_3 solution; (c) 200 ml of 1.25 M KOH solution.

12-32. Determine (1) the number of millimoles and (2) the number of grams of solute in each of the following: (a) 25 ml of 0.5 M H_2SO_4 solution; (b) 10 ml of 5 M NH_4OH solution; (c) 20 ml of 0.5 M $Al_2(SO_4)_3$ solution.

12-33. Find (1) the number of gram-equivalents and (2) the number of grams of solute in each of the following: (a) 1 l of 0.5 N $Mg(NO_3)_2$ solution; (b) 5 l of 9 N H_2SO_4 solution; (c) 2.5 l of 6 N NaOH solution.

12-34. Determine (1) the number of gram-equivalents and (2) the number of grams of solute in each of the following: (a) 3 l of 0.5 N $BaCl_2$ solution; (b) 200 ml of 9 N H_3PO_4 solution; (c) 250 ml of 5 N KOH solution.

12-35. Find (1) the molarity and (2) the normality of the following, which contain (a) 167 g of H_3PO_4 in 250 ml of solution, (b) 140.3 g of $SnCl_4$ in 250 ml of solution, and (c) 6.425 g of $Ba(OH)_2$ in 500 ml of solution.

12-36. Find (1) the molarity and (2) the normality of the following, which contain (a) 2 g of $Al(NO_3)_3$ in 100 ml of solution; (b) 11 g of H_2SO_4 in 15 ml of solution; (c) 12.45 g of $BaCl_2 \cdot 2H_2O$ in 50 ml of solution.

12-37. Calculate (1) molarity and (2) normality of the following "stock" reagents used in the chemical laboratory:

(a) Hydrochloric acid solution (sp gr 1.188 and containing 38 per cent by weight pure HCl).

(b) Sulfuric acid solution (sp gr 1.835 and containing 96 per cent by weight pure H_2SO_4).

(c) Nitric acid solution (sp gr 1.418 and containing 71 per cent by weight pure HNO_3).

(d) Ammonium hydroxide solution (ammonia in water) (sp gr 0.892 and containing 30 per cent by weight of NH_3).

12-38. A dilute phosphoric acid solution is made by diluting 100 ml of phosphoric acid solution (sp gr 1.426 and containing 60 per cent by weight pure H_3PO_4) to 1 l.   (a) What is the molarity?   (b) What is the normality of the dilute acid solution?

12-39. If 380 ml of nitric acid solution (sp gr 1.418 and containing 71 per cent by weight pure HNO_3) is mixed with 620 ml of water, what will be (a) the molarity and (b) the normality of this diluted acid solution?

12-40. If 35 ml of acetic acid solution (sp gr 1.052 and containing 99 per cent by weight pure $HC_2H_3O_2$) is mixed with 65 ml of water, what will be (a) the molarity and (b) the normality of this diluted acid solution?

12-41. Calculate the following: (a) the number of milliliters of potassium hydroxide solution (sp gr 1.546 and containing 50.6 per cent by weight pure KOH) necessary to prepare 500 ml 0.1 N KOH solution; (b) the number of grams of pure KOH contained in 100 ml of 0.1 N KOH solution; (c) the number of milliliters of 0.1 N KOH solution that will contain 10 g of pure KOH.

12-42. (a) How many milliliters of nitric acid solution (sp gr 1.255 and containing 40.58 per cent by weight pure HNO_3) is necessary to prepare 10 l of 0.25 N HNO_3 solution, used as ordinary acid? (b) How many grams of pure HNO_3 will be contained in 10 ml of 0.25 N HNO_3 solution? (c) How many milliliters of 0.25 N HNO_3 will contain 10 g of pure HNO_3?

12-43. Calculate the following: (a) the number of milliliters of phosphoric acid solution (sp gr 1.426 and 60 per cent by weight pure H_3PO_4) required in the preparation of 5 l of 5 N H_3PO_4 solution; (b) the number of grams of pure H_3PO_4 contained in 25 ml of 5 N H_3PO_4 solution; (c) the number of milliliters of 5 N H_3PO_4 that will contain 25 g of pure H_3PO_4.

12-44. How many milliliters of 6 N HCl solution can be prepared from 100 ml of hydrochloric acid solution (sp gr 1.188 and containing 38 per cent by weight pure HCl) by dilution with water?

12-45. Determine the number of liters of 9 N H_2SO_4 solution that can be obtained by dilution of 500 ml of sulfuric acid solution (sp gr 1.835 and containing 96 per cent by weight pure H_2SO_4) with water.

12-46. Determine the number of milliliters of 3 N H_3PO_4 solution that can be obtained by dilution of 20 ml of phosphoric acid solution (sp gr 1.426 and containing 60 per cent by weight pure H_3PO_4) with water.

12-47. Express (1) normal concentration in terms of molarity and (2) molar concentration in terms of normality, of the following solutions: (a) 0.25 N $Ba(OH)_2$; (b) 6 M $Al_2(SO_4)_3$; (c) 3.3 N H_3PO_4; (d) 0.6 M $Cr_2(SO_4)_3$; (e) 0.05 N $KMnO_4$ as oxidizer in acid medium.

12-48. Express (1) normal concentration in terms of molarity and (2) molar concentration in terms of normality, of the following solutions: (a) 0.33 N H_3AsO_4; (b) 0.2 M Na_3PO_4; (c) 0.25 M $(NH_4)_2CO_3$; (d) 1.05 N $AlCl_3$; (e) 0.5 M $K_2Cr_2O_7$ as oxidizer in acid medium.

CHAPTER XIII

PRINCIPLE OF EQUIVALENCY

OUTLINE

A standard solution is one whose concentration is known.

Volumetric chemical analysis consists in experimentally finding the volume of a standard solution which will react completely with a given quantity or a measured volume of a solution of unknown concentration by a process of *titration*.

Standardization is the determination of exact normality of a given solution: *1 g-eq wt of a given substance will react completely with 1 g-eq wt of any other substance.*

Application of this principle of equivalency to solution of problems in (*a*) dilution; (*b*) acidimetry-alkalimetry; (*c*) precipitimetry; (*d*) redoximetry.

STANDARD SOLUTIONS

A standard solution is one whose concentration is known. Generally speaking, **molar** and **normal solutions** come in the category of standard solutions. In making up a **standard solution,** one first calculates the weight of solid solute (or volume of liquid solute) required for a given normality of the solution. This quantity of solid (or volume of liquid) is added to water to effect complete solution, thence transferred to a **volumetric flask,** and water added to the required final volume indicated by the mark on the neck of the flask. After thorough mixing, the solution thus obtained is one of an approximate known concentration. The method of determining the exact concentration or normality will be considered in a later paragraph.

SIMPLE VOLUMETRIC ANALYSIS REACTIONS

Briefly, volumetric chemical analysis consists in experimentally finding the volume of a standard solution which will react completely with a given quantity or a measured volume of a solution of unknown concentration. The process is called **titration.** Thus, in determining the strength of a commercial nitric acid solution, one titrates a known volume of the nitric acid with a standard NaOH solution (known normality). This means the amount of active HNO_3 or the strength of acid solution is determined by finding the volume of standard alkali solution required for complete neutralization of the measured volume of acid solution, followed by the necessary computations.

A neutralization reaction carried out by the volumetric method is classed as **acidimetry-alkalimetry**. A few double decomposition reactions in volumetric analysis involve the formation of precipitates—these are classed as **volumetric precipitation** reactions or **precipitimetry**. Also, a great many volumetric analysis reactions involve oxidation-reduction reactions—these are classed as **redoximetry**.

STANDARDIZATION

To determine the exact normality of a given solution, a process of **standardization** is performed. This consists essentially of finding the number of milliliters of the solution required to react completely with a given weight of a pure solid substance as a volumetric standard, or a definite volume of a known standard solution. By employing the principle of equivalency, the exact normality of the given solution can be obtained.

In the preceding chapter it was stated that on a gram-equivalent basis

$$\text{Normality} = \frac{\text{number of gram-equivalent weights of solute}}{\text{number of liters of solution}}$$

$$N = \frac{\text{no. of g-eq wts solute}}{\text{no. of l solution}}$$

and

$$\text{No. of g-eq wts solute} = \text{no. of l solution} \times N$$

On a gram-milliequivalent basis,

$$\text{Normality} = \frac{\text{number of gram-milliequivalent weights of solute}}{\text{number of milliliters of solution}}$$

$$N = \frac{\text{no. of g-meq wts solute}}{\text{no. of ml of solution}}$$

and

$$\text{No. of g-meq wts solute} = \text{no. of ml solution} \times N$$

Now, in any double decomposition reaction (or oxidation-reduction reaction), 1 equivalent weight of a given substance will react completely with 1 equivalent weight of any other substance.

Then a solution containing a *given number* of gram-equivalent weights of acid ($_a$) will react completely with the *same number* of gram-equivalent weights of base ($_b$).

Since no. of g-eq wts solute = no. of l × N, then

$$\text{No. of l}_a \times N_a = \text{no. of l}_b \times N_b \tag{1}$$

Likewise, a *given number* of gram-milliequivalent weights of acid ($_a$) will react completely with the *same number* of gram-milliequivalent weights of base ($_b$).

Since no. of g-meq wts = no. of ml $\times$ N, then

$$\text{No. of ml}_a \times N_a = \text{no. of ml}_b \times N_b \qquad (2)$$

This relationship of reactions between normal solutions of acids and bases as expressed in Equations (1) and (2) can be extended to general chemical reactions between solutions of other substances involving normalities. Thus, 10 ml of 0.1 N $AgNO_3$ solution will react completely with 10 ml of 0.1 N $NaCl$ solution in the formation of $AgCl$, since both solutions contain the same number of gram-milliequivalent weights of solute.

The expressions (1) and (2) are particularly useful in making dilutions of normal solutions. This will be given consideration in the examples that follow.

DILUTION

Example 1. How many milliliters of 36 N H_2SO_4 solution is required in the preparation of 60 ml of 6 N H_2SO_4 solution?

For purpose of explanation, $a = 36\ N$ and $a' = 6\ N$.

$$\text{No. of ml}_a \times N_a = \text{no. of ml}_{a'} \times N_{a'}$$

Let x = number of milliliters of 36 N H_2SO_4 solution

$$x \times 36\ N = 60\ \text{ml} \times 6\ N$$
$$x = \frac{60\ \text{ml} \times 6\ N}{36\ N} = 10\ \text{ml}$$

or 10 ml of 36 N H_2SO_4 solution diluted to 60 ml with water = 60 ml of 6 N H_2SO_4 solution.

Example 2. What is the normality of a phosphoric acid solution made by diluting 15 ml of 9 N H_3PO_4 with sufficient water to a final volume of 90 ml?

$$a = \text{dilute } H_3PO_4 \text{ solution} \qquad a' = 9\ N\ H_3PO_4 \text{ solution}$$
$$\text{No. of ml}_a \times N_a = \text{no. of ml}_{a'} \times N_{a'}$$

Let x = normality of dilute phosphoric acid solution

$$90\ \text{ml} \times x = 15\ \text{ml} \times 9\ N$$
$$x = \frac{15\ \text{ml} \times 9\ N}{90\ \text{ml}} = 1.5\ N$$

Normality of dilute H_3PO_4 solution = 1.5 N.

ACIDIMETRY-ALKALIMETRY

Example 1.   How many milliliters of a 9 N H_2SO_4 solution will be required to neutralize completely 20 ml of 3.6 N NaOH solution?

$$\text{No. of ml}_a \times N_a = \text{no. of ml}_b \times N_b$$

Let x = number of milliliters of 9 N H_2SO_4 solution

$$x \times 9\ N = 20\ \text{ml} \times 3.6\ N$$
$$x = \frac{20\ \text{ml} \times 3.6\ N}{9\ N} = 8.0\ \text{ml}$$

or 8.0 ml of 9 N H_2SO_4 solution will exactly neutralize 20 ml of 3.6 N NaOH solution.

Example 2.   What is the normality of a sulfuric acid solution 18.6 ml of which neutralizes 30 ml of 1.55 N KOH solution?

$$\text{No. of ml}_a \times N_a = \text{no. of ml}_b \times N_b$$

Let x = normality of sulfuric acid solution

$$18.6\ \text{ml} \times x = 30\ \text{ml} \times 1.55\ N$$
$$x = \frac{30\ \text{ml} \times 1.55\ N}{18.6\ \text{ml}} = 2.5\ N$$

Example 3.   Calculate the number of milliliters of 0.1 N H_2SO_4 solution necessary to react completely with a solution that contains 0.125 g of pure Na_2CO_3.

Molecular weight Na_2CO_3 = 106, or 106 g Na_2CO_3/g-mole.

$$1\ \text{g-eq wt } Na_2CO_3 = \frac{106\ \text{g } Na_2CO_3/\text{g-mole}}{2\ \text{g-eq wt/g-mole}} = 53\ \text{g } Na_2CO_3/\text{g-eq wt}$$

Step 1.   Express the equivalent weight of Na_2CO_3 in terms of grams per gram-milliequivalent weight (g-meq wt).

$$\frac{53\ \text{g } Na_2CO_3}{1\ \text{g-eq wt}} = \frac{0.053\ \text{g } Na_2CO_3}{1\ \text{g-meq wt}}$$

or 0.053 g Na_2CO_3/g-meq wt.

Step 2.   Employ the following relationship:

$$\text{No. of ml} \times N = \frac{G}{\text{no. of g/g-meq wt}}.$$

Note that the left side of the foregoing equation represents the number of gram-milliequivalent weights of H_2SO_4 and the right side represents an equal number of gram-milliequivalent weights of Na_2CO_3.

Or a given number of gram-milliequivalent weights of H_2SO_4 will react completely with the same number of gram-milliequivalent weights of Na_2CO_3.

Let x = number of milliliters 0.1 N H_2SO_4

$$x \times \frac{0.1 \text{ g-meq wt}}{1 \text{ ml}} = \frac{0.125 \text{ g } Na_2CO_3}{0.053 \text{ g } Na_2CO_3/\text{g-meq wt}}$$

$$x = 0.125 \text{ g } Na_2CO_3 \times \frac{1 \text{ ml}}{0.1 \text{ g-meq wt}} \times \frac{1 \text{ g-meq wt}}{0.053 \text{ g } Na_2CO_3}$$

$$= 23.6 \text{ ml}$$

or 23.6 ml of 0.1 N H_2SO_4 reacts completely with 0.125 g pure Na_2CO_3.

Example 4.   It was found that 25.5 ml of sulfuric acid solution reacted completely with 1.96 g of pure Na_2CO_3. What was the normality of the acid solution?

$$\text{No. of l} \times N = \frac{G}{\text{no. of g/g-eq wt}}$$

Note that the left side of the foregoing equation represents the number of gram-equivalent weights of H_2SO_4 and the right side represents an equal number of gram-equivalent weights of Na_2CO_3.

$$25.5 \text{ ml} = 0.0255 \text{ l}$$

Molecular weight Na_2CO_3 = 106, or 106 g Na_2CO_3/g-mole.

$$1 \text{ g-eq wt } Na_2CO_3 = \frac{106 \text{ g } Na_2CO_3/\text{g-mole}}{2 \text{ g-eq wt/g-mole}} = 53 \text{ g } Na_2CO_3/\text{g-eq wt}$$

Let x = normality of acid solution

$$0.0255 \text{ l} \times x = \frac{1.96 \text{ g } Na_2CO_3}{53 \text{ g } Na_2CO_3/\text{g-eq wt}}$$

$$x = 1.96 \text{ g } Na_2CO_3 \times \frac{1}{0.0255 \text{ l}} \times \frac{1 \text{ g-eq wt}}{53 \text{ g } Na_2CO_3} = 1.45 \text{ g-eq wt/l}$$

or 1.45 N = normality of sulfuric acid solution.

Alternate Solution on Milliequivalent Basis.   See Example 3, page 190.

$$\text{No. of ml} \times N = \frac{G}{\text{no. of g/g-meq wt}}$$

Let x = normality of acid solution

$$25.5 \text{ ml} \times x = \frac{1.96 \text{ g } Na_2CO_3}{0.053 \text{ g } Na_2CO_3/\text{g-meq wt}}$$

$$x = 1.96 \text{ g } Na_2CO_3 \times \frac{1}{25.5 \text{ ml}} \times \frac{1 \text{ g-meq wt}}{0.053 \text{ g } Na_2CO_3} = 1.45 \text{ g-meq wt/ml}$$

or 1.45 N = normality of sulfuric acid solution.

Example 5. "Constant-boiling HCl" solution has a specific gravity of 1.10 and contains 20.2 per cent by weight pure HCl. How many milliliters of this acid solution will be required to neutralize 20.5 ml of 1.05 N NaOH solution?

Method 1. For convenience in dealing with dimensional units, constant-boiling HCl solution is abbreviated *cbh*.

Step 1. Determine the normality of hydrochloric acid solution (*cbh*). Since sp gr *cbh* = 1.10, or density *cbh* = 1.10 g *cbh*/ml *cbh*,

$$\frac{1.10 \text{ g } cbh}{1 \text{ ml } cbh} \times \frac{0.202 \text{ g pure HCl}}{1 \text{ g } cbh} = 0.222 \text{ g pure HCl/ml } cbh$$

$$\text{No. of ml} \times N = \frac{G}{\text{no. of g/g-meq wt}}$$

Molecular weight HCl = 36.5, or 36.5 g HCl/g-mole. Since 1 g-mole HCl contains 1 g-eq wt H^+, then 36.5 g HCl = 1 g-eq wt HCl, or 0.0365 g HCl = 1 g-meq wt.

Let x = normality of *cbh*

$$1 \text{ ml} \times x = \frac{0.222 \text{ g HCl}}{0.0365 \text{ g HCl/g-meq wt}}$$

$$x = 0.222 \text{ g HCl} \times \frac{1}{1 \text{ ml}} \times \frac{1 \text{ g-meq wt}}{0.0365 \text{ g HCl}} = \frac{6.09 \text{ g-meq wt}}{1 \text{ ml}}$$

$$= 6.09 \text{ } N$$

or normality of constant-boiling HCl solution is 6.09 N.

Step 2. Equate the number of gram-milliequivalent weights of base (NaOH) and the number of gram-milliequivalent weights of acid (HCl), thus

$$\text{No. of ml}_a \times N_a = \text{no. of ml}_b \times N_b$$

Let y = number of milliliters of *cbh*

$$y \times 6.09 \text{ } N = 20.5 \text{ ml} \times 1.05 \text{ } N$$

$$y = \frac{20.5 \text{ ml} \times 1.05 \text{ } N}{6.09 \text{ } N} = 3.5 \text{ ml}$$

or 3.5 ml of constant-boiling HCl solution will neutralize 20.5 ml of 1.05 N NaOH solution.

Method 2. On the basis of gram-milliequivalents: 1 gram-milliequivalent weight NaOH will react completely with 1 gram-milliequivalent weight HCl.

$$\text{No. of ml} \times N = \text{no. of g-meq wts}$$

$$20.5 \text{ ml} \times \frac{1.05 \text{ g-meq wt NaOH}}{1 \text{ ml}} = 21.5 \text{ g-meq wt NaOH}$$

then 21.5 g-meq wt NaOH will react completely with 21.5 g-meq wt HCl.

From Method 1, since 0.0365 g HCl = 1 g-meq wt HCl,

$$21.5 \text{ g-meq wt} \times \frac{0.0365 \text{ g HCl}}{1 \text{ g-meq wt}} = 0.785 \text{ g HCl}$$

$$\frac{1.10 \text{ g } cbh}{1 \text{ ml } cbh} \times \frac{0.202 \text{ g pure HCl}}{1 \text{ g } cbh} = 0.222 \text{ g pure HCl/ml } cbh$$

$$\frac{0.785 \text{ g HCl}}{0.222 \text{ g HCl/ml } cbh} = 3.5 \text{ ml } cbh$$

or 3.5 ml of constant-boiling HCl solution will neutralize 20.5 ml of 1.05 N NaOH.

Example 6. It required 25.5 ml of constant-boiling HCl solution (sp gr 1.10 and containing 20.2 per cent by weight pure HCl) to neutralize 21.5 ml of a sodium hydroxide solution. What is the normality of this sodium hydroxide solution?

NOTE. Constant-boiling HCl solution is abbreviated *cbh*.

Step 1. Determine the normality of *cbh* as in Example 5, Method 1.

$$\text{Normality of } cbh = 6.09 \ N$$

Step 2

$$\text{No. of ml}_a \times N_a = \text{no. of ml}_b \times N_b$$
$$25.5 \text{ ml} \times 6.09 \ N = 21.5 \text{ ml} \times N_b$$
$$N_b = \frac{25.5 \text{ ml} \times 6.09 \ N}{21.5 \text{ ml}} = 7.2 \ N$$

or normality of sodium hydroxide solution = 7.2 N.

Example 7. If 20 ml of 0.45 N NaOH solution is added to 30 ml of 0.32 N HCl, is the resulting solution basic or acidic? What is the normality with respect to (a) the basic or acidic final solution and (b) the salt formed by this neutralization?

$$20 \text{ ml} \times 0.45 \text{ g-meq NaOH/ml} = 9 \text{ g-meq wt NaOH}$$
$$30 \text{ ml} \times 0.32 \text{ g-meq HCl/ml} = 9.6 \text{ g-meq wt HCl}$$

Since 9 g-meq wt NaOH reacts with 9 g-meq wt HCl, there is an excess of 0.6 g-meq wt HCl which has not been neutralized; therefore the final solution is *acidic*.

(a) Assuming there is no change in volume due to chemical reaction, the total volume of final solution is 20 ml + 30 ml = 50 ml, and it contains 0.6 g-meq HCl. Then

$$N = \frac{0.6 \text{ g-meq HCl}}{50 \text{ ml}} = 0.012 \text{ g-meq HCl/ml}$$

or final solution is 0.012 N with regard to HCl.

(b) Since 9 g-meq NaOH will react completely with 9 g-meq HCl to form 9 g-meq NaCl in a total volume of 50 ml of solution,

$$N = \frac{9 \text{ g-meq NaCl}}{50 \text{ ml}} = 0.18 \text{ g-meq NaCl/ml}$$

or normality with respect to salt formed = 0.18 N NaCl.

PRECIPITIMETRY

Recall the important fact that 1 g-eq wt (or 1 g-meq wt) of a given substance will react completely with 1 g-eq wt (or 1 g-meq wt) of any other substance.

Example. Calculate (a) the number of milliliters of 0.5 N NaCl solution that will precipitate completely the AgCl from 20 ml of 0.15 N AgNO$_3$ solution and (b) the number of grams of AgCl obtained by this reaction.

No. of g-meq wts NaCl = same no. of g-meq wts AgNO$_3$
No. of ml$_{NaCl}$ × N_{NaCl} = no. of ml$_{AgNO_3}$ × N_{AgNO_3}

(a) Let x = number of milliliters 0.5 N NaCl

$$x \times 0.5 \ N = 20 \text{ ml} \times 0.15 \ N$$
$$x = \frac{20 \text{ ml} \times 0.15 \ N}{0.5 \ N} = 6 \text{ ml}$$

or 6 ml of 0.5 N NaCl will precipitate the AgCl from 20 ml of 0.15 N AgNO$_3$ solution.

(b) Since 0.15 N AgNO$_3$ = 0.15 g-meq wt AgNO$_3$/ml,

$$20 \text{ ml} \times \frac{0.15 \text{ g-meq wt AgNO}_3}{1 \text{ ml}} = 3 \text{ g-meq wt AgNO}_3$$

Now, 3 g-meq wt AgNO$_3$ will produce 3 g-meq wt AgCl. Since the molecular weight of AgCl is 143, or 143 g AgCl/g-mole, or 0.143 g AgCl/g-meq wt, then

$$3 \text{ g-meq wt} \times \frac{0.143 \text{ g AgCl}}{1 \text{ g-meq wt}} = 0.429 \text{ g AgCl}$$

or 0.429 g AgCl is precipitated by 6 ml of 0.5 N NaCl solution.

REDOXIMETRY

The principle of equivalency is definitely applicable to oxidation-reduction reactions (redoximetry). It can be stated that 1 g-eq wt of an oxidizer is reduced by 1 g-eq wt of a reducer. Also 1 g-meq wt of oxidizer is reduced by 1 g-meq wt of a reducer. Or 1 g-eq wt of reducer is oxidized by 1 g-eq wt of an oxidizer. Also 1 g-meq wt of reducer is oxidized by 1 g-meq wt of an oxidizer.

Example 1. How many grams of oxalic acid ($H_2C_2O_4 \cdot 2H_2O$) will be required to reduce 50.0 ml of 1.055 N $KMnO_4$ solution acidified with sulfuric acid?

$$\underbrace{5H_2C_2O_4}_{} + 2Mn^{+7}O_4^- + 6H^+ \rightarrow 10CO_2 + 2Mn^{+2} + 8H_2O$$

$$5 \times 2\text{\textcircled{e}} = 2 \times 5\text{\textcircled{e}}$$

Method 1. If 50 ml of 1.055 N $KMnO_4$ = 0.05 l of 1.055 N $KMnO_4$,

$$0.05 \text{ l} \times \frac{1.055 \text{ g-eq wt } KMnO_4}{1 \text{ l}} = 0.053 \text{ g-eq wt } KMnO_4$$

Since 1 g-eq wt $KMnO_4$ is reduced by 1 g-eq wt $H_2C_2O_4 \cdot 2H_2O$, then 0.053 g-eq wt $KMnO_4$ will be reduced by 0.053 g-eq wt $H_2C_2O_4 \cdot 2H_2O$. Molecular weight $H_2C_2O_4 \cdot 2H_2O$ = 126, or 126 g $H_2C_2O_4 \cdot 2H_2O$/g-mole. As a reducer 1 g-mole $H_2C_2O_4 \cdot 2H_2O$ loses 2 electrons per molecule, or a total change in oxidation number of 2; therefore 1 g-mole $H_2C_2O_4 \cdot 2H_2O$ contains 2 g-eq wt. Then

$$\frac{126 \text{ g } H_2C_2O_4 \cdot 2H_2O/\text{g-mole}}{2 \text{ g-eq wt/g-mole}} = \frac{63 \text{ g } H_2C_2O_4 \cdot 2H_2O}{1 \text{ g-eq wt}}$$

$$0.053 \text{ g-eq wt} \times \frac{63 \text{ g } H_2C_2O_4 \cdot 2H_2O}{1 \text{ g-eq wt}} = 3.3 \text{ g } H_2C_2O_4 \cdot 2H_2O$$

or 3.3 g of $H_2C_2O_4 \cdot 2H_2O$ will reduce 50 ml of 1.055 N $KMnO_4$ solution.

Method 2. Equate the number of gram-milliequivalent weights of $KMnO_4$ (oxidizer) and the number of gram-milliequivalent weights of $H_2C_2O_4 \cdot 2H_2O$ (reducer).

From Method 1 it was shown that 1 g-eq wt $H_2C_2O_4 \cdot 2H_2O$ = 63 g $H_2C_2O_4 \cdot 2H_2O$/g-eq wt; in terms of milliequivalents this becomes 0.063 g $H_2C_2O_4 \cdot 2H_2O$/g-meq wt.

Let x = number of grams $H_2C_2O_4 \cdot 2H_2O$

$$50 \text{ ml} \times \frac{1.055 \text{ g-meq wt}}{1 \text{ ml}} = \frac{x}{0.063 \text{ g } H_2C_2O_4 \cdot 2H_2O/\text{g-meq wt}}$$

$$x = 50 \text{ ml} \times \frac{1.055 \text{ g-meq wt}}{1 \text{ ml}} \times \frac{0.063 \text{ g } H_2C_2O_4 \cdot 2H_2O}{1 \text{ g-meq wt}}$$

$$= 3.3 \text{ g } H_2C_2O_4 \cdot 2H_2O$$

Example 2.   Calculate the number of milliliters of 0.125 N $K_2Cr_2O_7$ solution that will be required to oxidize 0.405 g $FeCl_2$ in a solution acidified with hydrochloric acid.

$$6Fe^{+2} + Cr_2^{+6}O_7^{-2} + 14H^+ \rightarrow 6Fe^{+3} + 2Cr^{+2} + 7H_2O$$

$$6 \times 1_{\textcircled{e}} \quad 2 \times 3_{\textcircled{e}}$$

From the foregoing equation, 1 Fe^{+2} is oxidized to 1 Fe^{+3}, or a change in oxidation number of $+1$.

Molecular weight $FeCl_2$ = 126.8, or 126.8 g $FeCl_2$/g-mole, and $\dfrac{126.8 \text{ g } FeCl_2/\text{g-mole}}{1 \text{ g-eq wt/g-mole}}$ or $\dfrac{0.127 \text{ g } FeCl_2}{1 \text{ g-meq wt}}$ as reducer.   The number of gram-milliequivalent weights of $K_2Cr_2O_7$ reacts with the same number of gram-milliequivalent weights of $FeCl_2$.

Let x = number of milliliters of 0.125 N $K_2Cr_2O_7$

$$x \times \frac{0.125 \text{ g-meq wt}}{1 \text{ ml}} = \frac{0.405 \text{ g } FeCl_2}{0.127 \text{ g } FeCl_2/\text{g-meq wt}}$$

$$x = 0.405 \text{ g } FeCl_2 \times \frac{1 \text{ ml}}{0.125 \text{ g-meq wt}} \times \frac{1 \text{ g-meq wt}}{0.127 \text{ g } FeCl_2}$$

$$= 25.5 \text{ ml}$$

Example 3.   It required 30 ml of a potassium dichromate solution to oxidize 1.52 g of $FeSO_4$ in a solution acidified with sulfuric acid. What is the normality of the potassium dichromate solution?

$$6Fe^{+2} + Cr_2^{+6}O_7^{-2} + 14H^+ \rightarrow 6Fe^{+3} + 2Cr^{+3} + 7H_2O$$

$$6 \times 1_{\textcircled{e}} \: 2 \times 3_{\textcircled{e}}$$

From the foregoing equation, 1 Fe^{+2} is oxidized to 1 Fe^{+3}, or a change in oxidation number of $+1$.

Molecular weight $FeSO_4$ = 151.9, or 151.9 g $FeSO_4$/g-mole, and $\dfrac{151.9 \text{ g } FeSO_4/\text{g-mole}}{1 \text{ g-eq wt/g-mole}}$ or $\dfrac{0.152 \text{ g } FeSO_4}{1 \text{ g-meq wt}}$ as reducer

No. of g-meq wts $K_2Cr_2O_7$ = same no. of g-meq wts $FeSO_4$

Let x = normality of potassium dichromate solution

$$30 \text{ ml} \times x = \frac{1.52 \text{ g } FeSO_4}{0.152 \text{ g } FeSO_4/\text{g-meq wt}}$$

$$x = 1.52 \text{ g } FeSO_4 \times \frac{1 \text{ g-meq wt}}{0.152 \text{ g } FeSO_4} \times \frac{1}{30 \text{ ml}}$$

$$= \frac{0.33 \text{ g-meq wt}}{1 \text{ ml}}$$

or normality of potassium dichromate solution = 0.33 N.

Problems

13-1. Determine (a) the number of milliliters of 15 N ammonia solution necessary to prepare 60 ml of 5 N ammonia solution and (b) the normality of nitric acid solution made by diluting 22.5 ml 16 N HNO_3 with water to 60 ml.   *Ans.* (a) 20 ml; (b) 6 N.

13-2. Calculate (a) the number of milliliters of 16 N HNO_3 solution required in the preparation of 60 ml of 3 N HNO_3 solution and (b) the normality of ammonia solution if 50 ml 15 N ammonia solution is diluted with water to 75 ml.   *Ans.* (a) 11.25 ml; (b) 10 N.

13-3. (1) What volume of 36 N H_2SO_4 solution will be necessary to prepare 30 ml of 1.2 N H_2SO_4 solution? (2) What is (a) the normality and (b) the molarity of phosphoric acid solution made by diluting 10 ml 9 N H_3PO_4 to 100 ml?   *Ans.* (1) 1 ml; (2) (a) 0.9N; (b) 0.3M.

13-4. How many milliliters of water is required to make 30 ml of 0.3 N HCl solution from 12 N HCl solution?   *Ans.* 29.25 ml.

13-5. How many milliliters of water is required to make 60 ml of 9 N H_2SO_4 solution from 18 M H_2SO_4 solution?   *Ans.* 45 ml.

13-6. What volume of water must be used in the preparation of 6 N HNO_3 solution from 12 ml of 16 N HNO_3?   *Ans.* 20 ml.

13-7. Find the volume of water necessary to prepare a 9 N H_2SO_4 solution from 6 ml of 36 N H_2SO_4.   *Ans.* 18 ml.

13-8. To what volume must 10 ml of 6 N H_3PO_4 solution be diluted to prepare a 1.5 N H_3PO_4 solution?   *Ans.* 40 ml.

13-9. If 50 ml of water is added to 10 ml of 6 N HNO_3 solution, what is the normality of this acid solution?   *Ans.* N.

13-10. A dilute sulfuric acid solution is made by adding 5 ml of 36 N H_2SO_4 to 245 ml of water. What is (a) the normality and (b) the molarity of this dilute acid solution?   *Ans.* (a) 0.7 N; (b) 0.35 M.

13-11. A dilute nitric acid solution is prepared by adding 38 ml of 16 N HNO_3 to 62 ml of water. Find (a) the normality and (b) the molarity of this dilute acid solution.   *Ans.* (a) 6 N; (b) 6 M.

13-12. Convert 32.8 ml of 0.1452 N H_2SO_4 to the equivalent volume of N H_2SO_4.   *Ans.* 4.76 ml.

13-13. Convert 29.8 ml of 0.1383 N KOH to the equivalent volume of N KOH.   *Ans.* 4.12 ml.

13-14. How many milliliters of 0.15 N NaOH will be required to neutralize completely 60 ml of 0.25 N H_2SO_4?   *Ans.* 100 ml.

13-15. Calculate the number of milliliters of 0.498 N KOH that is necessary to neutralize 25.0 ml of 0.259 N H_2SO_4.   *Ans.* 13 ml.

13-16. A solution of nitric acid is 0.2532 N. Calculate the number of milliliters of 0.2225 N NaOH required to neutralize 15.5 ml of the acid.   *Ans.* 17.6 ml.

13-17. How many milliliters of 0.4 N KOH solution will be necessary to neutralize 10 ml of the following acids: (a) 0.1 N HCl; (b) 0.1 N H_2SO_4; (c) 0.05 N H_3PO_4; (d) N HNO_3?   *Ans.* (a) 2.5 ml; (b) 2.5 ml; (c) 1.25 ml; (d) 25 ml.

13-18. What volume of 0.5 M $Ba(OH)_2$ solution will react completely with 25 ml of 3 N H_3PO_4?   *Ans.* 75 ml.

13-19. What volume of 0.5 N H_3PO_4 solution will neutralize exactly 16 ml of 0.05 M $Ba(OH)_2$?   *Ans.* 3.2 ml.

13-20. Determine the volume of 1.5 M H_3PO_4 solution required to neutralize exactly 90 ml of 0.5 M $Ba(OH)_2$ solution. *Ans.* 20 ml.

13-21. Calculate the normality of a nitric acid solution 50.0 ml of which was neutralized by 48.5 ml of 0.4 N KOH. *Ans.* 0.388 N.

13-22. What is the normality of a potassium hydroxide solution 30 ml of which neutralized 31.8 ml of 0.1198 N H_2SO_4? *Ans.* 0.127 N.

13-23. What is the normality of a phosphoric acid solution 35 ml of which neutralized 125 ml of 0.56 N KOH? *Ans.* 2 N.

13-24. What weight of $BaCl_2$ is needed to precipitate completely $BaSO_4$ from 30.5 ml of 0.1 N H_2SO_4? *Ans.* 0.318 g.

13-25. Calculate the weight of lead sulfate obtained by the action of excess sulfuric acid with 47 ml of 0.5 N $Pb(C_2H_3O_2)_2$. *Ans.* 3.6 g.

13-26. How many milliliters of 1.2 N HCl solution will react completely with a solution containing 0.267 g of pure Na_2CO_3? *Ans.* 4.2 ml.

13-27. How many milliliters of 2.5 N H_2SO_4 solution will neutralize completely a solution containing 0.25 g sodium hydroxide (85 per cent pure NaOH)? *Ans.* 2.12 ml.

13-28. How many milliliters of 0.5 N HCl solution will react completely with 0.51 g of limestone (96 per cent pure $CaCO_3$)? *Ans.* 19.6 ml.

13-29. What weight in grams of calcite (pure $CaCO_3$) will be necessary to react completely with 25 ml of 0.225 N H_2SO_4 solution? *Ans.* 0.281 g.

13-30. Determine the weight of pure Na_2CO_3 required to react completely with 22.4 ml of 0.525 N HNO_3 solution. *Ans.* 0.623 g.

13-31. A sample of calcite (pure $CaCO_3$) weighing 1.00 g required 39.5 ml of a hydrochloric acid solution for complete reaction. Calculate the normality of the acid. *Ans.* 0.506 N.

13-32. If 20.0 ml of a sulfuric acid solution reacts completely with 0.265 g of pure Na_2CO_3, calculate the normality of the acid. *Ans.* 0.25 N.

13-33. In standardizing a hydrochloric acid solution it was found that 28.5 ml of the acid reacted completely with 0.40 g of pure Na_2CO_3. What is the normality of the acid solution? *Ans.* 0.265 N.

13-34. Calculate the number of milliliters of 2.5 N NaOH solution necessary to neutralize completely 10 ml of sulfuric acid solution which has a specific gravity of 1.84 and contains 98.0 per cent by weight pure H_2SO_4. *Ans.* 147 ml.

13-35. Calculate the number of milliliters of 0.2 N ammonia solution that will exactly neutralize 5 ml of acetic acid, which has a specific gravity of 1.04 and contains 30 per cent by weight pure $HC_2H_3O_2$. *Ans.* 130 ml.

13-36. How many milliliters of 0.6 N HNO_3 solution will react completely with 31.1 ml of sodium carbonate solution (sp gr 1.10 and containing 10 per cent by weight pure Na_2CO_3)? *Ans.* 107 ml.

13-37. It required 25.0 ml of constant-boiling HCl solution (sp gr 1.10 and containing 20.2 per cent by weight active HCl) to neutralize 30.4 ml of a potassium hydroxide solution. Determine the normality of the potassium hydroxide solution. *Ans.* 5 N.

13-38. It was found that 30 ml of constant-boiling HCl solution (sp gr 1.10 and containing 20.2 per cent by weight pure HCl) was required to neutralize 20.5 ml of sodium hydroxide solution. What is the normality of the sodium hydroxide solution? *Ans.* 8.8 N.

13-39. Excess hydrochloric acid was added to 13.8 ml of a silver nitrate solution, and 0.990 g of AgCl was obtained in the reaction. What was the normality of the silver nitrate solution? *Ans.* 0.5 *N*.

13-40. Excess NaOH was added to 100 ml of a ferric chloride solution. This caused the precipitation of 1.425 g of $Fe(OH)_3$. Calculate the normality of the ferric chloride solution. *Ans.* 0.4 *N*.

13-41. A solution contains 2.5 g of $(NH_4)_2SO_4$. How many milliliters of 0.4 *N* $BaCl_2$ solution would be required to react completely with SO_4^{-2} in the original solution? *Ans.* 94.6 ml.

13-42. Calculate the number of milliliters of 0.5 *N* $K_4Fe(CN)_6$ that will be required for complete precipitation of ferric ferrocyanide from a solution containing 1.5 g of ferric chloride. *Ans.* 55.5 ml.

13-43. Calculate the number of milliliters of 0.122 *N* $AgNO_3$ required to precipitate the chloride ion from a sample of rock salt weighing 0.234 g and containing 99.23 per cent of NaCl. *Ans.* 32.5 ml.

13-44. How many milliliters of 0.1 *N* $KMnO_4$ solution would be required to oxidize a solution that contains 0.45 g of $H_2C_2O_4$? *Ans.* 100 ml.

13-45. How many milliliters of 0.2 *N* $K_2Cr_2O_7$ solution would be required to liberate the chlorine from a solution made acid with concentrated sulfuric acid and containing 1.0 g of NaCl? *Ans.* 85.5 ml.

13-46. Calculate the number of grams of $FeSO_4$ that will be oxidized in a solution acidified with sulfuric acid by 25.8 ml of 0.1235 *N* $KMnO_4$.
Ans. 0.484 g.

13-47. Calculate the weight of iodine that will be liberated by the action of 30.5 ml of 0.259 *N* $K_2Cr_2O_7$ with a solution acidified with sulfuric acid and containing an excess of potassium iodide. *Ans.* 1 g.

13-48. (a) Calculate the number of milliliters of hydriodic acid (sp gr 1.343 and containing 36 per cent by weight pure HI) that will react completely with 100 ml of 0.125 *N* $K_2Cr_2O_7$. (b) Calculate the weight of iodine obtained by this reaction. *Ans.* (a) 7.68 ml; (b) 1.585 g.

13-49. Calculate the number of milliliters of 8 *N* HNO_3 that would be necessary to dissolve 10 g of copper turnings. Assume the reduction of NO_3^- to NO.
Ans. 52.5 ml.

13-50. Calculate the number of milliliters of 8 *N* HNO_3 that would be necessary to react completely with 10 g of Ag_2S. Assume the reduction of NO_3^- to NO, and oxidation of S^{-2} to S^0. *Ans.* 13.4 ml.

13-51. (a) Calculate the number of milliliters of 8 *N* HNO_3 that would be necessary to react completely with 10 g of As. (b) Calculate the weight of arsenic acid formed in this reaction. Assume the reduction of NO_3^- to NO.
Ans. (a) 27.8 ml; (b) 18.9 g.

13-52. (a) Calculate the number of milliliters of 12 *N* HCl necessary to react completely with 100 g of potassium permanganate. (b) Calculate the volume of chlorine collected at 25°C and 750 mm Hg by this action.
Ans. (a) 421.6 ml; (b) 39.25 l.

13-53. (a) What volume of hydrogen sulfide gas (STP) is required to precipitate completely the Pb^{+2} from 100 ml of 0.2 *N* $Pb(C_2H_3O_2)_2$? (b) What weight of PbS is produced? *Ans.* (a) 224 ml; (b) 2.39 g.

13-54. What volume of hydrogen sulfide gas (STP) will be required to reduce completely 25.5 ml of 0.1535 *N* $KMnO_4$, which has been acidified with dilute hydrochloric acid? *Ans.* 87.7 ml.

13-55. A solution of ferrous sulfate acidified with sulfuric acid is titrated with $K_2Cr_2O_7$ solution. Calculate the normality of the $K_2Cr_2O_7$ solution if 1 ml of $K_2Cr_2O_7$ is equivalent to 0.01 g of Fe. *Ans.* 0.179 *N*.

13-56. A solution of ferrous sulfate acidified with sulfuric acid is titrated with $KMnO_4$ solution. What is the normality of the $KMnO_4$ solution if 1 ml of $KMnO_4$ is equivalent to 0.005 g of Fe_2O_3? *Ans.* 0.0626 *N*.

13-57. How many milliliters of 0.456 *N* HCl solution should be diluted with water in the preparation of 500 ml of 0.2 *N* HCl?

13-58. A solution of potassium hydroxide was found to be 0.252 *N*. How many milliliters of this solution should be diluted with water to prepare 1 l of 0.1 *N* KOH solution?

13-59. Determine (*a*) the number of milliliters of 15 *N* ammonia solution required in the preparation of 1 l of 3.6 *N* ammonia solution and (*b*) the normality of a sulfuric acid solution made by diluting 50 ml of 36 *N* H_2SO_4 with water to 1 l.

13-60. (*a*) How many milliliters of 16 *N* HNO_3 solution is necessary in the preparation of 5 l of 9 *N* HNO_3 solution? (*b*) What is the normality of a caustic soda solution if 10 ml of 10 *N* NaOH solution is diluted to 500 ml?

13-61. (*a*) If 25 ml of 16 *N* HNO_3 solution is diluted to 100 ml, what is the normality of the dilute solution? (*b*) How many milliliters of 4.5 *M* H_3PO_4 solution is necessary in the preparation of 1 l of 5 *N* H_3PO_4 solution?

13-62. What volume of water is required in the preparation of 250 ml of 0.1 *N* NaOH solution from 5 *N* NaOH solution?

13-63. Determine the volume of water necessary to prepare 5 l of 0.1 *N* HNO_3 solution from 16 *N* HNO_3 solution.

13-64. How much water must be used in the preparation of 250 ml of 5 *N* H_3PO_4 from a 10 *M* H_3PO_4 solution?

13-65. To what volume must 10 ml of 18 *N* H_2SO_4 solution be diluted to prepare a 0.6 *N* H_2SO_4 solution?

13-66. To what volume must 17 ml of 15 *N* NaOH solution be diluted to make a 0.25 *N* NaOH solution?

13-67. Calculate the number of milliliters of water necessary to add to 250 ml of a 1.25 *N* solution in order to make it 0.5 *N*.

13-68. How many milliliters of 0.432 *N* KOH solution is necessary to neutralize 20.0 ml of 0.387 *N* HNO_3 solution?

13-69. What volume of 0.2530 *N* H_2SO_4 solution will exactly neutralize 30.0 ml of 0.137 *N* NaOH solution?

13-70. Calculate the normality of a sodium hydroxide solution 35 ml of which neutralized 46.5 ml of 0.1 *N* HCl solution.

13-71. It was found that to neutralize 25.0 ml of a dilute nitric acid solution, 30.5 ml of 0.125 *N* NaOH solution was required. Calculate the normality of the nitric acid solution.

13-72. It was found that 2.0 ml of a dilute oxalic acid solution required 22.6 ml of 0.255 *N* KOH solution for complete neutralization. Calculate the normality of the oxalic acid solution.

13-73. What volume of 0.5 *M* $Ba(OH)_2$ solution will react completely with 5 ml of 6 *N* H_3PO_4 solution?

13-74. Determine the volume of 0.6 *M* H_3PO_4 solution required to react completely with 10.5 ml of 0.6 *M* $Ba(OH)_2$ solution.

13-75. Calculate the number of grams of NaCl necessary for complete precipitation of Ag^+ from 20.5 ml of 0.2 N $AgNO_3$ solution.

13-76. Calculate the weight of AgCl precipitated when 20.0 ml of 2.5 N HCl solution is added to excess $AgC_2H_3O_2$ solution.

13-77. How many milliliters of 0.2 N HCl will be required to precipitate completely the Ag^+ from 25.0 ml of 0.25 N $AgNO_3$ solution?

13-78. Calculate the number of milliliters of 0.5 N H_2SO_4 that will react completely with 20 ml of sodium carbonate solution (sp gr 1.15 and 14.2 per cent by weight pure Na_2CO_3).

13-79. How many milliliters of 0.2 N H_2SO_4 is required to neutralize 25.0 ml of a solution known to contain 25.0 ml of KOH solution (sp gr 1.34 and 35 per cent by weight pure KOH) per liter?

13-80. Calculate the number of milliliters of 0.108 N NaOH solution required to neutralize 25.0 ml of a solution known to contain 20.0 ml of sulfuric acid (sp gr 1.84 and 93.2 per cent by weight pure H_2SO_4) per liter.

13-81. How many milliliters of 6 N HCl solution will react completely with a solution containing 1.60 g of pure Na_2CO_3?

13-82. What volume of 0.25 N HNO_3 solution will react completely with 1.0 g of limestone (97.5 per cent pure $CaCO_3$)?

13-83. What volume of 1.25 N HNO_3 solution will react completely with 1.0 g of hydrated lime [$Ca(OH)_2$] containing 70 per cent pure CaO?

13-84. In standardizing a hydrochloric acid solution, it was found that 25.8 ml was required for complete reaction with a solution containing 1.2588 g of Na_2CO_3. Calculate the normality of this hydrochloric acid solution.

13-85. In standardizing a sodium hydroxide solution with pure benzoic acid, C_6H_5COOH (equivalent weight, 122) it was found that 28.9 ml of alkali was required for complete neutralization of a solution containing 1.0043 g of benzoic acid. Calculate the normality of the sodium hydroxide solution.

13-86. In standardizing a sulfuric acid solution with pure sodium carbonate, it was found that 27.3 ml of sulfuric acid was required for complete reaction with 0.1312 g of Na_2CO_3. Calculate the normality of the sulfuric acid solution.

13-87. A sulfuric acid solution contains 0.2198 g-eq wt of H_2SO_4 per liter. Calculate the number of milliliters of N NaOH necessary for the complete neutralization of 20.0 ml of the acid.

13-88. A nitric acid solution contains 0.1878 g-eq wt of HNO_3 per 500 ml. Calculate the number of milliliters of 0.2 N KOH necessary for complete neutralization of 10 ml of the acid.

13-89. A potassium hydroxide solution contains 0.1237 g-eq wt of KOH per 500 ml. Calculate the number of milliliters of 0.5 N H_2SO_4 that will be required for complete neutralization of 25 ml of the base.

13-90. A sodium hydroxide solution contains 0.2456 g-eq wt of NaOH per liter. Calculate the number of milliliters of 6 N $HC_2H_3O_2$ that will be required for complete neutralization of 10 ml of the base.

13-91. A barium chloride solution contains 0.1782 g-eq wt of $BaCl_2$ per liter. Calculate the number of milliliters of 0.5 N $(NH_4)_2SO_4$ that will be required for complete precipitation of the Ba^{+2} ion in 10 ml of the barium chloride solution.

13-92. (a) What volume of hydrogen sulfide gas, at STP, is required to precipitate completely the HgS from 75 ml of 0.1 N HgCl₂ solution? (b) What weight of HgS is produced?

13-93. Excess carbon dioxide is bubbled through 100 ml of 0.1 N Ba(OH)₂ solution. Calculate the weight of BaCO₃ that is precipitated.

13-94. Excess (NH₄)₂CO₃ was added to 50.0 ml of a barium acetate solution, forming a precipitate of BaCO₃ which was found to weigh 1.234 g. Calculate the normality of the barium acetate solution.

13-95. Excess K₂S was added to 75.0 ml of a hydrochloric acid solution, thereby generating 2 l of hydrogen sulfide at STP. Calculate the normality of the hydrochloric acid solution.

13-96. When excess sodium chloride was added to 75.0 ml of silver nitrate solution, it was found that 0.429 g of AgCl was precipitated. What is the normality of silver nitrate solution?

13-97. If 6 ml of 0.5 N ammonia solution is added to 14 ml of 0.3 N H₂SO₄, (a) will the final solution have an acid or basic reaction? (b) Determine the normality of the final solution with respect to this acid or base.

13-98. If 6 ml of 0.3 N H₂SO₄ is mixed with 4 ml of 0.5 N KOH, (1) is the final solution acidic or basic? (2) What is the normality with respect to (a) the acidic or basic final solution and (b) the salt formed by this neutralization?

13-99. If 10.5 ml of 0.525 N NaCl is added to 13.5 ml of 0.425 N AgNO₃, (a) which substance is in excess? (b) How many milligrams of the excess substance in solution remains unused? (c) How many grams of AgCl is precipitated?

13-100. If 60 ml of 1.25 N Na₂CO₃ solution is reacted with 50 ml of 1.75 N H₂SO₄, (a) which substance is in excess? (b) How many milligrams of the excess substance in solution remains unused? (c) How many milliliters at STP of CO₂ will be formed in this reaction?

CHAPTER XIV

COMBINATION OF GASES

OUTLINE

Further extension of law of volumes and law of Avogadro dealing with volume-volume relations in various reactions between gases.

Combustion reactions.

Gas analysis: (a) absorption method; (b) slow-combustion method. The composition of a fuel gas can be determined by a combination of the two methods. The preliminary absorption measurements of such constituents as carbon dioxide, illuminants (unsaturated hydrocarbon), oxygen is followed by oxidation of hydrogen and carbon monoxide in the "copper oxide tube." The remaining constituents, principally methane and ethane, are determined by slow-combustion method.

COMBINATION OF GASES

The fundamental law of volumes (Gay-Lussac) and law of Avogadro were given preliminary consideration in Chap. VII. It is the purpose of this chapter to extend further these important principles by dealing with volume-volume relations in various reactions between gases and then dealing with the fundamentals of gas analysis.

It is well to be reminded of the volume-volume relationship which is expressed by the balanced chemical equation representing a given gaseous reaction. Thus, in the burning of 10 l of acetylene (C_2H_2) with oxygen:

$2C_2H_2$	$+ 5O_2$	$\rightarrow 4CO_2$	$+ 2H_2O$	
2 moles	5 moles	4 moles	2 moles	*mole relationship*
2 vol	5 vol	4 vol	2 vol	*volume relationship*

It is advisable to express the volume of the gas undergoing combustion in terms of unit volume. Then

1 vol	2½ vol	2 vol	1 vol	
10 l	10 × 2½ l	10 × 2 l	10 l	*liter relationship*

or

10 l	25 l	20 l	10 l	

From the foregoing one observes that, for the combustion of 1 l of C_2H_2, 2½ l of oxygen will be required. For the burning of 10 l of C_2H_2 there will be 25 l of oxygen necessary for complete combustion, and 20 l of

203

CO_2 and 10 l of water vapor will be formed. It should also be noted there is a change in the theoretical initial volume of 35 l to theoretical final volume of 30 l, or a contraction of 5 l.

It should be mentioned that in solving problems involving gases, the volumes of all gases in a given reaction must be measured at *same temperature and pressure.*

Example 1. If 30 l of nitrogen and 30 l of hydrogen react to form ammonia, which gas is in excess and by what amount? What is the final volume composition of residual gas?

$$\begin{matrix} 30\ l & 30\ l & \\ N_2 & +\ 3H_2 & \to 2NH_3 \\ 1\ vol & 3\ vol & 2\ vol \end{matrix}$$

From the equation, 1 volume of N_2 requires 3 volumes of H_2, or 1 volume of H_2 requires $\frac{1}{3}$ volume of N_2 for complete reaction. Since 30 l of each gas is available, there will be an excess of nitrogen, as only 10 l of N_2 will react with 30 l of H_2. Thus

Reaction: N_2 + $3H_2$ $\to$ $2NH_3$ Volume relation: 1 vol 3 vol 2 vol	N_2, liters	H_2, liters	NH_3, liters
Initial volumes...........................	30	30	
Reacting volumes + product volume........	10	30	20
Excess (unused) volume...................	20	0	
Final volume composition.................	20	0	20

Example 2. (*a*) Find the volume of air necessary for complete combustion of 25 cu ft of acetylene (C_2H_2). (*b*) What is the final volume composition of residual, assuming H_2O to remain in the vapor phase? The composition by volume of air, neglecting the gases present in small amounts, CO_2, moisture, argon, etc., is oxygen = 20.8 per

Reaction: $2C_2H_2$ + $5O_2$ $\to$ $4CO_2$ + $2H_2O$ Volume relation: 2 vol 5 vol 4 vol 2 vol or 1 vol $2\frac{1}{2}$ vol 2 vol 1 vol	C_2H_2, cu ft	O_2, cu ft	CO_2, cu ft	H_2O, cu ft	Air, cu ft	N_2, cu ft
Initial volume........................	25					
Reacting volumes + product volumes.............	25	$62\frac{1}{2}$	50	25		
Volume of air required for combustion = $62\frac{1}{2}$ cu ft						
$O_2 \times 4.8$ cu ft air/cu ft O_2......................	..	....	..	..	300	
Volume of nitrogen (300 cu ft − $62\frac{1}{2}$ cu ft).........	..	....	..	..	...	$237\frac{1}{2}$
Final volume composition.......................	0	0	50	25	...	$237\frac{1}{2}$

cent by volume and nitrogen = 79.2 per cent by volume. That is, 100 cu ft air contains 20.8 cu ft O_2 and 79.2 cu ft N_2. The ratio is

$$100 \text{ cu ft air} : 20.8 \text{ cu ft } O_2 = 4.8 \text{ cu ft air} : 1 \text{ cu ft } O_2$$

or 1 cu ft O_2 is contained in 4.8 cu ft air.

Example 3. (a) In burning 200 lb of anthracite coal (93.5 per cent C) with 10 per cent of excess air, what volume (STP) of CO_2 will be produced? (b) What volume of air is used in the combustion? (c) What is the final residual volume?

(a) Since 200 lb coal × 0.935 lb C/lb coal = 187 lb C,

$$\frac{187 \text{ lb C}}{12 \text{ lb C/lb-mole}} = 15.6 \text{ lb-moles}$$

C	+	O_2	→	CO_2	
1 lb-mole		1 lb-mole		1 lb-mole	*lb-mole relation*
1 lb-mole		358 cu ft/lb-mole		358 cu ft/lb-mole	*lb-mole-vol relation*
15.6 lb-moles		15.6 × 358 cu ft		15.6 × 358 cu ft	
15.6 lb-moles		5,585 cu ft		5,585 cu ft	

Then 5,585 cu ft CO_2 will be produced by the burning of 200 lb coal, 93.5 per cent C.

(b) It is noted that 5,585 cu ft of O_2 is needed for combustion. Since 1 cu ft O_2 is contained in 4.8 cu ft air, 5,585 cu ft O_2 is contained in 5,585 × 4.8 cu ft air = 27,808 cu ft air.

Actual volume of air required for combustion......... 27,808 cu ft
10 per cent excess air = 0.1 × 27,808 cu ft........... 2,781 cu ft
Total volume air used......................... 30,589 cu ft

(c) Since nitrogen does not enter into the combustion reaction it will remain unused.

Actual volume air required for combustion = 27,808 cu ft
Volume of N_2 unused = 79.2 per cent of 27,808 cu ft air

0.792 cu ft N_2/cu ft air × 27,808 cu ft air............ 22,024 cu ft
Volume of 10 per cent excess air (unused)............ 2,781 cu ft
Volume of CO_2 produced........................... 5,585 cu ft
Final volume (residual)............................ 30,390 cu ft

GAS ANALYSIS

In this section on gas analysis two general methods will be considered. They are generally called (1) the selective **absorption method** and (2) the **slow-combustion method**.

Absorption Methods of Gas Analysis. The absorption method is employed to determine the proportional amounts of the components in a mixture of gases. The general practice is to treat the mixture of gases with different absorbing reagents or absorbents, maintaining a constant temperature and pressure during the entire analysis. The difference in volume of the gas before and after treatment with an absorbent gives the actual volume of the gas absorbed. If the original volume of the sample of gas is 100.0 ml, obviously the amounts absorbed would be directly expressible on a percentage-by-volume basis. If the original volume is less than 100.0 ml, it is a simple mathematical process to convert each amount into terms of percentage by volume.

Table XV giving the absorbing reagents and the gases that each reagent will absorb is shown herewith.

TABLE XV. ABSORBENTS FOR GASES

Absorbing Reagents	Gases Absorbed
Strong caustic potash (KOH)......................	{ Carbon dioxide { Sulfur dioxide
Fuming sulfuric acid..............................	Illuminants (unsaturated hydrocarbons)
Yellow phosphorus Alkaline pyrogallol solution [trihydroxy benzene, $C_6H_3(OH)_3$]	} Oxygen
Ammoniacal cuprous chloride......................	Carbon monoxide
Palladous chloride solution.......................	Hydrogen
Anhydrous cupric sulfate..........................	Hydrogen sulfide
Ascarite (sodium hydroxide-asbestos)..............	Carbon dioxide
Dehydrite $[Mg(ClO_4)_2.3H_2O]$ Anhydrone $[Mg(ClO_4)_2]$ Drierite $(CaSO_4)$ Anhydrous calcium chloride	} Water vapor

It should be mentioned that in ordinary gas analysis, where results are expressed on a per cent by volume basis, only relative values are sought. Then if temperature, pressure, and water-vapor content of the gas are maintained constant during the analysis, the results obtained are comparable to the results of any other gas analysis made under the same conditions, and corrections to standard conditions of temperature and pressure are unnecessary for purposes of comparison.

Also, gas volumes are measured in a burette over a confining liquid— water, aqueous sodium sulfate solution, or mercury. It should be noted that the solubility of gases in water varies with the given gas, its partial pressure in the gas mixture, the pressure of the gas above the liquid, and the temperature of the liquid. If the gas is measured over ordinary water, large errors in analysis, due to solubility, would be expected. To avoid these errors, the water should be saturated with the gas by bubbling it through the water for a long period of time before any analysis is undertaken. The solubility of gases may be further decreased by using an aqueous solution of sodium sulfate (20 per cent Na_2SO_4 by weight) and 5 per cent sulfuric acid by volume, with methyl orange as an indicator to note any change in the acidity of the solution. This salt solution should also be saturated with the gas in question prior to analysis.

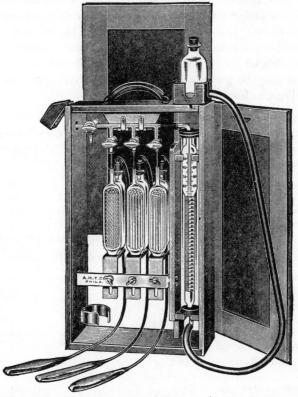

FIG. 9. Orsat portable gas-analysis apparatus. (*Arthur H. Thomas Co.*)

If the gas is measured over mercury, the errors due to solubility are eliminated. Errors due to the pressure of water vapor when mercury is used are compensated for by saturating the original sample with water vapor in the burette.

For detailed explanation of gas analysis, it is well to refer to standard textbooks on this subject.

For the determination of CO, O_2, and CO_2 in flue or furnace gases, a portable gas-analysis apparatus, known as an Orsat apparatus (Fig. 9), is used. It consists essentially of a 100-ml measuring burette with water jacket, aspirator bottle, and three absorption pipettes. A

100-ml sample is usually taken for analysis. The CO_2 is first removed by absorption in a KOH pipette and residual volume measured; the decrease in volume gives the percentage of CO_2 in the sample. The oxygen in the sample is next absorbed in a pipette containing alkaline pyrogallol solution, and the decrease in volume is measured, which gives the percentage of O_2 in the sample. The CO is then absorbed in a pipette containing ammoniacal cuprous chloride and the decrease in volume measured; this gives percentage CO in the sample. A typical flue gas under favorable operating conditions will contain 12 to 14 per cent CO_2, about 8 per cent O_2, and 0.5 or less per cent CO. The other gases that may be present in a flue gas are hydrogen, water vapor, hydrocarbons, sulfur compounds, and dust.

Example. A sample of a gaseous mixture analyzed by absorption methods for CO_2, illuminants, O_2, CO, and N_2, each measurement made under the same conditions of temperature and pressure, gave the following data:

Volume of sample taken	70.5 ml
Volume after treatment with caustic potash	66.5 ml
Volume after treatment with fuming sulfuric acid	61.5 ml
Volume after treatment with alkaline pyrogallol	61.0 ml
Volume after treatment with ammoniacal cuprous chloride	51.8 ml

Calculate the percentage of each component in the gaseous mixture.

Initial volume (CO_2, illuminants, O_2, CO, N_2)	70.5 ml
Residual volume (1) after KOH absorption	66.5 ml
Volume of CO_2	4.0 ml
Residual volume (1)	66.5 ml
Residual volume (2) after fuming H_2SO_4	61.5 ml
Volume of illuminants	5.0 ml
Residual volume (2)	61.5 ml
Residual volume (3) after pyrogallol	61.0 ml
Volume of O_2	0.5 ml
Residual volume (3)	61.0 ml
Residual volume (4) after cuprous chloride	51.8 ml
Volume of CO	9.2 ml
Residual volume (4) = volume of N_2	51.8 ml

To express each of these volumes on a percentage basis:

70.5 ml of gaseous mixture contains 4.0 ml of CO_2

1.0 ml of gaseous mixture contains $\dfrac{1}{70.5} \times 4.0$ ml of CO_2

100.0 ml of gaseous mixture contains $100 \times \dfrac{1}{70.5} \times 4.0$ ml = 5.67 ml of CO_2

5.67 ml in 100 ml = 5.67 per cent of CO_2

Similarly

$100.0 \times \dfrac{5.0}{70.5}$ ml = 7.09 ml = 7.09 per cent of illuminants

$100.0 \times \dfrac{0.5}{70.5}$ ml = 0.70 ml = 0.70 per cent of O_2

$100.0 \times \dfrac{9.2}{70.5}$ ml = 13.04 ml = 13.04 per cent of CO

$100.0 \times \dfrac{51.8}{70.5}$ ml = 73.47 ml = 73.47 per cent of N_2

The Slow-combustion Method of Gas Analysis. The slow-combustion method is employed in gas analysis when a gas mixture contains components that are combustible and particularly when it contains several hydrocarbons. The analytical procedure is to introduce a known and sufficient volume of oxygen into what is called a "slow-combustion pipette" (see Fig. 10) and then, by an electrically heated filament inside the pipette, cause a slow burning of the combustible gas by slowly and gradually transferring a known volume of the gas to the pipette while keeping the wire hot. After the reaction has gone to completion, the products of combustion are allowed to cool, and their volume is measured. The contraction in volume, as a result of the slow combustion, is noted. The volume of CO_2 obtained from the reaction and the volume of excess oxygen are measured by the absorption method. The percentage by volume of each gas is then determined by calculations that will be illustrated by an example later on in this chapter.

When a sample of illuminating gas is to be analyzed, both absorption and slow-combustion methods are employed. It is the usual practice first to pass the gas through each of the various absorption pipettes to remove, respectively, CO_2, illuminants (unsaturated compounds), and O_2. After each successive treatment, the contraction in volume is measured and noted. The newer type of gas-analysis apparatus (Fig. 10) also employs copper oxide in a U tube, which might be called an "oxidation tube," for the purpose of oxidizing CO and H_2 simultaneously. After the preliminary absorption measurements, the residual gas is passed over heated copper oxide (290°C to 310°C) in the U tube. The CO is oxidized to CO_2, and H_2 to H_2O. The contraction in volume observed is due to the oxidation of hydro-

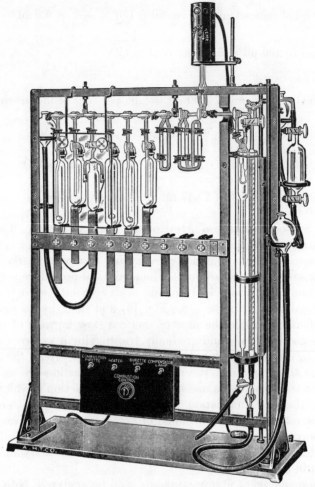

Fig. 10. Gas-analysis apparatus, Shepherd Volumetric. (*Arthur H. Thomas Co.*)

gen to water, and the contraction is equal to the volume of hydrogen in the sample.[1]

[1] Suppose 1 ml CO and 1 ml O_2 is oxidized in copper oxide tube.

$$2CO + O_2 = 2CO_2$$
1 ml   0.5 ml   1 ml
$$2H_2 + O_2 = 2H_2O$$
1 ml   0.5 ml   1 ml

Upon cooling, 1 ml H_2O condenses to liquid water whose volume is negligible. Then 2 ml (CO + H_2) contracts to 1 ml (equal to volume of CO_2) which equals the volume of hydrogen in the original mixture of 2 ml (CO + H_2).

The amount of CO is found by absorbing the CO_2 obtained from the oxidation of CO by the copper oxide in the caustic-potash pipette. This contraction in volume is measured and noted. To determine the volume of saturated hydrocarbons (CH_4, C_2H_6) after the removal of the components just mentioned, a known volume of oxygen is transferred to the slow-combustion pipette. Then a known volume of the residual gas is gradually admitted into this pipette. When the two gases, together, come in contact with the electrically heated filament, a slow burning process ensues and is carried to completion with the complete mixing of the residual gas with the oxygen. After the reaction has cooled to approximately room temperature, the total contraction due to the combustion is determined. The volume of CO_2, formed in the burning process, is obtained by transferring the residual gas to the caustic-potash pipette and measuring the contraction after this absorption has taken place. This is followed by calculations of the volumes of each of the combustible components, which involve considerations of (a) the total number and volume of the combustible components, (b) the total contraction after burning, and (c) the total volume of CO_2 formed by the combustion.

The components of a gas mixture are usually removed in the following order: CO_2 illuminants, O_2, H_2, CO, CH_4, and C_2H_6.

Example 2. A mixture of gases consists of CO, CH_4, and C_2H_2. A sample of this gas mixture, measuring 50.0 ml, was transferred to a combustion pipette, 150.0 ml of oxygen added, and the mixture burned. This is more than enough oxygen for complete combustion of the 50.0 ml of gas. The gases, after combustion, were allowed to cool, this causing condensation of the water vapor. The volume after cooling measured 122.5 ml. This residual gas was next transferred to the caustic-potash pipette; after absorption of CO_2, the volume measured 57.5 ml. (a) From these data calculate the number of milliliters of each of the gases, CO, CH_4, and C_2H_2, in 50.0 ml of the original sample. (b) How much oxygen was consumed by the combustion of these gases? (c) How much oxygen remained unused?

(a) The number of milliliters are calculated as follows:

Volume of sample (CO, CH_4, C_2H_2)	50.0 ml
Volume of oxygen added	150.0 ml
Total volume of mixture	200.0 ml
Residual volume after combustion (with cooling)	122.5 ml
Volume contraction due to combustion	77.5 ml
Residual volume	122.5 ml
Residual volume after KOH absorption	57.5 ml
Volume of CO_2 produced by combustion	65.0 ml

Let x = number of milliliters of CO
y = number of milliliters of CH_4
z = number of milliliters of C_2H_2

Combustion reactions	V_i	V_{bc}	V_{ac}*	$V_{bc} - V_{ac}$	V_{CO_2}	V_{O_2} used
CO $+ \frac{1}{2}O_2 = CO_2$						
$x \quad + \frac{1}{2}x \quad = x$	x	$\frac{3}{2}x$	x	$\frac{1}{2}x$	x	$\frac{1}{2}x$
$CH_4 + 2O_2 \quad = CO_2 + 2H_2O$						
$y \quad + 2y \quad = y \quad + 2y$	y	$3y$	y	$2y$	y	$2y$
$C_2H_2 + \frac{5}{2}O_2 = 2CO_2 + H_2O$						
$z \quad + \frac{5}{2}z = 2z \quad + z$	z	$\frac{7}{2}z$	$2z$	$\frac{3}{2}z$	$2z$	$\frac{5}{2}z$
Total volume (ml).............	50	...	..	77.5	65.0	

V_i = initial volume.
V_{bc} = volume before combustion.
V_{ac} = volume after combustion.
$V_{bc} - V_{ac}$ = volume contraction after burning and cooling.

* When products of combustion are cooled, the water vapor formed condenses and volume of liquid water obtained is negligible. This volume of water is neglected in determining the final volume.

From the foregoing table, the total contraction due to combustion is $\frac{1}{2}x + 2y + \frac{3}{2}z$ and this measures 77.5 ml. Also, the total volume of CO_2 produced by the combustion is $x + y + 2z$, and this measures 65.0 ml.

To find the volume of each component in the original sample, which contains three unknowns, requires solving three simultaneous equations in x, y, and z. Thus

(1) $\qquad\qquad\qquad x + y + z = 50.0$ ml
(2) $\qquad\qquad\qquad \frac{1}{2}x + 2y + \frac{3}{2}z = 77.5$ ml
or
$\qquad\qquad\qquad\qquad x + 4y + 3z = 155.0$ ml
(3) $\qquad\qquad\qquad x + y + 2z = 65.0$ ml

Solving these simultaneous equations,

$$
\begin{array}{r}
x + y + 2z = 65.0 \text{ ml} \\
x + y + z = 50.0 \text{ ml} \\
\hline
z = 15.0 \text{ ml}
\end{array}
$$

$$
\begin{array}{r}
x + 4y + 3z = 155.0 \text{ ml} \\
x + y + 2z = 65.0 \text{ ml} \\
\hline
3y + z = 90.0 \text{ ml} \\
z = 15.0 \text{ ml} \\
\hline
3y = 75.0 \text{ ml} \\
y = 25.0 \text{ ml}
\end{array}
$$

$$x + y + z = 50.0 \text{ ml}$$
$$x + 25.0 \text{ ml} + 15.0 \text{ ml} = 50.0 \text{ ml}$$
$$x = 10.0 \text{ ml}$$

$$x = 10.0 \text{ ml of CO}$$
$$y = 25.0 \text{ ml of CH}_4$$
$$z = 15.0 \text{ ml of C}_2\text{H}_2$$
$$\overline{50.0 \text{ ml of original mixture}}$$

(b) From the foregoing table, the total volume of O_2 required for complete combustion was $\frac{1}{2}x + 2y + \frac{5}{2}z$. Since $x = 10.0$ ml, $y = 25.0$ ml, $z = 15.0$ ml, by substituting these values in $\frac{1}{2}x + 2y + \frac{5}{2}z$, one obtains 5 ml + 50 ml + 37.5 ml = 92.5 ml of O_2 consumed by the combustion.

(c) The amount of oxygen that remained unused is given in the following data:

Volume of O_2 added to original sample................. 150.0 ml
Volume of O_2 consumed by combustion................. 92.5 ml
Volume of O_2 remained unused....................... 57.5 ml

Example 3.   Given a mixture of CH_4, CO, and N_2, calculate the volume composition from the following data:

Volume of mixture taken............................. 60.0 ml
Volume of O_2 added................................. 42.0 ml
Residual volume after combustion (without cooling)...... 96.0 ml
Residual volume after removal of water vapor by $CaCl_2$... 66.0 ml
Residual volume after KOH........................... 39.0 ml

Solution

Volume of sample (CH_4, CO, N_2)..................... 60.0 ml
Volume of O_2 added................................. 42.0 ml
Total volume of mixture.............................. 102.0 ml
Residual volume after combustion (without cooling)..... 96.0 ml
Volume contraction due to combustion................. 6.0 ml

Residual volume...................................... 96.0 ml
Residual volume after $CaCl_2$......................... 66.0 ml
Volume of water vapor produced by combustion......... 30.0 ml

Residual volume...................................... 66.0 ml
Residual volume after KOH........................... 39.0 ml
Volume of CO_2 produced by combustion................ 27.0 ml

Let x = number of milliliters of CH_4
y = number of milliliters of CO
z = number of milliliters of N_2

Combustion reactions	V_i	V_{bc}	V_{ac}	$V_{bc} - V_{ac}$	V_{CO_2}	V_{H_2O}	V_{O_2}
$CH_4 + 2O_2 = CO_2 + 2H_2O$							
$x\ \ \ + 2x\ \ = x\ \ \ + 2x$	x	$3x$	$3x$	0	x	$2x$	$2x$
$CO\ + \frac{1}{2}O_2 = CO_2$							
$y\ \ + \frac{1}{2}y\ = y$	y	$\frac{3}{2}y$	y	$\frac{1}{2}y$	y		$\frac{1}{2}y$
$N_2\ + O_2\ \ = $ no reaction	z						
Total volume (ml)..........	60	...	..	6.0	27.0	30.0	

From the foregoing table, the total contraction due to combustion is $\frac{1}{2}y$ and this measures 6.0 ml.

Also, the total volume of CO_2 produced is $x + y$, which measures 27.0 ml, and the volume of water vapor produced is $2x$, which measures 30.0 ml.

To find the volume of each constituent in the original sample, the following equations are available:

(1) $\qquad\qquad x + y + z = 60.0$ ml
(2) $\qquad\qquad\qquad \frac{1}{2}y = 6.0$ ml
(3) $\qquad\qquad\qquad x + y = 27.0$ ml
(4) $\qquad\qquad\qquad\quad 2x = 30.0$ ml

Solving these equations gives the following values:

$$x = 15.0 \text{ ml of } CH_4$$
$$y = 12.0 \text{ ml of } CO$$
$$z = 33.0 \text{ ml of } N_2$$

Example 4. A sample of carbureted water gas was analyzed employing both absorption and slow-combustion methods. From the corresponding data, find the percentage of each constituent determined in the following order: CO_2, illuminants, O_2, H_2, CO, CH_4, C_2H_6, N_2.

Volume of sample taken.............................	100.0 ml
Volume after KOH....................................	97.0 ml
Volume after fuming sulfuric acid......................	87.0 ml
Volume after alkaline pyrogallol.......................	86.4 ml
Volume after copper oxide.............................	51.9 ml
Volume after KOH (residual gas)......................	19.4 ml

A volume of *residual gas* (*i.e.*, a sample of the 19.4 ml) measuring 10.0 ml was burned with 88.0 ml of oxygen.

Volume after combustion (with cooling)................	84.5 ml
Volume after KOH....................................	76.7 ml

Solution

Volume of sample.....................................	100.0 ml
Residual volume (1) after KOH........................	97.0 ml
Volume of CO_2.....................................	3.0 ml
	= 3.0 per cent CO_2

Residual volume (1)...................................	97.0 ml
Residual volume (2) after fuming sulfuric acid.........	87.0 ml
Volume of illuminants................................	10.0 ml
	= 10.0 per cent illuminants

Residual volume (2)...................................	87.0 ml
Residual volume (3) after alkaline pyrogallol............	86.4 ml
Volume of O_2......................................	0.6 ml
	= 0.6 per cent O_2

Residual volume (3)...................................	86.4 ml
Residual volume (4) after copper oxide.................	51.9 ml
Volume of H_2......................................	34.5 ml
	= 34.5 per cent H_2

Residual volume (4)...................................	51.9 ml
Residual volume (5) after KOH........................	19.4 ml
Volume of CO..	32.5 ml
	= 32.5 per cent CO

Let x = number of milliliters of CH_4

y = number of milliliters of C_2H_6

z = number of milliliters of N_2

Volume of residual (5) gas taken......................	10.0 ml
Volume of O_2 added...............................	88.0 ml
Total volume of mixture..............................	98.0 ml
Residual volume (6) after burning.....................	84.5 ml
Volume contraction due to burning....................	13.5 ml

Residual volume (6)...................................	84.5 ml
Residual volume after KOH...........................	76.7 ml
Volume of CO_2 produced in burning process.............	7.8 ml

Combustion reactions	V_i	V_{bc}	V_{ac}	$V_{bc} - V_{ac}$	V_{CO_2}
$CH_4 + 2O_2 = CO_2 + 2H_2O$					
$x \quad + 2x \quad = x \quad + 2x$	x	$3x$	x	$2x$	x
$C_2H_6 + \frac{7}{2}O_2 = 2CO_2 + 3H_2O$					
$y \quad + \frac{7}{2}y = 2y \quad + 3y$	y	$\frac{9}{2}y$	$2y$	$\frac{5}{2}y$	$2y$
$N_2 \quad + O_2 \quad = $ no reaction	z				
Total volume (ml).....................	10	...	..	13.5	7.8

Setup of equations:

(1) $$x + y + z = 10.0 \text{ ml}$$
(2) $$2x + \tfrac{5}{2}y = 13.5 \text{ ml}$$

or

$$4x + 5y = 27.0 \text{ ml}$$
(3) $$x + 2y = 7.8 \text{ ml}$$

Solving

$$4x + 8y = 31.2 \text{ ml}$$
$$\underline{4x + 5y = 27.0 \text{ ml}}$$
$$3y = 4.2 \text{ ml}$$
$$y = 1.4 \text{ ml}$$

$$x + 2y = 7.8 \text{ ml}$$
$$\underline{2y = 2.8 \text{ ml}}$$
$$x = 5.0 \text{ ml}$$

$$x + y + z = 10 \text{ ml}$$
$$5 \text{ ml} + 1.4 \text{ ml} + z = 10 \text{ ml}$$
$$z = 3.6 \text{ ml}$$

Then 10 ml of residual volume (5) contains 5.0 ml of CH_4, 1.4 ml of C_2H_6, and 3.6 ml of N_2. To express these volumes on a percentage basis, it is only necessary to compute the volume of each gas contained in 19.4 ml of the residual volume (5), since this volume is on a basis of 100 ml of sample. Then

10.0 ml of residual volume (5) contains 5.0 ml CH_4

19.4 ml of residual volume (5) will contain $19.4 \times \dfrac{5.0}{10.0}$ ml

CH_4 = 9.7 ml CH_4 = 9.7 per cent CH_4

10.0 ml of residual volume (5) contains 1.4 ml C_2H_6

19.4 ml of residual volume (5) will contain $19.4 \times \dfrac{1.4}{10.0}$ ml

C_2H_6 = 2.7 ml C_2H_6 = 2.7 per cent C_2H_6

10.0 ml of residual volume (5) contains 3.6 ml N_2

19.4 ml of residual volume (5) will contain $19.4 \times \dfrac{3.6}{10.0}$ ml

N_2 = 7.0 ml N_2 = 7.0 per cent N_2

To check the results, one needs only to add the percentages of all constituents, which should total 100 per cent.

Problems

In solving problems involving reactions between gases, the volumes of all gases must be measured at same temperature and pressure.

14-1. (a) What volume (liters at STP) of air is necessary for complete combustion of 20 l of methane (CH_4)? (b) What volume (liters at STP) of CO_2 is formed by this combustion? *Ans.* (a) 192 l; (b) 20 l.

14-2. (a) Determine the volume (cubic feet at STP) of air required for complete combustion of 200 cu ft of acetylene (C_2H_2). (b) What volume (cubic feet at STP) of CO_2 is produced by this reaction? *Ans.* (a) 2,400 cu ft; (b) 400 cu ft.

14-3. (a) Find the volume (cubic meters at STP) of air required for complete combustion of 1,000 cu m of carbon monoxide. (b) What volume (cubic meters at STP) of CO_2 is produced by this combustion? (c) What is the volume composition of the residual gas? *Ans.* (a) 2,400 cu m air; (b) 1,000 cu m CO_2; (c) 1,900 cu m N_2; 1,000 cu m CO_2.

14-4. (a) What volume (cubic feet at STP) of air is necessary for complete combustion of 1 ton of coke (98 per cent pure C)? (b) What volume (cubic feet at STP) of CO_2 is produced by this reaction? (c) What is the volume composition of the residual gases? *Ans.* (a) 280,615 cu ft air; (b) 58,461 cu ft CO_2; (c) 222,154 cu ft N_2; 58,461 cu ft CO_2.

14-5. (a) If 10 ml of oxygen and 30 ml of nitric oxide reacted to form nitrogen dioxide (gas), what would be the volume composition of residual gas? (b) If the nitrogen dioxide formed in (a) was dissolved in water, what would be the volume composition of the residual gas? *Ans.* (a) 10 ml NO; 20 ml NO_2.

14-6. (a) A mixture of 15 cu ft of C_2H_4 and 15 cu ft of oxygen was burned. What is the volume composition of cooled residual gas? (b) If 15 cu ft of C_2H_4 and 15 cu ft of air was burned, what would be the volume composition of the cooled residual gas? *Ans.* (a) 10 cu ft CO_2; 10 cu ft C_2H_4; (b) 14 cu ft C_2H_4; 11.9 cu ft N_2; 2.1 cu ft CO_2.

14-7. Calculate the volume (cubic feet at STP) of air necessary for the complete combustion of 1,000 cu ft of water gas which has the following composition by volume: 1.4 per cent methane, 45.7 per cent carbon monoxide, 46.2 per cent hydrogen, 4.0 per cent nitrogen, 2.4 per cent carbon dioxide. *Ans.* 2,340 cu ft.

14-8. Calculate the volume (cubic feet at STP) of air required for the complete combustion of 500 cu ft of coal gas that has the following composition: 49.0 per cent hydrogen, 34.8 per cent methane, 4.2 per cent ethylene (C_2H_4), 6.0 per cent carbon monoxide, 4.0 per cent nitrogen, 1 per cent carbon dioxide. *Ans.* 2,636 cu ft.

14-9. How many cubic feet (STP) of carbon dioxide is produced in the burning of 1,000 cu ft of coal gas that has the following analysis: 36.8 per cent methane, 47.2 per cent hydrogen, 7.0 per cent carbon monoxide. 4.8 per cent ethylene (C_2H_4), 4.0 per cent nitrogen? *Ans.* 534 cu ft.

14-10. A sample of a gaseous mixture, measuring 100 ml and containing 40 per cent hydrogen, 10 per cent ethane (C_2H_6), 20 per cent methane, 30 per cent carbon monoxide, was mixed with 150 ml of oxygen in a combustion pipette, and the mixture ignited.   Calculate the volume of each of the products of combustion.   *Ans.* 110 ml H_2O; 70 ml CO_2.

14-11. A sample of a gaseous mixture containing CO_2, C_2H_4, O_2, CO, and N_2, measuring 100 ml, analyzed by the absorption method gave the following data:

Volume after treatment with KOH............................. 93.4 ml
Volume after treatment with fuming H_2SO_4................... 90.2 ml
Volume after treatment with alkaline pyrogallol.............. 88.3 ml
Volume after treatment with ammoniacal Cu_2Cl_2.............. 87.8 ml

Calculate the percentage of CO_2, C_2H_4, O_2, CO, and N_2 in the original mixture.

Ans.   6.6 per cent CO_2; 3.2 per cent C_2H_4; 1.9 per cent O_2; 0.5 per cent CO;
87.8 per cent N_2.

14-12. A sample of illuminating gas was analyzed by absorption methods for CO_2, illuminants, O_2, CO, and H_2.   Calculate the percentage of each of these constituents from the following data:

Volume of sample taken.................................... 90.0 ml
After treatment with KOH.................................. 88.0 ml
After fuming H_2SO_4 treatment............................. 84.5 ml
After alkaline pyrogallol treatment........................ 84.2 m[
After ammoniacal Cu_2Cl_2 treatment........................ 48.6 ml
After palladous chloride treatment......................... 11.1 ml

Ans.   2.22 per cent CO_2; 3.88 per cent illuminants; 0.33 per cent O_2;
39.55 per cent CO; 41.66 per cent H_2.

14-13. Given 100 ml of a mixture containing CS_2 vapor and CO, to which 200 ml of oxygen was added, and the total mixture burned.   After the combustion the residual volume measured 245 ml.   Calculate (*a*) the volume of each of the constituents in the original mixture and (*b*) the volume of oxygen that remained.   *Ans.* (*a*) 10 ml CS_2, 90 ml CO; (*b*) 125 ml O_2.

14-14. Given 90 ml of mixture of CH_4 and CO, to which 126 ml of O_2 was added, and the total mixture burned.   After the combustion the volume of the cooled gas was found to be 150 ml.   Calculate the volume of each of the constituents in the original mixture.   *Ans.* 14 ml CH_4; 76 ml CO.

14-15. Given 94 ml of a mixture of H_2 and CO, to which 100 ml of O_2 was added, and the total mixture burned in a combustion pipette.   The residual volume of the cooled gas after combustion measured 136 ml.   Calculate the percentage composition of the original mixture.

Ans. 11.7 per cent H_2; 88.3 per cent CO.

14-16. A gaseous mixture consisting of CO and C_2H_2, measuring 40 ml, was mixed with 100 ml of O_2 and burned.   The volume of cooled gas after the combustion measured 105 ml.   Calculate the composition of the original mixture.   *Ans.* 25 ml CO; 15 ml C_2H_2.

14-17. Calculate the volume of CO and C_2H_2 in a mixture of the two gases from the following:

Volume of mixture taken................................... 40.0 ml
Volume of O_2 added....................................... 100.0 ml
Volume after combustion (with cooling)..................... 96.0 ml

Ans. 16 ml CO; 24 ml C_2H_2.

14-18. Given a mixture of 50 ml of C_2H_4 and C_2H_2, to which 150 ml of oxygen was added, and the total mixture burned. The volume of cooled gas after the combustion measured 112.5 ml. Calculate the volume of each gas in the original mixture. *Ans.* 25 ml C_2H_4; 25 ml C_2H_2.

14-19. A gaseous mixture, containing carbon monoxide, methane, and acetylene, measuring 100 ml, was mixed with 400 ml of oxygen, and the total mixture burned. After cooling, the volume of gas remaining measured 375 ml. This volume was further reduced to 224 ml by passing the gas through a strong caustic potash solution. Calculate the percentage composition of the original mixture.

Ans. 16.0 per cent CH_4; 33.0 per cent CO; 51.0 per cent C_2H_2.

14-20. Given 50 ml of a mixture of H_2, C_2H_2, CO, to which was added 80 ml of oxygen, and the total mixture burned. The volume of the cooled gas after the combustion measured 65 ml. This was reduced to 15 ml by treatment with KOH solution. Calculate the volume of each of the three gases in the original mixture. *Ans.* 20 ml H_2; 20 ml C_2H_2; 10 ml CO.

14-21. Given 30 ml of a mixture of CO, CH_4, and C_2H_2, to which 65 ml of O_2 was added, and the total mixture burned. The volume of cooled gas after the combustion measured 55 ml. This was further reduced to 15 ml by absorption of the CO_2 by KOH solution. Calculate the volume of each gas in the original mixture. *Ans.* 10 ml CO; 10 ml CH_4; 10 ml C_2H_2.

14-22. Given 100 ml of a mixture of CH_4, CO, and N_2, to which was added 100 ml of oxygen, and the total mixture burned. Volume of cooled gas after the combustion was 125 ml. By absorption with KOH solution the volume was further reduced to 65 ml. Calculate the volume of each of the gases in the original mixture. *Ans.* 30 ml CH_4; 30 ml CO; 40 ml N_2.

14-23. Given a mixture of CH_4, C_2H_2, and C_3H_8, calculate the volume of each gas from the following:

Volume of gas taken...................................... 25.0 ml
Volume of O_2 added...................................... 75.0 ml
Volume of cooled gas after combustion..................... 49.5 ml
Volume after CO_2 absorption............................. 17.5 ml

Ans. 20 ml CH_4; 3 ml C_2H_2; 2 ml C_3H_8.

14-24. Given 65.0 ml of a mixture of CH_4 and C_2H_2, to which 144.5 ml of O_2 was added, and the total mixture burned in a combustion pipette. The residual volume after the combustion, without cooling, measured 195.0 ml. When the products of combustion were passed through calcium chloride tubes, to remove the water vapor, the final volume measured 94.0 ml. Calculate (a) the volume of each of the constituents in the original mixture and (b) the volume of water vapor produced.

Ans. (a) 36 ml CH_4, 29 ml C_2H_2; (b) 101 ml water vapor.

14-25. Given a mixture of CO, CH₄, C₂H₄, and N₂, calculate the volume of each gas in the original mixture from the following data:

Volume of gas taken.. 30.0 ml
Volume of O₂ added.. 50.0 ml
Volume after combustion (without cooling)................... 75.0 ml
Volume after removing the water vapor by CaCl₂............. 45.0 ml
Volume after absorption of CO₂ by KOH.................... 15.0 ml

Ans. 10 ml CO; 10 ml CH₄; 5 ml C₂H₄; 5 ml N₂.

14-26. Calculate the volume of CO, H₂, C₂H₄, and N₂ from the following data:

Volume of sample taken.................................. 80.0 ml
Volume of O₂ added.. 100.0 ml
Residual volume after combustion (without cooling)........... 160.0 ml
Volume after removal of water vapor by CaCl₂.............. 100.0 ml
Volume after removal of CO₂ by KOH...................... 40.0 ml

Ans. 20 ml CO; 20 ml H₂; 20 ml C₂H₄; 20 ml N₂.

14-27. A gaseous mixture consisting of CO₂, CO, H₂, and N₂, upon analysis, gave the following data:

Volume of sample taken.................................. 100.0 ml
Volume after KOH treatment............................... 93.3 ml
Volume after ammoniacal Cu₂Cl₂ treatment................. 72.9 ml

To 50 ml of residual volume (*i.e.*, of 72.9 ml), 50 ml of O₂ was added, and this mixture burned (assume a constant temperature of 100°C). The residual volume after the combustion measured 80 ml. Calculate the percentages of the constituents in the original mixture.

Ans. 6.7 per cent CO₂; 20.4 per cent CO; 58.32 per cent H₂; 14.58 per cent N₂.

14-28. A 10-ml sample of natural gas is burned with 90.0 ml of oxygen.

Volume after combustion (with cooling)...................... 76.4 ml
Volume after KOH.. 58.0 ml

Determine the percentage of ethane, methane, and nitrogen in this gas.

Ans. Ethane, 88.0 per cent; methane, 8.0 per cent.

14-29. A sample of coke-oven gas was analyzed by absorption and slow-combustion methods. From the corresponding data, find the percentage of each constituent in the gas, determined in the following order: CO₂, illuminants, O₂, H₂, CO, CH₄, C₂H₆, and N₂.

Volume of sample taken.................................. 100.0 ml
Volume after KOH.. 98.3 ml
Volume after fuming sulfuric acid.......................... 95.2 ml
Volume after alkaline pyrogallol........................... 94.8 ml
Volume after copper oxide................................ 35.9 ml
Volume after KOH.. 31.1 ml

To 10 ml of residual volume (*i.e.*, of 31.1 ml), 80.0 ml of O₂ was added, and this mixture burned.

Volume after combustion (with cooling)..................... 72.9 ml
Volume after KOH....................................... 63.6 ml

Ans. 1.7 per cent CO_2; 3.1 per cent illuminants; 0.4 per cent O_2; 58.9 per cent H_2; 4.8 per cent CO; 22.7 per cent CH_4; 3.1 per cent C_2H_6; 5.3 per cent N_2.

14-30. A 100-ml sample of a producer gas analyzed in the following order for CO_2 illuminants, O_2, H_2, CO, CH_4, and N_2 gave these corresponding data:

Volume after KOH....................................... 90.2 ml
Volume after fuming sulfuric acid......................... 90.0 ml
Volume after pyrogallol.................................. 89.9 ml
Volume after copper oxide............................... 77.0 ml
Volume after KOH....................................... 58.7 ml

To 10.0 ml of residual gas (*i.e.*, of 58.7 ml), 90.0 ml of O_2 was added and this mixture burned.

Volume after combustion (with cooling)..................... 99.0 ml
Volume after KOH....................................... 98.5 ml

Determine the percentage composition of this gas.

Ans. CO_2, 9.8 per cent; illuminants, 0.2 per cent; O_2, 0.1 per cent; H_2, 12.9 per cent; CO, 18.3 per cent; CH_4, 2.9 per cent; N_2, 55.8 per cent.

14-31. Find the final volume (STP) of products obtained when 10 l of ethane (C_2H_6) is burned with the theoretical volume of (*a*) oxygen and (*b*) air.

14-32. What is the final volume (STP) of products obtained when 100 cu ft of propane (C_3H_8) is burned with the theoretical volume of (*a*) oxygen and (*b*) air?

14-33. What is the volume (STP) of the residual gas when 10 l of carbon monoxide is burned with 10 per cent excess air?

14-34. What is the volume composition of the residual gas (without subsequent cooling) when 100 cu ft of acetylene (C_2H_2) is burned with 5 per cent excess oxygen?

14-35. Determine the volume composition of residual gas (without subsequent cooling) when 1,000 cu ft of ethylene (C_2H_4) is burned with 5 per cent excess air.

14-36. In the Ostwald process, ammonia is oxidized to nitric oxide and water vapor is formed. If 100 cu ft of NH_3 and 100 cu ft O_2 are caused to react, what is the volume composition of the residual gas?

14-37. (*a*) If 25 ml of air and 25 ml of nitric oxide react to form nitrogen dioxide, what is the volume composition of the residual gas? (*b*) If the nitrogen dioxide formed in (*a*) is dissolved in water, what is the volume composition of the residual gas?

14-38. Calculate the percentage composition of a gaseous mixture of CH_4 and C_3H_8 from the following data.

Volume of gas taken.................................... 30.0 ml
Volume of O_2 added.................................... 105.0 ml
Volume of cooled gas after combustion .... 60.0 ml

14-39. Given 75.0 ml of a mixture containing CH_4, CO, and C_2H_2, to which was added 125.0 ml of oxygen, and the whole mixture burned. The volume of the cooled gas after combustion measured 132.0 ml, and this was further reduced by absorption of CO_2, by strong KOH solution, to 52.0 ml. Calculate (a) the volume of each of the gases in the original mixture and (b) the volume of oxygen that was not consumed in the burning.

14-40. Calculate the volume of each gas in a mixture of H_2, CO, and N_2 from the following:

Volume of sample taken.................................... 50.0 ml
Volume of O_2 added.. 20.0 ml
Volume of cooled gas after combustion...................... 44.9 ml
Volume after removal of CO_2.............................. 32.5 ml

14-41. Given 30 ml of a mixture of CH_4, C_2H_4, and N_2, to which was added 60.0 ml of oxygen, and the total mixture burned. Residual volume of cooled gas after combustion measured 50.0 ml. After removal of CO_2 the volume was 20.0 ml. Calculate the percentage composition of the original mixture.

14-42. Given 50 ml of a mixture of H_2, CO, and CO_2, to which is added 75 ml of O_2 and the whole mixture burned. The volume of cooled gas after combustion was 87.5 ml; after removal of CO_2 with KOH, the volume measured 57.5 ml. Calculate the volume of each gas in the original mixture.

14-43. Given 45 ml of a mixture of CO, CH_4, and C_2H_2, to which 97.5 ml of O_2 was added, and the total mixture burned. Volume of cooled gas after the combustion measured 82.5 ml. This was further reduced to 22.5 ml by absorption of the CO_2, by KOH solution. Calculate the volume of each gas in the original mixture.

14-44. Given a mixture of CH_4, C_2H_2, and C_3H_8. Calculate the percentage composition of the original mixture from the following data:

Volume of gas taken.. 30.0 ml
Volume of O_2 added....................................... 90.0 ml
Volume of cooled gas after combustion...................... 59.4 ml
Volume after CO_2 absorption .... 21.0 ml

14-45. Given 25 ml of a mixture of H_2, C_2H_2, and CO, to which was added 40 ml of O_2, and the total mixture burned. The volume of cooled gas after combustion measured 32.5 ml. This was reduced to 7.5 ml by treatment with KOH solution. Calculate the volume of each gas in original mixture.

14-46. To a 60-ml mixture of CH_4, CO, and C_3H_8 is added 200 ml of O_2 and the total mixture burned. The volume of cooled gas after combustion was 140 ml; after treatment with KOH solution, the volume remaining was 20 ml. What is the percentage of each gas in the original mixture?

14-47. A sample of 70 ml of a mixture of C_2H_2, C_2H_4, and C_3H_8 is taken for analysis. To this is added 250 ml of O_2 and the mixture burned. The volume of the cooled gas after combustion was 165 ml; the volume remaining after the CO_2 was absorbed was 0 ml. Calculate the volume of each gas in the original mixture.

14-48. A gas mixture containing CO_2, illuminants, O_2, CO, CH_4, and N_2 upon analysis gave the following data:

Volume of sample... 50 ml
Volume after KOH.. 42 ml
Volume after fuming H_2SO_4................................. 37 ml
Volume after pyrogallol...................................... 25 ml
Volume of residual gas (*i.e.*, of 25 ml) used for combustion analysis 10 ml
Volume O_2 added... 90 ml
Volume after burning and cooling............................ 94 ml
Volume after KOH.. 88 ml

Determine the percentage of each constituent in the original mixture.

14-49. Analysis of a gas sample said to contain CO_2, illuminants, O_2, CO, CH_4, and N_2 gave the following data:

Volume of sample... 50 ml
Volume after KOH.. 40 ml
Volume after fuming H_2SO_4................................. 34 ml
Volume after pyrogallol...................................... 30 ml
Volume of residual gas (*i.e.*, of 30 ml) used for combustion analysis 10 ml
Volume of O_2 added.. 100 ml
Volume after combustion and cooling......................... 108 ml
Volume after KOH.. 107 ml

Calculate the percentage of each gas in the original sample.

14-50. A sample of coke-oven gas was analyzed by absorption and slow-combustion methods. From the corresponding data, find the percentage of each constituent in the gas, determined in the following order: CO_2, illuminants, O_2, H_2, CO, CH_4, C_2H_6, and N_2.

Volume of sample taken................................... 100.0 ml
Volume after KOH.. 97.7 ml
Volume after fuming sulfuric acid......................... 93.7 ml
Volume after alkaline pyrogallol.......................... 93.4 ml
Volume after copper oxide................................ 37.8 ml
Volume after KOH.. 29.6 ml
Volume of residual gas (*i.e.*, of 29.6 ml) used for combustion
    analysis... 10.0 ml
Volume of oxygen added.................................. 90.0 ml
Volume after combustion (with cooling).................... 83.4 ml
Volume after KOH.. 74.5 ml

CHAPTER XV

THERMOCHEMICAL REACTIONS

OUTLINE

Thermochemical reactions. Heat is evolved or absorbed when a chemical reaction takes place.

Exothermal reaction: heat is given up to the surroundings.

Endothermal reaction: heat is absorbed from the surroundings.

Heat energy units: (a) calorie; (b) British thermal unit.

Heat of combustion.

The calorific power of a substance is the heat evolved (calories) during the combustion of a unit weight of a substance. In the case of gases it is often considered as the heat evolved by the combustion of a unit volume of the gas.

Calorific power of some substances is expressed in calories per mole. Heats of formation of some oxides are expressed in calories per gram, or kilocalories per kilogram, and Btu per pound. Calorific power of some gases and liquids is expressed in calories per liter, or kilocalories per cubic meter, and Btu per cubic foot.

Calorific power.

Specific heat of a body is the number of heat units required to raise its temperature by one degree.

Heat content of a substance is the quantity of substance multiplied by the mean specific heat between 0 and $t°C$ multiplied by the temperature.

Mean specific heats of gases between 0 and $t°C$ are expressed in kilocalories per cubic meter, and calories per liter; calories per gram, and kilocalories per kilogram.

Maximum theoretical temperature of combustion, calorific intensity, is the maximum theoretical temperature (starting from $0°C$) to which the products of combustion of a substance are raised in the production of a flame.

Total calories (available) = volume of gases $\times$ specific heat $\times$ temperature.

When a chemical reaction takes place, the original substances disappear, and new substances are formed. Coincident with this change, there occurs a transformation of energy, with the result that the chemical reaction is accompanied by the evolution or absorption of heat.

A reaction in which heat is given up to the surroundings is known as an **exothermal reaction;** and one in which heat is absorbed from the surroundings, an **endothermal reaction.** Exothermal reactions by far outnumber endothermal reactions.

224

CALORIE AND BRITISH THERMAL UNIT

Heat energy is measured in terms of units known as (1) the **calorie** (**cal**) and (2) the **British thermal unit** (**Btu**).

The calorie is the quantity of heat necessary to raise the temperature of 1 g of water 1°C, from 15 to 16°C.   Frequently the larger unit, kilogram-calorie (kg-cal) or kilocalorie (kcal) equal to 1000 cal, is employed.

The British thermal unit is the quantity of heat necessary to raise the temperature of 1 lb of water 1°F.   Since 1 lb = 453 g and 1°F = $\frac{5}{9}$ of 1°C, then 1 Btu = 453 g of water raised $\frac{5}{9}$°C = $\frac{5}{9} \times 453$ = 252, or 1 Btu = 252 cal = 0.252 kcal.

HEAT OF COMBUSTION

The quantity of heat liberated when 1 g-atom or 1 g-mole of a substance is burned is known as the **heat of combustion.**

The quantity of heat liberated in forming 1 g-mole of a substance is known as the **heat of formation** of that product.

Thus, when a piece of magnesium ribbon burns in air, the quantity of heat liberated is represented by the equation:

$$Mg + \tfrac{1}{2}O_2 \rightarrow MgO + 146{,}100 \text{ cal}$$
$$\text{24.3 g}\quad\text{16 g}$$

The value 146,100 cal represents the heat of combustion, or the quantity of heat liberated when 1 g-atom of Mg is burned, or 146,100 cal/g-atom.   Expressed in calories per gram of Mg, it would be

$$\frac{146{,}100 \text{ cal/g-atom}}{24.3 \text{ g/g-atom}} = 6012 \text{ cal/g}$$

Also, 146,100 cal represents the heat of formation of 1 g-mole of MgO.

To measure the quantity of heat liberated in a chemical reaction, an instrument known as a **calorimeter** is employed.   In measuring the heating value (calorific power) of a coal, a bomb-type calorimeter is used.   The essential procedure is to place a weighed sample of powdered coal mixed with an excess of solid oxidizer (Na_2O_2) in the bomb and fasten the cover securely.   The bomb is next completely immersed in water, the mixture ignited by electrically heating a wire in contact with the mixture, and the heat liberated by the reaction is measured by observing the rise in temperature of the water.   By making certain corrections the heat of combustion or calorific power of the fuel can be computed.

CALORIFIC POWER

The **calorific power,** or **heating value,** of a substance is the quantity of heat liberated by the combustion of a unit weight of the substance. In the case of solids it can be expressed in calories per gram-mole (cal/g-mole), calories per gram (cal/g), kilocalories per gram (kcal/g), or Btu per pound (Btu/lb). In dealing with gases, the calorific power can be expressed in calories per liter (cal/l), kilocalories per cubic meter (kcal/cu m), or Btu per cubic foot (Btu/cu ft). It should be stated calorific power or heat of combustion of a substance is the same whether the substance is burned in air or in pure oxygen.

Table XVI gives the calorific power of several substances expressed in calories per gram-mole. The designation

$$(C, O_2) \qquad 12 + 32 = 44 \qquad 97,200$$

simply means that when 12 g C combines with 32 g O_2, 44 g CO_2 is formed, and 97,200 cal/g-mole is liberated (heat of formation of CO_2), or 97,200 cal/g-atom C, or 97.2 kcal/g-atom C is liberated when carbon burns to carbon dioxide. On the basis of calories per gram of C, the calorific power of C would be

$$\frac{97,200 \text{ cal/g-atom}}{12 \text{ g/g-atom}} = 8100 \text{ cal/g}$$

TABLE XVI. CALORIFIC POWER OF SOME SUBSTANCES

Substance	Molecular weights (approx.)	Heat evolved, cal/mole
C, ½O₂	12 + 16 = 28	29,160
C, O₂	12 + 32 = 44	97,200
H₂, ½O₂	2 + 16 = 18	68,718 (liquid)* 57,801 (gas)
S, O₂	32 + 32 = 64	70,940
2P, 2½O₂	62 + 80 = 142	366,900
CO, ½O₂	28 + 16 = 44	68,040
Zn, ½O₂	65 + 16 = 81	83,500
Mn, ½O₂	55 + 16 = 71	96,500
Si, O₂	28 + 32 = 60	201,000
Sn, O₂	118 + 32 = 150	138,000
2Fe, 1½O₂	112 + 48 = 160	198,500

* In ordinary work the moisture formed by the combustion of hydrogen passes off as vapor, but if it is condensed, as is the case in calorific measurements, then taking the products cold, the heat of condensation of water (606.5 cal per gram of water) is liberated and the total heat evolved = 57,801 + (18 × 606.5) = 68,718.

TABLE XVII. HEATS OF FORMATION OF SOME OXIDES

$H_2, \frac{1}{2}O_2$	34,000 cal/g (or kcal/kg) of H	61,200 Btu/lb of H
$C, \frac{1}{2}O_2$	2,430 cal/g (or kcal/kg) of C	4,374 Btu/lb of C
C, O_2	8,100 cal/g (or kcal/kg) of C	14,580 Btu/lb of C
S, O_2	2,212 cal/g (or kcal/kg) of S	3,982 Btu/lb of S
$2P, 2\frac{1}{2}O_2$	5,912 cal/g (or kcal/kg) of P	10,642 Btu/lb of P

NOTE. To convert cal/g to Btu/lb, multiply by 1.8.

TABLE XVIII. CALORIFIC POWER

(A) Calorific Power (Low) of Some Gases*

		Cal/l (STP) or kcal/cu m (STP)	Btu/cu ft (STP)
Hydrogen	H_2	2,582	290
Hydrogen sulfide	H_2S	5,514	620
Carbon monoxide	CO	3,034	341
Methane	CH_4	8,560	962
Acetylene	C_2H_2	13,440	1,510
Ethylene	C_2H_4	14,480	1,627
Ethane	C_2H_6	15,110	1,698
Propane	C_3H_8	21,650	2,433
Butane (iso)	C_4H_{10}	28,220	3,171
Benzene (benzol)	C_6H_6	33,490	3,763

(B) Calorific Power (Low) of Some Liquids

		Cal/g, or kcal/kg	Btu/lb
Benzene (benzol)	C_6H_6	9,632	17,340
Toluene (toluol)	C_7H_8	9,708	17,470
Methyl alcohol	CH_3OH	4,676	8,417
Ethyl alcohol	C_2H_5OH	6,435	11,580
Acetone	CH_3COCH_3	6,810	12,260
Carbon disulfide	CS_2	2,880	5,185

NOTE. Water vapor formed in combustion not condensed. To obtain high calorific powers (water vapor condensed), add the following: for gases, 471 kcal/cu m or 53 Btu/cu ft for each mole of H_2 in the gas; for liquids, 10,560 kcal/kg-mole or 19,000 Btu/lb-mole for each mole of H_2 in the liquid.

* Data in this table are compiled from Allison Butts, "Metallurgical Problems," McGraw-Hill Book Company, Inc., New York, p. 422.

In solving the following examples concerned with calorific power from composition of fuels, it should be noted that nitrogen, carbon dioxide, ash, and moisture do not enter into the combustion reactions and are therefore not to be considered in determining the heating values of the various fuels.

Example 1. Calculate the calorific power in calories per liter of a natural gas which has the following composition by volume: 32.3 per cent CH_4; 67.0 per cent C_2H_6; 0.7 per cent N_2.

Calorific power of CH_4 = 8560 cal/l of CH_4
32.3 per cent CH_4 = 0.323 l of CH_4/l of gas
0.323 l of CH_4/l of gas × 8560 cal/l of CH_4 =   2765 cal/l of gas
Calorific power of C_2H_6 = 15,110 cal/l of C_2H_6
67.0 per cent C_2H_6 = 0.67 l of C_2H_6/l of gas
0.67 l of C_2H_6/l of gas × 15,110 cal/l of C_2H_6 = 10,124 cal/l of gas
                Calorific power of natural gas = 12,889 cal/l of gas

NOTE. N_2 is inert and does not enter into combustion.

In dealing with gaseous fuels the calorific power is obtained by taking the sum of the calorific powers of the combustible constituents. Any hydrogen in the gas is considered to be contained in the water vapor and no correction for heat of vaporization of water is necessary, when low calorific powers of gases are used.

Example 2. Calculate the low calorific power in Btu per cubic feet of a producer gas which has the following composition by volume: 2.6 per cent CH_4; 0.4 per cent C_2H_4; 22.0 per cent CO; 5.7 per cent CO_2; 10.5 per cent H_2; 58.8 per cent N_2.

Calorific power CH_4 = 962 Btu/cu ft CH_4
2.6 per cent CH_4 = 0.026 cu ft CH_4/cu ft gas
0.026 cu ft CH_4/cu ft gas × 962 Btu/cu ft CH_4 =   25.0 Btu/cu ft gas
Calorific power C_2H_4 = 1627 Btu/cu ft C_2H_4
0.4 per cent C_2H_4 = 0.004 cu ft C_2H_4/cu ft gas
0.004 cu ft C_2H_4/cu ft gas
                        × 1627 Btu/cu ft C_2H_4 =   6.5 Btu/cu ft gas
Calorific power CO = 341 Btu/cu ft CO
22.0 per cent CO = 0.22 cu ft CO/cu ft gas
0.22 cu ft CO/cu ft gas × 341 Btu/cu ft CO   =   75.0 Btu/cu ft gas
Calorific power H_2 = 290 Btu/cu ft H_2
10.5 per cent H_2 = 0.105 cu ft H_2/cu ft gas
0.105 cu ft H_2/cu ft gas × 290 Btu/cu ft H_2 =   30.4 Btu/cu ft gas
Calorific power of producer gas   = 136.9 Btu/cu ft gas

NOTE. CO_2 and N_2 do not enter into computation, as they are not concerned with combustion reaction.

SPECIFIC HEAT

Heat capacity of a body is the number of heat units required to raise its temperature by 1°.

The heat capacity of water is numerically equal to unity, which is ascertained from the definition of the calorie or Btu. The ratio of the heat capacity of a given substance to the heat capacity of water is called the **specific heat** of that substance. This ratio would make the specific heat a *pure number* (without dimension). The heat capacity of a body equals the product of its mass and its specific heat, or $C = mc$. The specific heat of a given substance is usually defined as the *number* of calories required to raise the temperature of 1 g of that substance 1°C (cal/g °C); or the *number* of Btu required to raise the temperature of 1 lb of the given substance 1°F (Btu/lb °F). Then, the specific heat of water is unity in any system of units of heat measure. Furthermore, the specific heat of any given substance has the same numerical value in any system of units of heat measure. The specific heat of aluminum is 0.218; the heat capacity of aluminum may be expressed as 0.218 cal/g °C, 0.218 kcal/kg °C, or 0.218 Btu/lb °F.

In dealing with gases the specific heat is frequently expressed in calories per liter (STP) per degree centigrade or kilocalories per cubic meter per degree centigrade.

The specific heat of a substance increases with temperature. In determining the heat content Q of a substance, the mean specific heat between 0 and $t°$ must be used. Thus, the heat content of a substance is equal to the quantity W of substance multiplied by mean specific heat between 0 and $t°$, c_m, multiplied by temperature t or

$$Q = W \times c_m \times t$$

Q will be expressed in calories at $t°C$, if W is in grams and c_m is the mean specific heat per gram between 0 and $t°$. Q will be expressed in kilocalories at $t°C$, if W is in kilograms and c_m is the mean specific heat per kilogram between 0 and $t°$.

When dealing with gases, the foregoing relation for Q becomes

$$Q = V \times c_m \times t$$

Q will be expressed in calories at $t°C$, if volume V is in liters and c_m is the mean specific heat per liter between 0 and $t°$. Q will be expressed in kilocalories at $t°C$, if volume V is in cubic meters and c_m is the mean specific heat per cubic meter between 0 and $t°$.

The following expressions give the change in specific heat of substances with temperature: $A + Bt + Ct^2$, or $A + Bt - Ct^{-2}$. For practical purposes in calculations to be considered in this discussion, the expression for change in specific heat can be simplified to $A + Bt$, where A = specific heat at 0°C and B is a constant. The expression for the mean specific heat between 0 and $t°$ is $A + \frac{1}{2}Bt$.

Table XIX gives the mean specific heats of gases between 0° and $t°C$:

TABLE XIX

	Kcal/cu m (STP); cal/l (STP)	Mean specific heat by weight, cal/g; kcal/kg
Nitrogen...........	$0.302 + 0.000\ 022t$	$0.241 + 0.000\ 018t$
Hydrogen..........	$0.301 + 0.000\ 02t$	$3.35\ \ + 0.000\ 22t$
Oxygen............	$0.302 + 0.000\ 022t$	$0.211 + 0.000\ 015t$
Air................	$0.302 + 0.000\ 022t$	$0.234 + 0.000\ 017t$
Carbon monoxide...	$0.302 + 0.000\ 022t$	$0.242 + 0.000\ 018t$
Carbon dioxide......	$0.406 + 0.000\ 090t$	$0.205 + 0.000\ 046t$
Sulfur dioxide.......	$0.406 + 0.000\ 090t$	$0.139 + 0.000\ 031t$
Water vapor........	$0.373 + 0.000\ 050t$	$0.463 + 0.000\ 062t$

MAXIMUM THEORETICAL TEMPERATURE OF COMBUSTION

When a fuel burns, definite weights and volumes of products are formed, and a definite quantity of heat is liberated. This quantity of heat raises the temperature of the products of combustion sufficiently to produce a flame. The maximum theoretical temperature (starting from 0°C) to which the products of combustion of a substance are raised in the production of a flame may be called the **calorific intensity.** In order to calculate this maximum temperature, the assumption is made that the total heat available in the combustion (chiefly calorific power of fuel) is equal to the heat taken up by the products of combustion immediately after the reaction. Then

Total calories (available)

$$= \text{volume of gases} \times \text{specific heat} \times \text{temperature}$$

or

$$t = \frac{\text{cal (available)}}{\Sigma(V \times \text{sp ht})}$$

Example. Calculate the maximum theoretical temperature attained when hydrogen is burned (a) in oxygen and (b) in 20 per cent excess air.

The burning of hydrogen in oxygen or in air is represented by the following relations:

$$H_2 + \tfrac{1}{2}O_2 \rightarrow H_2O_{vapor} + cal$$
$$1\,l \quad \tfrac{1}{2}\,l \quad\quad 1\,l \quad\quad + 2582\ cal$$

The assumption is made that all the heat produced by the burning of a substance is utilized in raising the temperature of the products of combustion, and the heat utilized in raising the temperature of surrounding bodies is disregarded.

(a) In the foregoing reaction, 2582 cal (available heat) is used in raising the temperature of the 1 l of water vapor produced.

Reaction: $H_2 + \tfrac{1}{2}O_2 \rightarrow H_2O + heat$

Gases	V_{bc}, liters	Cal power, cal/l	V_{ac}, liters	Specific heats, cal/l °C
H_2	1	2582		
O_2	0.5			
H_2O			1	$0.373 + 0.00005t$

$$t = \frac{cal\ (available)}{\Sigma(V \times sp\ ht)}$$

$$t = \frac{2582}{0.373 + 0.00005t}$$

$$0.00005t^2 + 0.373t - 2582 = 0$$

To solve this quadratic equation by the usual formula,[1] multiply both sides of this equation by 10^4 and rearrange.

$$0.5t^2 + (0.373 \times 10^4)t - (0.2582 \times 10^8) = 0$$

$$t = \frac{-(0.373 \times 10^4) + \sqrt{(0.373 \times 10^4)^2 + 4(0.5)\,(0.2582 \times 10^8)}}{2 \times 0.5}$$

$$t = 4366$$

Starting from 0°C, the maximum theoretical temperature attainable is 4366°C.

---

[1] The general quadratic equation is

$$ax^2 + bx + c = 0$$
$$x = \frac{-b + \sqrt{b^2 - 4ac}}{2a}$$

(*b*) When hydrogen is burned in excess air, the products of combustion will consist of water vapor and excess air ($O_2 + N_2$).

The heat produced per liter of hydrogen is the same as in part (*a*), *viz.*, 2582 cal, but the heat liberated raises the temperature of water vapor and also the excess air. It is necessary to determine this volume of excess O_2 and N_2.

The volume of oxygen required to burn 1 l of hydrogen is 0.5 l.

The composition of dry air by volume (at sea level) is 78.03 per cent nitrogen, 20.99 per cent oxygen, and 0.98 per cent other gases (chiefly argon, CO_2).

Since dry air contains 20.99 l O_2 in 100 l air,

$$0.5 \text{ l } O_2 \text{ in } 0.5 \text{ l } O_2 \times \frac{100 \text{ l air}}{20.99 \text{ l } O_2} = 0.5 \text{ l } O_2 \times 4.76 \text{ l air/l } O_2$$

$$= 2.38 \text{ l air needed}$$

Since 20 per cent excess air is used,

2.38 l air $\times$ 0.20 l excess air/l air.......................... 0.48 l excess air

Total volume of air needed (2.38 l) and excess air (0.48 l)..... 2.86 l ($O_2 + N_2$)

Volume O_2 needed for combustion 1 l H_2.................... 0.5 l O_2

Volume ($O_2 + N_2$) which will absorb heat in addition to 1 l H_2O
  vapor.. 2.36 l ($O_2 + N_2$)

Reaction: $H_2 + \frac{1}{2}O_2 \rightarrow H_2O +$ heat

Gases	V_{bc}, liters	Cal power, cal/l	V_{ac}, liters	Specific heats, cal/l °C
H_2	1	2582		
O_2	0.5			
Air ($O_2 + N_2$)	2.38			
Excess air	0.48			
Air unused ($O_2 + N_2$)			2.36	$2.36(0.302 + 0.000022t)$
H_2O			1	$0.373 + 0.00005t$

$\Sigma = 1.086 + 0.0001t$

$$t = \frac{2582}{(1.086 + 0.0001t)}$$

$$0.0001t^2 + 1.086t - 2582 = 0$$

Multiplying both sides of this equation by 10^4 and rearranging,

$$t^2 + (1.086 \times 10^4)t - (0.2582 \times 10^8) = 0$$
$$t = 2007$$

or maximum theoretical temperature of hydrogen burned with 20 per cent excess air is 2007°C.

Problems

15-1. Calculate the calorific power in calories per liter (STP) of a producer gas that gave the following analysis by volume: 6.0 per cent CO_2; 22.0 per cent CO; 12.0 per cent H_2; 60.0 per cent N_2. *Ans.* 977 cal/l.

15-2. A natural gas has the following percentage composition by volume: 0.6 per cent CO; 0.2 per cent CO_2; 1.8 per cent H_2; 93.5 per cent CH_4; 3.4 per cent N_2. What is the calorific power of this gas in calories per liter (STP)? *Ans.* 8068 cal/l.

15-3. Calculate the calorific power in kilocalories per cubic meter (STP) of a water gas that has the following percentage composition by volume: 1.4 per cent CH_4; 45.5 per cent CO; 47.4 per cent H_2; 2.0 per cent CO_2; 4.0 per cent N_2. *Ans.* 2724 kcal/cu m.

15-4. Calculate the calorific power in Btu per pound of a powdered coal used in a rotary cement kiln. This coal gave the following analysis: 2.17 per cent moisture; 85.00 per cent carbon; 8.83 per cent ash; 4.12 per cent S. *Ans.* 12,557 Btu/lb.

15-5. Calculate the calorific power in Btu per cubic foot of an oil gas that has the following percentage composition by volume: 30.0 per cent H_2; 49.5 per cent CH_4; 15.0 per cent C_2H_4; 3.5 per cent N_2. *Ans.* 807 Btu/cu ft.

15-6. A carbureted water gas has the following percentage composition by volume: 29.8 per cent CO; 40.0 per cent H_2; 17.0 per cent CH_4; 7.8 per cent C_2H_4; 3.8 per cent N_2; 1.5 per cent CO_2. Calculate the calorific power (low) of this gas in Btu per cubic foot. *Ans.* 508 Btu/cu ft.

15-7. Calculate the maximum theoretical temperature obtained when carbon monoxide is burned in oxygen. *Ans.* 3972°C.

15-8. Calculate the maximum theoretical temperature obtained when carbon monoxide is burned in air. *Ans.* 2350°C.

15-9. Methane is burned in air. Calculate the maximum theoretical temperature reached. *Ans.* 2083°C.

15-10. Calculate the theoretical temperature of the oxyhydrogen blowtorch. *Ans.* 4366°C.

15-11. Calculate the calorific intensity of hydrogen when burned in air. *Ans.* 2250°C.

15-12. Calculate the maximum theoretical temperature of combustion of acetylene in air. *Ans.* 2603°C.

15-13. Calculate the theoretical temperature of the oxyacetylene blowtorch. *Ans.* 5489°C.

15-14. Calculate the calorific intensity when pure carbon is burned in air. *Ans.* 3036°C.

15-15. Calculate the maximum theoretical temperature of combustion of ethylene when burned in air. *Ans.* 2274°C.

15-16. Calculate the calorific intensity of benzene when burned in air. *Ans.* 2233°C.

15-17. C_6H_6 is burned in a blast lamp with 10 per cent excess air. Calculate the maximum theoretical temperature attained. *Ans.* 2085°C.

15-18. Calculate the temperature of the flame of an air-blast lamp that burns carbon monoxide and uses 25 per cent excess air over that needed for combustion. *Ans.* 2090°C.

15-19. A coke-oven gas has the following composition by volume: 10.0 per cent CO; 1.5 per cent CO_2; 33.5 per cent CH_4; 48 per cent H_2; 5.0 per cent C_2H_4; 2.0 per cent N_2. What is the calorific power of this gas in kilocalories per kilogram?

15-20. Calculate the calorific power in kilocalories per kilogram of water gas which has the following percentage composition by volume: 37.0 per cent CO; 1.0 per cent CO_2; 2.0 per cent CH_4; 49.5 per cent H_2; 10.5 per cent H_2O.

15-21. A natural gas has the following percentage composition by volume: 61.0 per cent CH_4; 29.0 per cent H_2; 0.5 per cent CO; 7.5 per cent C_2H_6; 2.0 per cent N_2. Calculate the calorific power in Btu per cubic foot of this gas.

15-22. A producer-gas analysis gave the following results: 23.0 per cent CO; 3.5 per cent CH_4; 10.5 per cent H_2; 56.0 per cent N_2; 4.5 per cent CO_2; 2.5 per cent H_2O. Calculate the calorific power in Btu per cubic foot of this producer gas.

15-23. A blast-furnace gas analysis gave the following percentage composition by volume: 60 per cent N_2; 12.5 per cent CO_2; 2.5 per cent H_2; 25 per cent CO. What is the calorific power in kilocalories per kilogram of blast-furnace gas?

15-24. Calculate the calorific intensity of ethane (C_2H_6) when burned in air.

15-25. Calculate the maximum theoretical temperature of combustion of butane (iso) (C_4H_{10}) when burned in air.

15-26. Calculate the temperature of the flame of an oxyacetylene blowtorch that uses 15 per cent excess oxygen over that needed for complete combustion.

15-27. Acetylene is burned in a blast lamp using 20 per cent excess air. Calculate the maximum theoretical temperature of combustion under these conditions.

15-28. Calculate the flame temperature when propane (C_3H_8) is burned with 15 per cent excess air.

15-29. What is the theoretical temperature of combustion when hydrogen sulfide burns with 10 per cent excess air?

15-30. A mixture which is 50 per cent CH_4 and 50 per cent CO is burned in oxygen. (*a*) What is the low calorific power in kilocalories per cubic meter? (*b*) What is the maximum theoretical temperature of combustion?

15-31. Calculate the maximum theoretical temperature of combustion when methanol (methyl alcohol, CH_3OH) is burned in air.

15-32. Calculate the maximum theoretical temperature of combustion when ethyl alcohol (C_2H_5OH) is burned in air.

15-33. Calculate the maximum theoretical temperature of combustion when benzene (C_6H_6), a liquid, is burned with 20 per cent excess air.

15-34. Calculate the maximum theoretical temperature of combustion when toluol (C_7H_8), a liquid, is burned with 10 per cent excess air.

CHAPTER XVI

ELECTROCHEMISTRY

OUTLINE

Electrochemical reactions.

Electrolytic reactions—chemical reactions brought about by the electric current.

Electrogenetic reactions—chemical reactions which produce electrical energy.

Oxidation-reduction reactions are electrochemical; the loss and/or gain of electrons will take place at an electrode during electrolytic or electrogenetic cell reactions.

Electrolysis of cupric chloride solution.

Reduction takes place at the cathode and the best oxidizer is reduced. Oxidation takes place at the anode and the best reducer is oxidized.

Electrochemical series. Redox-couple reaction potentials listed (Appendix) with the strongest reducers at the top of the list and poorest reducers lower down on the list.

Electrolysis of potassium sulfate solution.

Electrogenetic cell reaction. Gravity cell.

Electrical units: ampere, coulomb, ohm, volt, watt.

Ohm's law.

Faraday's laws of electrolysis.

1. The amount of any substance liberated at an electrode during an electrolysis is proportional to the quantity of current which has passed through the cell.

2. The same quantity of current, when passed through cells containing different electrolytes, liberates amounts of different substances that are proportional to the chemical equivalents of the various substances.

Electrochemical equivalent—the number of grams of a substance liberated by the passage of unit quantity of electricity (one coulomb). The electrochemical equivalent of silver is 0.0011180 g.

The Faraday, or F: 1 F equals 96,500 coulombs, the quantity of electricity required to deposit or liberate 1 g-eq wt of a substance or liberate 1 l-eq (STP) of gas at an electrode.

Many chemical reactions can be brought about by the electric current (electrolytic reactions), and some chemical reactions will produce electrical energy (electrogenetic reactions). These types of reactions come under the category of **electrochemistry.**

It has been shown in Chap. X that chemical reactions which involve changes in oxidation numbers and/or valence numbers are oxidation-reduction reactions. An *increase* in oxidation number and/or valence number is qualitatively and quantitatively equivalent to a *loss of electrons* (oxidation), and a decrease in oxidation number and/or valence number, to a *gain of electrons* (reduction).   Then oxidation-reduction reactions are in reality electrochemical, and the loss or gain of electrons will take place at an electrode during electrolytic or electrogenetic cell reactions.

Electrolytic Cell Reactions. If two pieces of platinum foil are suspended in a solution of cupric chloride ($CuCl_2$) and the pieces, commonly called "electrodes," are connected by a copper wire to the terminals (poles) of a battery, it will be observed that metallic copper plates out, or is deposited on the electrode connected to the negative $(-)$ terminal of the battery, and that chlorine gas escapes at the electrode connected to the positive $(+)$ terminal. The electrode connected to the *negative* terminal is the **cathode** and the one attached to the *positive* terminal is the **anode.** The direction of flow of the electrons through the wire is from anode to cathode.

In a solution (acids, bases, salts) the conduction of electricity is due to the presence of ions, and the conductivity is a measure of the degree of ionization. Many salts are highly ionized. There would then be a large number of cupric ions, Cu^{+2} (*cations*), and chloride ions, Cl^- (*anions*), in a solution of cupric chloride. The electrode reactions taking place may be expressed as follows:

The chloride ions are attracted to the anode (positive electrode) where they give up electrons, with the subsequent formation of, first, atomic chlorine and then molecular chlorine. Under the impulse of the battery, these electrons are pulled away from the anode and forced through the outside metallic conductor (copper wire) into the cathode (negative electrode), from the surface of which electrons are acquired by the cupric ions, resulting in a deposition of metallic copper.

Ions present at cathode: Cu^{+2} and H^+.

Reduction takes place at the cathode, and the *best oxidizer is reduced.* Since cupric ion (Cu^{+2}) is a better oxidizer than H^+, the following electrode reaction occurs:

Cathode ($-$ electrode) reaction:

$$Cu^{+2} + 2\text{\textcircled{e}} \rightarrow Cu^0 \qquad \textit{reduction}$$

Ions present at anode: Cl^- and OH^-.

Oxidation takes place at the anode, and the *best reducer is oxidized.* The chloride ion (Cl^-) is the best reducer, and the following electrode reaction takes place:

Anode ($+$ electrode) reaction:

$$2Cl^- \rightarrow 2Cl^0 + 2\text{\textcircled{e}} \rightarrow Cl_2^0 \qquad \textit{oxidation}$$

ELECTROCHEMICAL SERIES

There is an analogy between oxidation-reduction reactions and acid-base reactions.[1] An acid gives up a proton to form a conjugate base, and the base may regain the proton to produce the acid. Every reducer has a conjugate oxidizer, and the oxidizer may gain the electron to produce the reducer.

$$\text{Reducer} \rightleftharpoons \text{oxidizer} + \text{ⓔ}$$

This is analogous to the relationship

$$\text{Acid} \rightleftharpoons \text{base} + \text{proton}$$

Both fundamental processes are reversible. A solution containing a reducer and its conjugate oxidizer is said to contain a *redox couple*. Just as acids vary in strength, so do oxidizers. The strength of a couple is measured in volts relative to the strength of a hydrogen electrode, whose potential is arbitrarily taken as zero. The electrochemical series (see Table VI, Appendix) is a list of these couple potentials. A relatively negative voltage, indicating the reducer of the couple is strong, is placed at the top of the list, that is, it has a high tendency to lose electrons (or conjugate oxidizer is weak). A relatively positive voltage, indicating the reducer of the couple is weak, is lower down on the list, and its tendency to lose electrons is low (or conjugate oxidizer is strong). The farther apart two reducers are in the series, the larger is the difference in their tendencies to lose electrons. Thus if a strip of zinc is immersed in cupric sulfate solution, the zinc atoms will readily displace cupric ions from solution primarily because of the great tendency for zinc atoms to lose electrons (reducer) to cupric ions (oxidizer).

To obtain the standard electrode potential of the zinc couple, the latter must be compared with the hydrogen couple.

$$\overset{\longleftarrow \text{ⓔ} \longrightarrow}{\text{H}_2 \text{ (1 atm)} \left| \underset{1M}{\text{H}_3\text{O}^+} \right\| \left. \underset{1M}{\text{Zn}^{+2}} \right| \text{Zn}}$$

Couple reaction, hydrogen electrode:

$$\text{H}_2 + 2\text{H}_2\text{O} \rightleftharpoons 2\text{H}_3\text{O}^+ + 2\text{ⓔ} \qquad E = 0 \text{ volt}$$

Couple reaction, zinc electrode:

$$\text{Zn}^0 \rightleftharpoons \text{Zn}^{+2} + 2\text{ⓔ} \qquad E = -0.76 \text{ volt}$$

[1] Hazelhurst, T. H. *J. Chem. Educ.*, **17**, 466 (1940).

The electromotive force for this cell is 0.76 volt.   Since the zinc electrode is negative with respect to the hydrogen electrode and the potential of the hydrogen electrode is zero, the standard electrode potential of zinc is -0.76 volt.

Further consideration of electrolytic cell reaction in the light of the electrochemical series is apropos.   In the electrolysis of a potassium sulfate solution, K_2SO_4 furnishes a high concentration of K^+ and SO_4^{-2} ions, and H_2O a low concentration of H^+ and OH^- ions.

NOTE.   The hydrogen ion, H^+, is in reality the hydronium ion, H_3O^+.

Ions present at cathode: K^+ and H^+ ions.

Ions present at anode: SO_4^{-2} and OH^- ions.

Reference to the electrochemical series gives information that H^+ is a better oxidizer than K^+, and H^+ ions will be reduced, since the best oxidizer present in solution will be reduced.   Likewise, the OH^- ion will be oxidized, since it is the best reducer present; thus, OH^- ions are more readily discharged than SO_4^{-2} ions.   There is no accumulation of OH^- ions; as soon as they are discharged they combine to form H_2O and O_2.

Cathode reaction:

$$2H^+ + 2\text{\textcircled{e}} \rightleftharpoons 2H^0 \rightarrow H_2^0 \qquad\qquad reduction$$

Anode reaction:

$$2OH^- \rightleftharpoons \tfrac{1}{2}O_2 + H_2O + 2\text{\textcircled{e}} \qquad\qquad oxidation$$

Thus, in electrolysis of potassium sulfate solution, the products of the reaction are hydrogen liberated at the cathode and oxygen liberated at the anode; K^+ and SO_4^{-2} ions remain in the solution.

Electrogenetic Cell Reaction.   In the familiar gravity cell, a heavy zinc electrode, crowfoot in shape for large surface area, is immersed in dilute zinc sulfate solution, and thin copper strips at the bottom of the container are immersed in a saturated solution of cupric sulfate, in contact with excess crystals of $CuSO_4 \cdot 5H_2O$.   The dilute zinc sulfate solution, having a much lower density than that of the saturated cupric sulfate solution, is made to float on the latter solution with very little mixing.   When the two electrodes are connected by a conducting wire, an electric current is produced.   From the electrochemical series one notes that the tendency for Zn to lose electrons is much greater than that of metallic copper.   Then, when metallic zinc is in contact with a solution containing Zn^{+2} ions, zinc atoms lose electrons, thereby becoming zinc ions (oxidation).   These electrons are in turn taken up by the zinc electrode, which becomes negative with respect to the surrounding solution.   When a connection is made between the two electrodes, the electrons are conducted from the zinc to the copper electrode, where the cupric ions gain electrons (reduction) and become metallic copper. These reactions constitute a source of electrical energy.

$$\xrightarrow{-\textcircled{\epsilon}\rightarrow} Zn^0 \left|\begin{matrix}Zn^{+2}\\1M\end{matrix}\right|\left|\begin{matrix}Cu^{+2}\\1\,M\end{matrix}\right| Cu^0$$

Cathode reaction:

$$Cu^{+2} + 2\textcircled{\epsilon} \rightarrow Cu^0 \qquad E = +0.34 \text{ volt} \qquad reduction$$

Anode reaction:

$$Zn^0 \rightarrow Zn^{+2} + 2\textcircled{\epsilon} \qquad E = -0.76 \text{ volt} \qquad oxidation$$

The electromotive force of cell = 0.34 volt − (−0.76) volt = 1.1 volts

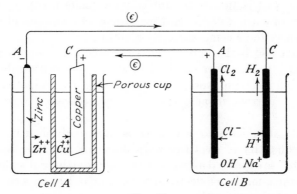

Fig. 11

Cell *A*, Electrogenetic Type

A, anode (Zn—best reducer). Electrolyte: $ZnSO_4$ solution

C, cathode (Cu) Electrolyte: $CuSO_4$ solution

Anode reaction:

$$Zn^0 \rightarrow Zn^{+2} + 2\textcircled{\epsilon}$$
$$(oxidation)$$
$$E = +0.34 \text{ volt}$$

Cathode reaction:

$$Cu^{+2} + 2\textcircled{\epsilon} \rightarrow Cu^0$$
$$(reduction)$$
$$E = -0.76 \text{ volt}$$

emf of cell = 0.34 volt − (−0.76) volt
= 1.1 volts

Cell *B*, Electrolytic Type

Carbon electrodes (inert). *A*, anode; *C*, cathode. Electrolyte: NaCl solution

$$NaCl \rightleftharpoons Na^+ + Cl^-$$
$$H_2O \rightleftharpoons H^+ + OH^-$$

cations	anions
at cathode	at anode
(oxidizers)	(reducers)

Cathode reaction: best oxidizer is reduced at cathode, or

$$2H^+ + 2\textcircled{\epsilon} \rightarrow H_2^0$$

Anode reaction: best reducer is oxidized at anode, or

$$2Cl^- \rightarrow Cl_2^0 + 2\textcircled{\epsilon}$$

$$Na^+ + OH^- \rightarrow NaOH \text{ accumulates}$$

ELECTRICAL UNITS

The **ampere (amp)** is the unit of current. One ampere is that current which, when passing through a silver nitrate solution, deposits 0.0011180 g or 1.1180 mg of silver in one second. Current is measured by an ammeter.

The **coulomb** is the unit quantity of electricity; it is that quantity of electricity which must pass through a given cross section of a conductor in one second when the current is one ampere. One coulomb deposits 1.1180 mg of silver. One ampere is one coulomb per second. If Q = coulombs, I = amperes, t = time in seconds, $Q = It$.

The **ohm** is the unit of electric resistance; it is the resistance offered to the passage of an electric current by a column of mercury 106.30 cm in length and 1 sq mm in cross section at 0°C.

The **volt** is the unit of electromotive force and/or potential difference. One volt is the electromotive force (emf) necessary to maintain a flow of current of one ampere through a resistance of one ohm. Electromotive force is measured by a voltmeter.

The **watt (w)** is the unit of electrical power and equals one joule per second. It should be emphasized that power represents the *time rate* of doing electrical work. The product of electromotive force in volts (E) × current in amperes (I) equals power in watts (P), or $P = EI$.

The rate at which electrical work is done multiplied by the time gives the quantity of electrical work done. When time is in hours, this quantity is expressed as watthours: 1,000 watthr = 1 kwhr. Then 1 kwhr is the quantity of electrical work done in 1 hr by a current that does work at the rate of 1 kw.

LAWS OF ELECTRICITY

Ohm's law: The current in amperes I through a conductor is directly proportional to the electromotive force in volts E and inversely proportional to the resistance in ohms R of the conductor, or $I = E/R$.

Faraday's laws of electrolysis: 1. The amount of any substance liberated at an electrode during an electrolysis is proportional to the quantity of current which has passed through the cell.

2. The same quantity of current, when passed through cells containing different electrolytes, liberates amounts of different substances that are proportional to the chemical equivalents of the various substances.

ELECTROCHEMICAL EQUIVALENT

The number of grams of a substance liberated by the passage of unit quantity of electricity (1 coulomb) is called the **electrochemical equivalent.**

The electrochemical equivalent of silver is 0.0011180 g Ag, since this is the amount deposited by 1 coulomb of electricity. To deposit 1 g-eq wt of Ag, or 107.88 g Ag, would require

$$\frac{107.88 \text{ g Ag}}{0.001118 \text{ g Ag/coulomb}} = 96{,}494 \text{ coulombs}$$

or approximately 96,500 coulombs. The value 96,500 coulombs is called the **faraday** (F). The faraday is defined as the quantity of electricity (coulombs) required to deposit or liberate 1 g-eq wt of a substance. In accordance with Faraday's second law of electrolysis, the passage of $1\ F$ of electricity will liberate 1 g-eq wt of various substances and/or 1 l-eq (STP) of gases at each electrode.

Example 1. Determine the electrochemical equivalent of zinc. Atomic weight Zn = 65.4.

$$1 \text{ g-eq wt Zn} = \frac{65.4 \text{ g Zn}}{2 \text{ g-eq wt}} = 32.7 \text{ g Zn/g-eq wt}$$

$$\frac{1 \text{ g-eq wt of element}}{\text{Electrochemical eq of element}} = 96{,}500 \text{ coulombs/g-eq wt}$$

$$\text{Electrochemical eq of element} = \frac{1 \text{ g-eq wt of element (g/g-eq wt)}}{96{,}500 \text{ coulombs/g-eq wt}}$$

Let x = electrochemical equivalent of Zn

$$= \frac{32.7 \text{ g Zn/g-eq wt}}{96{,}500 \text{ coulombs/g-eq wt}} = 0.0003388 \text{ g Zn/coulomb}$$

Example 2. What weights of nickel and silver will be liberated by a current of 1 amp flowing for 50 min through solutions of $NiSO_4$ and $AgNO_3$? Atomic weights: Ni = 58.7; Ag = 107.9.

Step 1. Determine the gram-equivalent weights of Ni and Ag.

$$1 \text{ g-eq wt Ni} = \frac{58.7 \text{ g Ni}}{2 \text{ g-eq wt}} = 29.4 \text{ g Ni/g-eq wt}$$

$$1 \text{ g-eq wt Ag} = \frac{107.9 \text{ g Ag}}{1 \text{ g-eq wt}} = 107.9 \text{ g Ag/g-eq wt}$$

Step 2

$$50 \text{ min} = 3{,}000 \text{ sec}$$
$$\text{Amperes} \times \text{seconds} = \text{coulombs}$$
$$1 \text{ amp} \times 3{,}000 \text{ sec} = 3{,}000 \text{ coulombs}$$
$$1\ F = 96{,}500 \text{ coulombs}$$

Step 3.   To express any given number of coulombs in terms of the number of faradays,

$$\text{No. of faradays} = \frac{\text{no. of coulombs}}{96,500 \text{ coulombs/faraday}}$$

Let x = number of faradays in 3,000 coulombs

$$= \frac{3,000 \text{ coulombs}}{96,500 \text{ coulombs/}F} = 0.0311 \, F$$

Step 4.   Since 1 faraday (F) deposits or liberates 1 g-eq wt of a substance, 1 faraday is equivalent to 1 g-eq wt, or $1 \, F \backsimeq 1$ g-eq wt. Then $0.0311 \, F \backsimeq 0.0311$ g-eq wt, or $0.0311 \, F$ will deposit 0.0311 g-eq wt Ni and 0.0311 g-eq wt Ag.   Then

$$0.0311 \text{ g-eq wt Ni} \times \frac{29.4 \text{ g Ni}}{1 \text{ g-eq wt Ni}} = 0.914 \text{ g Ni}$$

and

$$0.0311 \text{ g-eq wt Ag} \times \frac{107.9 \text{ g Ag}}{1 \text{ g-eq wt Ag}} = 3.36 \text{ g Ag}$$

Alternate Method.   Combining Steps 3 and 4 as factors, let x = weight of Ni liberated by 3,000 coulombs

$$x = 3,000 \text{ coulombs} \times \frac{1 \, F}{96,500 \text{ coulombs}} \times \frac{1 \text{ g-eq wt Ni}}{1 \, F} \times \frac{29.4 \text{ g Ni}}{1 \text{ g-eq wt Ni}}$$

$$= \frac{3,000 \times 29.4}{96,500} \text{ g Ni} = 0.914 \text{ g Ni}$$

Let y = weight of Ag liberated by 3,000 coulombs

$$y = 3,000 \text{ coulombs} \times \frac{1 \, F}{96,500 \text{ coulombs}} \times \frac{1 \text{ g-eq wt Ag}}{1 \, F} \times \frac{107.9 \text{ g Ag}}{1 \text{ g-eq wt Ag}}$$

$$= \frac{3,000 \times 107.9}{96,500} \text{ g Ag} = 3.36 \text{ g Ag}$$

Example 3.   How many milliliters (STP) of oxygen and hydrogen will be liberated by 5 amp flowing for 25 min through acidulated water?

Step 1

$$25 \text{ min} = 1,500 \text{ sec}$$
$$\text{Amperes} \times \text{seconds} = \text{coulombs}$$
$$5 \text{ amp} \times 1,500 \text{ sec} = 7,500 \text{ coulombs}$$

Step 2

$$\text{No. of faradays} = \frac{\text{no. of coulombs}}{96,500 \text{ coulombs/faraday}}$$

Let x = number of faradays in 7,500 coulombs

$$= \frac{7{,}500 \text{ coulombs}}{96{,}500 \text{ coulombs}/F} = 0.078\,F$$

Step 3. By definition, $1\,F$, or 96,500 coulombs, liberates 1 l-eq (STP) of gas, or $1\,F \approx 1$ l-eq (STP) of gas; then $0.078\,F \approx 0.078$ l-eq (STP) gas.

Step 4. If 1 l-eq (STP) H = 11.2 l (STP) H, or 11.2 l (STP) H/l-eq (STP) H,

$$0.078 \text{ l-eq (STP) H} \times \frac{11.2 \text{ l (STP) H}}{1 \text{ l-eq (STP) H}} = 0.87 \text{ l (STP) H}$$

or 870 ml (STP) H. Then 1 l-eq (STP) O = 5.6 l (STP) O, or 5.6 l (STP) O/l-eq (STP) O, and

$$0.078 \text{ l-eq (STP) O} \times \frac{5.6 \text{ l (STP) O}}{1 \text{ l-eq (STP) O}} = 0.435 \text{ l (STP) O}$$
$$= 435 \text{ ml (STP) O}$$

or 7,500 coulombs liberates 870 ml (STP) H and 435 ml (STP) O.

Alternate Solution. Combining Steps 2, 3, and 4 as factors, let x = number of liters (STP) H liberated by 7,500 coulombs

$$x = 7{,}500 \text{ coulombs} \times \frac{1\,F}{96{,}500 \text{ coulombs}} \times \frac{1 \text{ l-eq (STP) H}}{1\,F}$$
$$\times \frac{11.2 \text{ l (STP) H}}{1 \text{ l-eq (STP) H}}$$

$$= \frac{7{,}500 \times 11.2}{96{,}500} \text{ l (STP) H} = 0.870 \text{ l (STP) H}$$
$$= 870 \text{ ml (STP) H}$$

Let y = number of liters (STP) O liberated by 7,500 coulombs

$$y = 7{,}500 \text{ coulombs} \times \frac{1\,F}{96{,}500 \text{ coulombs}} \times \frac{1 \text{ l-eq (STP) O}}{1\,F}$$
$$\times \frac{5.6 \text{ l (STP) O}}{1 \text{ l-eq (STP) O}}$$

$$= \frac{7{,}500 \times 5.6}{96{,}500} \text{ l (STP) O} = 0.435 \text{ l (STP) O}$$
$$= 435 \text{ ml (STP) O}$$

Example 4. What time will be required for a current of 2 amp to deposit 8.12 g of antimony from $SbCl_3$ solution? Atomic weight Sb = 121.8.

$$1 \text{ g-eq wt Sb} = \frac{121.8 \text{ g Sb}}{3 \text{ g-eq wt}} = 40.6 \text{ g Sb/g-eq wt}$$

Step 1. Determine the number of gram-equivalents in 8.12 g SbCl₃.

Let x = number of gram-equivalents

$$= \frac{8.12 \text{ g Sb}}{40.6 \text{ g Sb/g-eq wt}} = 0.2 \text{ g-eq}$$

Step 2. Since 1 g-eq $\backsimeq$ 1 F, then 0.2 g-eq $\backsimeq$ 0.2 F.

Step 3. Then

$$0.2 \, F \times \frac{96,500 \text{ coulombs}}{1 \, F} = 19,300 \text{ coulombs (amp-sec)}$$

Step 4. Let y = number of seconds for 2 amp to deposit 8.12 g Sb

$$y = \frac{19,300 \text{ amp-sec}}{2 \text{ amp}} = 9,650 \text{ sec}$$

Alternate Solution. Combining the foregoing steps as factors, let x = number of seconds for 2 amp to deposit 8.12 g Sb

$$x = 8.12 \text{ g Sb} \times \frac{1 \text{ g-eq wt}}{40.6 \text{ g Sb}} \times \frac{1 \, F}{1 \text{ g-eq wt}} \times \frac{96,500 \text{ coulombs}}{1 \, F}$$
$$\times \frac{1 \text{ amp-sec}}{1 \text{ coulomb}} \times \frac{1}{2 \text{ amp}}$$

$$= \frac{8.12 \times 96,500 \text{ sec}}{40.6 \times 2} = 9,650 \text{ sec}$$

or 9,650 sec, or 2 hr 40 min 50 sec, is the time required to deposit 8.12 g of Sb.

Example 5. How many amperes of current are required to liberate 5.6 l (STP) of chlorine in 3 hr in the electrolysis of brine (NaCl) solution?

Step 1. Determine the number of liter-equivalents (STP) of Cl in 5.6 l (STP) Cl.

$$1 \text{ l-eq (STP) Cl} = 11.2 \text{ l (STP) Cl}$$

or 11.2 l (STP) Cl/l-eq (STP) Cl.

Let x = number of liter-equivalents (STP) of Cl

$$= \frac{5.6 \text{ l (STP) Cl}}{11.2 \text{ l (STP) Cl/l-eq (STP) Cl}} = 0.5 \text{ l-eq (STP) Cl}$$

Step 2. Since 1 l-eq (STP) gas $\backsimeq$ 1 g-eq wt gas $\backsimeq$ 1 F, then 0.5 l-eq (STP) Cl $\backsimeq$ 0.5 F.

Step 3. Determine the number of coulombs in 0.5 F.

$$0.5 \, F = 0.5 \, F \times \frac{96,500 \text{ coulombs}}{1 \, F} = 48,250 \text{ coulombs}$$

Step 4

$$3 \text{ hr} = 3 \text{ hr} \times \frac{3,600 \text{ sec}}{1 \text{ hr}} = 10,800 \text{ sec}$$

Step 5

$$48,250 \text{ coulombs} \times \frac{1 \text{ amp-sec}}{1 \text{ coulomb}} = 48,250 \text{ amp-sec}$$

Let y = number of amperes

$$= \frac{48,250 \text{ amp-sec}}{10,800 \text{ sec}} = 4.5 \text{ amp}$$

Alternate Solution. Combining foregoing steps as factors, let x = number of amperes required to liberate 5.6 l (STP) Cl in 3 hr

$$x = 5.6 \text{ l (STP) Cl} \times \frac{1 \text{ l-eq (STP) Cl}}{11.2 \text{ l (STP) Cl}} \times \frac{1 F}{1 \text{ l-eq (STP) Cl}}$$
$$\times \frac{96,500 \text{ coulombs}}{1 F} \times \frac{1 \text{ amp-sec}}{1 \text{ coulomb}} \times \frac{1}{10,800 \text{ sec}}$$
$$= \frac{5.6 \times 96,500}{11.2 \times 10,800} \text{ amp} = 4.5 \text{ amp}$$

Example 6. A 100-watt 110-volt incandescent lamp is connected in series with an electrolytic cell containing cadmium sulfate solution. What weight of cadmium should be deposited by the current flowing for 10 hr? Atomic weight Cd = 112.4.

$$1 \text{ g-eq wt Cd} = \frac{112.4 \text{ g Cd}}{2 \text{ g-eq wt}} = 56.2 \text{ g Cd/g-eq wt}$$

Step 1

$$P = EI \quad \text{or} \quad I = \frac{P}{E}$$

P = 100 watts (volt-amp) $\quad E$ = 110 volts $\quad I$ = amperes

$$I = \frac{100 \text{ volt-amp}}{110 \text{ volts}} = \frac{100}{110} \text{ amp}$$

Step 2

$$Q = It \quad t = 10 \text{ hr} \times 3,600 \text{ sec/hr} = 36,000 \text{ sec}$$
$$Q = {}^{100}\!/_{110} \text{ amp} \times 36,000 \text{ sec} = 32,724 \text{ amp-sec (coulombs)}$$

Step 3. Determine the number of faradays in 32,724 coulombs.

$$32,724 \text{ coulombs} = 32,724 \text{ coulombs} \times \frac{1 F}{96,500 \text{ coulombs}}$$
$$= 0.34 F$$

Step 4. If $0.34 F \approx 0.34$ g-eq wt Cd,

$$0.34 \text{ g-eq wt Cd} \times \frac{56.2 \text{ g Cd}}{1 \text{ g-eq wt Cd}} = 19.1 \text{ g Cd}$$

or 19.1 g Cd could be deposited in 1 hr.

Example 7. In the electrolysis of a dilute sulfuric acid solution a current flowing through the solution for 20 min liberated a total volume of 56 ml (STP) of gas. Find (a) the number of coulombs used and (b) the number of amperes of current.

(a) In the electrolysis of a dilute acid solution, 1 F liberates 1 l-eq (STP) of H and 1 l-eq (STP) of O, and 1 l-eq (STP) H = 11.2 l (STP) H and 1 l-eq (STP) O = 5.6 l (STP) O, or 1 F liberates 11.2 l (STP) H + 5.6 l (STP) O = 16.8 l (STP) gas. Then 16.8 l (STP) gas = 16,800 ml (STP) gas liberated by 1 F.

Let x = number of faradays required to liberate 56 ml (STP) gas

$$= \frac{56 \text{ ml (STP) gas}}{16,800 \text{ ml (STP) gas/faraday}} = 0.0033 \ F$$

Then $0.0033 \ F \times 96,500$ coulombs/faraday = 318 coulombs (amp-sec), or 318 coulombs are used in the electrolysis.

(b) In the electrolysis of a dilute acid solution,

$$Q = It \qquad \text{or} \qquad I = \frac{Q}{t}$$

$$t = 20 \text{ min} \times 60 \text{ sec/min} = 1,200 \text{ sec}$$

$$I = \frac{318 \text{ amp-sec}}{1,200 \text{ sec}} = 0.26 \text{ amp}$$

or 0.26 amp is used in the electrolysis.

Problems

16-1. Determine the electrochemical equivalent of (a) cadmium and (b) hydrogen.   *Ans.* (a) 0.58 mg Cd.

16-2. How much antimony will be deposited in 2 hr by the passage of a current of 6 amp through a solution of antimony trichloride?   *Ans.* 18.2 g.

16-3. Calculate the number of grams of copper that will be deposited in 5 hr by a current of 5 amp from a solution of $CuSO_4$.   *Ans.* 29.6 g.

16-4. How much copper will be deposited by a current of 0.5 amp flowing for 30 min through a solution of (a) cuprous chloride and (b) cupric chloride?   *Ans.* (a) 0.59 g; (b) 0.295 g.

16-5. Calculate the weight of Co deposited from a solution of a cobaltous salt by 23,247 coulombs.   *Ans.* 7.10 g.

16-6. A current of 0.55 amp was passed through a dilute sulfuric acid solution for 75 min. Calculate (a) the volume in ml (STP) of hydrogen liberated at the cathode and (b) the volume of oxygen in ml (STP) liberated at the anode.   *Ans.* (a) 287 ml (STP); (b) 144 ml (STP).

16-7. A current of 0.1 amp passing for 24 hr through separate electrolytic cells containing solutions of $HgCl_2$, $Cd(NO_3)_2$, and $AgNO_3$ will deposit what respective weights of Hg, Cd, and Ag?   *Ans.* 8.99 g Hg; 5.02 g Cd; 9.67 g Ag.

16-8. How much silver will be deposited by a current of 1 amp passing through a solution of silver nitrate in 1 sec? How should you define an ampere on this basis?

16-9. (a) How many coulombs of electricity will be necessary to deposit 2.5 g of nickel from a solution of $NiSO_4$? (b) Calculate how many amperes will be necessary to deposit 2.5 g of nickel in 10 min.

Ans. (a) 8,222 coulombs; (b) 13.7 amp.

16-10. It is desired to deposit 50 g of tin from a stannous chloride solution with a current of 1 amp. How much time will be required? *Ans.* 22.6 hr.

16-11. A quantity of current passing through a solution of a cadmium salt deposited 1.02 g of cadmium in 20 min. Calculate the amperage. *Ans.* 1.45 amp.

16-12. A certain current can deposit 200 g of zinc in 8 hr. What time will be required for this current passing through a brine solution to liberate a cubic meter of chlorine at 0°C and 760 mm Hg? *Ans.* 116.7 hr.

16-13. A 50-watt 110-volt incandescent lamp is placed in series with an electrolytic cell containing a solution of zinc sulfate. Calculate the weight of the Zn that could be deposited in 1 hr from the solution by the current that will flow. *Ans.* 0.55 g.

16-14. A current passed through a dilute hydrochloric acid solution for 20 min liberated 100 ml of hydrogen, at STP. Calculate (a) the number of coulombs of electricity required and (b) the amperage needed.

Ans. (a) 862 coulombs; (b) 0.7 amp.

16-15. A current is passed through a dilute sulfuric acid solution for 15 min, thereby liberating 50 ml of hydrogen at 22°C and 750 mm Hg. Calculate (a) the number of coulombs of electricity required and (b) the amperage needed. *Ans.* (a) 397 coulombs; (b) 0.44 amp.

16-16. A 100-watt 110-volt incandescent lamp is placed in series with an electrolytic cell containing a dilute solution of phosphoric acid. Calculate the volume of hydrogen measured at 18°C and 750 mm Hg that will be liberated in 15 min. *Ans.* 103 ml.

16-17. What time will be required for a current of 0.2 amp to deposit all the silver from 50 ml of 0.1 N $AgNO_3$ solution? *Ans.* 40 min 10 sec.

16-18. How many cubic meters of Cl_2 (STP) could be obtained from the electrolysis of molten sodium chloride in a cell that produces 100 kg of sodium? *Ans.* 48.7 cu m.

16-19. A flat piece of metal measuring 5 cm by 7 cm is made the cathode in a cell containing cupric sulfate solution. If a current of 0.1 amp flows through the cell for 20 min, what should be the thickness of the copper plating? Density of copper = 8.9 g/cu cm. *Ans.* 0.6 μ.

NOTE. Consult Table VI, Appendix, Electrochemical Series, for electrode potentials.

16-20. What is the theoretical voltage for the reaction of a cell setup consisting of a zinc electrode in a dilute zinc sulfate solution and a tin electrode in a stannous chloride solution?

16-21. Determine the theoretical potential difference corresponding to each of the following redox-couple reactions: (a) $Zn^0 + 2Ag^+ \rightarrow Zn^{+2} + 2Ag^0$; (b) $2Sb^0 + 3Sn^{+4} \rightarrow 2Sb^{+3} + 3Sn^{+2}$; (c) $Sn^0 + Sn^{+4} \rightarrow 2Sn^{+2}$.

16-22. Find the theoretical emf corresponding to each of the following redox-couple reactions: (a) $Cl_2^0 + Sn^{+2} \rightarrow 2Cl^- + Sn^{+4}$; (b) $Hg^0 + Hg^{+2} \rightarrow Hg_2^{+2}$; (c) $Cu^0 + Hg^{+2} \rightarrow Cu^{+2} + Hg^0$.

16-23. Calculate the theoretical potential difference corresponding to each of the following redox-couple reactions: (a) $Hg^{+2} + Sn^{+2} \rightarrow Hg^0 + Sn^{+4}$; (b)

$5Sn^{+2} + 2MnO_4^- + 16H^+ \rightarrow 2Mn^{+2} + 5Sn^{+4} + 8H_2O$; (c) $6Br^- + Cr_2O_7^{-2}$ $+ 14H^+ \rightarrow 3Br_2^0 + 2Cr^{+3} + 7H_2O$.

16-24. Determine the electrochemical equivalent of (a) oxygen and (b) chromium.

16-25. How many grams of metal should be deposited by $0.25F$ from each of the following solutions: (a) $Ag(NH_3)_2Cl$; (b) $CdSO_4$; (c) $Bi(NO_3)_3$?

16-26. Determine the number of grams of metal that should be liberated by $0.125F$ from each one of the following solutions: (a) $Ni(NH_3)_4SO_4$; (b) $Cr_2(SO_4)_3$; (c) $CuCl$.

16-27. Determine the number of liters (STP) of gas that should be liberated by $0.35F$ from the electrolysis of (a) molten NaCl, (b) dilute sulfuric acid solution, and (c) dilute NaCl solution.

16-28. How many coulombs are required to liberate 145 ml (STP) of Cl_2 from the electrolysis of a brine solution in 30 min?

16-29. How many amperes are required to liberate 392 ml (STP) of H_2 from the electrolysis of acidulated water in 15 min?

16-30. A current of 2 amp is flowing through an electrolytic cell containing dilute cupric sulfate solution. What weight of copper will be liberated in 20 min?

16-31. How many minutes is required to plate out 2.46 g of Zn from a zinc chloride solution using a current of 5 amp?

16-32. It is desired to deposit 2.95 g of nickel from a nickel sulfate solution employing a current of 1.5 amp. How much time will be required?

16-33. How much time, in minutes, is required to liberate 280 ml (STP) of Cl_2 from the electrolysis of a brine solution using a current of 2.5 amp?

16-34. How much time, in minutes, is necessary to liberate a total volume of 252 ml (STP) gas from the electrolysis of acidulated water by a current of 3 amp?

16-35. A 100-watt 220-volt incandescent lamp is placed in series with a cell containing dilute solution of sulfuric acid. Calculate the number of milliliters of gas at 21°C and 750 mm Hg liberated in 10 min.

16-36. A current from a battery deposits 100 g of nickel in 5 hr. If this same current is passed through a sodium chloride solution, what time will be required to liberate a total volume of 2 cu m (STP) of gas?

16-37. What weight of chromium should be deposited from a chromic acid solution by a current of 5 amp flowing for 25 hr, assuming an efficiency of 95 per cent?

16-38. What weight of silver should be deposited from a solution of $KAg(CN)_2$ by a current of 2 amp flowing for 25 hr, assuming an efficiency of 92 per cent?

16-39. Determine the time required to deposit 4 g of antimony from a solution of antimony trichloride by 4 amp, assuming a current efficiency of 90 per cent.

CHAPTER XVII

CHEMICAL EQUILIBRIUM; REVERSIBLE REACTIONS

OUTLINE

Equilibrium is a condition in which two opposing tendencies balance one another. (1) Physical equilibrium; (2) chemical equilibrium.

Le Châtelier principle. When a reaction in a state of equilibrium is subjected to a stress, such as change in pressure, temperature, or concentration, the tendency is to shift the equilibrium in such a way as to relieve the stress, and a new equilibrium will be established under the new conditions. Example: the ammonia equilibrium reaction.

Law of mass action. The rate of a chemical reaction is proportional to the molecular concentrations of the reacting substances. Derivation of the mass-action expression.

Ionization constants. $K_{\text{ionization}}$ for acetic acid. $K_{\text{ionization}}$ for ammonia solution.

Common-ion effect. If to a solution of a weak acid, or a weak base, a salt is added that has an ion in common with the weak acid or weak base, the ionization of the weak electrolyte is repressed; that is, the acidity of the acid solution is decreased, or the basicity of the base solution is decreased.

Significance and determination of pH value. pH represents the effective $[H_3O^+]$ of a dilute acid solution.

An equilibrium is a condition in which two opposing tendencies balance one another. There are two types of equilibrium: (1) physical equilibrium and (2) chemical equilibrium.

Examples of Physical Equilibrium. 1. The change of state when liquid water is converted into water vapor, and the simultaneous reverse process, or condensation of water vapor. This may be represented by

$$H_2O_{\text{liquid}} \rightleftharpoons H_2O_{\text{vapor}}$$

2. The condition existing when a saturated solution of sodium chloride is in contact with excess solid sodium chloride, represented by

$$NaCl_{\text{solid}} \rightleftharpoons NaCl_{\text{dissolved}}$$

Examples of Chemical Equilibrium. 1. The reaction between carbon monoxide and steam in a sealed tube at 400°C may be represented by

$$CO + H_2O \rightleftharpoons CO_2 + H_2$$

2. The synthesis of ammonia by the Haber process may be expressed as follows:

$$N_2 + 3H_2 \rightleftharpoons 2NH_3$$

3. The addition of water to a bismuth chloride solution followed by the addition of hydrochloric acid, or

$$BiCl_3 + H_2O \rightleftharpoons BiOCl\downarrow + 2HCl$$

A chemical reaction that is capable of proceeding in either of two directions is a reversible reaction. In dealing with this type of reaction, the term "velocity, or rate of reaction" is employed. The **rate of reaction** may be defined as the quantity of substance reacting in unit time. The factors affecting the rate of reaction are (a) temperature, (b) concentration, and (c) catalyst. These influences will be dealt with briefly in subsequent paragraphs.

Any system in equilibrium is governed by the **principle of Le Châtelier: When a reaction in a state of equilibrium is subjected to a stress, such as changes in pressure, temperature, or concentration, the tendency is to shift the equilibrium in such a way as to relieve the stress, and a new equilibrium will be established under the new conditions.**

The ammonia synthesis affords an excellent example of the application of the Le Châtelier principle. The equilibrium reaction is

$$\underset{1 \text{ vol}}{N_2} + \underset{3 \text{ vol}}{3H_2} \rightleftharpoons \underset{2 \text{ vol}}{2NH_3} + 24{,}500 \text{ cal}$$

1. Influence of temperature on this equilibrium reaction: The forward reaction (combination of N_2 and $3H_2$) is an exothermic reaction; the reverse reaction (decomposition of NH_3) is an endothermic reaction. Increase of temperature increases the rate of any reaction, but in this instance the reverse reaction is favored. Raising the temperature increases the rate of decomposition of ammonia to a much greater extent than it does the rate of combination of nitrogen and hydrogen. The equilibrium is displaced in the direction which absorbs heat, i.e., decomposition of NH_3. Thus, the yield of ammonia is decreased by an increase in temperature.

2. Influence of pressure on this reaction: Since the total initial volume of reacting gases is 4 volumes and the total final volume of products is 2 volumes, any application of pressure to this equilibrium system would favor the forward reaction, since the ammonia produced occupies a smaller volume, and the applied pressure would work in the same direction, i.e., toward a decrease in volume. For

this reason the Claude process uses a pressure up to 1,000 atm in the ammonia synthesis. Then increase in pressure on this equilibrium reaction would increase the yield of ammonia. In passing, it should be noted that in equilibrium reactions in which the total initial volume of reactants equals the total final volume of products, an applied pressure will not affect the equilibrium.

3. Influence of catalyst: The use of a catalyst increases the rate of both forward reaction and reverse reaction equally. It does not shift the equilibrium, but decreases the time required to reach equilibrium. The catalyst then has no effect on the yield of ammonia.

The conditions most favorable for producing ammonia would be a low temperature and high pressure under the influence of a catalyst. The accompanying table shows the effect of changes in temperature and pressure on the percentage yield (by volume) of ammonia at equilibrium.

Temperature, °C	Yield, per cent		
	1 atm	200 atm	1,000 atm
200	15.3	85.8	98.3
400	0.44	36.3	80.0
500	0.13	17.6	58
600	0.05	8.25	35

A glance at the table suggests operating this process at 200°C and 1,000 atm for the highest yield of ammonia. However, the reaction is slow at this temperature and yield is sacrificed to speed. The practical operating temperature range is about 450 to 600°C and pressure range of 100 to 300 atm. The Claude process operates at 1,000 to 2,000 atm.

The Influence of Concentration on a Chemical Equilibrium. The influence of concentration may well be illustrated by the equilibrium reaction

$$BiCl_3 + H_2O \rightleftharpoons BiOCl\downarrow + 2HCl$$

To alter this reversible reaction, one may change the concentration either of the reacting substances or of the products. If hydrochloric acid is slowly added to this system, the BiOCl precipitate will eventually dissolve. If to this solution more water is added, the BiOCl precipitate will form again. Of course these procedures could be repeated with similar results. Thus, an increase in concentration of HCl (a product of the reaction) causes a displacement of this equilibrium reaction to the left; the addition of water (a reactant) to this solution causes the reaction to proceed to the right. Of course a new equilibrium is established under the new conditions of concentration.

LAW OF MASS ACTION; EQUILIBRIUM CONSTANT

The **law of mass action** states: **The rate of a chemical reaction is proportional to the molecular concentrations of the reacting substances.**

Consider the reaction

$$A + B \rightleftharpoons C + D$$

In line with common practice the square bracket [ ] enclosing a given substance denotes the concentration of that substance in moles per liter. Thus $[A]$ = concentration of A in moles per liter (moles/l).

Let $V \rightarrow$ = rate of forward reaction

$V \leftarrow$ = rate of reverse reaction

In accordance with the law of mass action, the reaction rate depends on the molecular concentrations of reacting substances and will be proportional to the product of their molecular concentrations, or

$$V \rightarrow = k' \times [A] \times [B]$$
$$V \leftarrow = k'' \times [C] \times [D]$$

k' and k'' are proportionality factors and are dependent on temperature, pressure, and catalysts.

At equilibrium the two rates of reaction are exactly equal, or

$$V \rightarrow = V \leftarrow$$

Hence

$$k' \times [A] \times [B] = k'' \times [C] \times [D]$$
$$\frac{[C] \times [D]}{[A] \times [B]} = \frac{k'}{k''} = K$$

K = equilibrium constant of the reversible or equilibrium reaction.

IONIZATION CONSTANTS

The following examples of the application of the foregoing law will deal essentially with ionic reactions of weak electrolytes.

1. The ionization of the weak acid, acetic acid, is represented by the ionic equilibrium

$$HC_2H_3O_2 + H_2O \rightleftharpoons H_3O^+ + C_2H_3O_2^-$$

According to the law of mass action

$$\frac{[H_3O^+] \times [C_2H_3O_2^-]}{[HC_2H_3O_2] \times [H_2O]} = K_{\text{equilibrium}}$$

$[H_2O]$ is practically constant, or $[H_2O] = k$.

$$\frac{[H_3O^+] \times [C_2H_3O_2^-]}{[HC_2H_3O_2]} = [H_2O] \times K_{\text{equilibrium}} = K_{\text{ionization}}$$

$K_{\text{ionization}}$ is known as the ionization constant.

2. The ionization constant of the weak base ammonia in water, commonly called ammonium hydroxide, is formulated as follows:

$$NH_3 + H_2O \rightleftharpoons NH_4^+ + OH^-$$

Then

$$\frac{[NH_4^+] \times [OH^-]}{[NH_3] \times [H_2O]} = K_{\text{equilibrium}}$$

$$[H_2O] = \text{constant}$$

$$\frac{[NH_4^+] \times [OH^-]}{[NH_3]} = [H_2O] \times K_{\text{equilibrium}} = K_{\text{ionization}}$$

Example 1. A 0.1 M acetic acid solution is ionized to the extent of 1.34 per cent. Find (a) $[H_3O^+]$, (b) $[C_2H_3O_2^-]$, (c) $[HC_2H_3O_2]$, (d) $K_{\text{ionization}}$ of acetic acid.

The ionic equilibrium for acetic acid is

$$HC_2H_3O_2 + H_2O \rightleftharpoons H_3O^+ + C_2H_3O_2^-$$

Gross concentration of $HC_2H_3O_2 = 0.1$ M, or 0.1 g-mole/l
Ion concentration = gross concentration $\times$ fraction ionized

(a) $[H_3O^+] = 0.1$ g-mole/l $\times$ 0.0134 = 0.00134 g-ion/l
$$= 1.34 \times 10^{-3} \text{ g-ion/l}$$

(b) $[C_2H_3O_2^-] = 0.1$ g-mole/l $\times$ 0.0134 = 0.00134 g-ion/l
$$= 1.34 \times 10^{-3} \text{ g-ion/l}$$

(c) Un-ionized acetic acid = $[HC_2H_3O_2]$
Un-ionized concentration
$$= \text{gross concentration} \times \text{fraction un-ionized}$$

If 1.34 per cent of 0.1 M $HC_2H_3O_2$ solution is ionized, 98.66 per cent of it is un-ionized.

$$[HC_2H_3O_2] = 0.1 \text{ g-mole/l} \times 0.9866 = 0.09866 \text{ g-mole/l}$$

or

Un-ionized concentration = gross concentration − ion concentration then

$$[HC_2H_3O_2] = 0.1 \text{ g-mole/l} - 0.00134 \text{ g-ion/l} = 0.09866 \text{ g-mole/l}$$
$$= 9.87 \times 10^{-2} \text{ g-mole/l}$$

(d) The mass-action expression of acetic acid is

$$\frac{[H_3O^+] \times [C_2H_3O_2^-]}{[HC_2H_3O_2]} = K_{\text{ionization}}$$

where $[H_3O^+]$ and $[C_2H_3O_2^-]$ represent the concentration of hydronium ion and acetate ion in moles per liter (or gram-ions/l), respectively, and $[HC_2H_3O_2]$ = concentration of un-ionized acetic acid in moles per liter. Substituting the concentration values obtained in parts (a), (b), and (c) in the foregoing mass-action expression,

$$\frac{(1.34 \times 10^{-3})(1.34 \times 10^{-3})}{(9.87 \times 10^{-2})} = 0.000018 = 1.8 \times 10^{-5} = K_{\text{ionization}}$$

A convention frequently employed in determining ion concentrations of weak electrolytes is to designate the gross concentration (molarity) by M, and the degree of ionization (as a decimal fraction) by α. Then in determining $K_{\text{ionization}}$ of acetic acid, part (d) of the foregoing example, one may proceed as follows:

$$[H_3O^+] = M\alpha \qquad [C_2H_3O_2^-] = M\alpha$$
$$[HC_2H_3O_2] = M - M\alpha = M(1 - \alpha)$$

The mass-action expression would be

$$\frac{(M\alpha)(M\alpha)}{M(1 - \alpha)} = M\left(\frac{\alpha^2}{1 - \alpha}\right) = K_{\text{ionization}}$$

$M = 0.1$, and $\alpha = 1.34 \times 10^{-2}$.
Then

$$0.1\left[\frac{(1.34 \times 10^{-2})^2}{1 - (1.34 \times 10^{-2})}\right] = 0.000018 = K_{\text{ionization}}$$

It is essential to grasp the idea that the value of $K_{\text{ionization}}$ of acetic acid will not change, even though the concentration of the solution is changed or some other acetate is present in the same solution. The following table illustrates the constancy of K despite changes in the concentration of the solution. It gives the experimentally determined value of the percentage ionization of acetic acid and the value of $K_{\text{ionization}}$ for solutions of acetic acid of different concentrations. It will be noted that for a tenfold change in the concentration of the solution the value of $K_{\text{ionization}}$ remains constant within the limit of error of such measurements.

Concentration of acetic acid, moles per liter	Percentage ionization	$K_{\text{ionization}}$
0.1	1.34	1.82×10^{-5}
0.08	1.50	1.83×10^{-5}
0.03	2.45	1.85×10^{-5}
0.01	4.17	1.81×10^{-5}

Example 2. Find (a) $[H_3O^+]$ and (b) percentage ionization of 0.2 M acetic acid solution. The ionization constant of acetic acid = 1.8×10^{-5}.

$$\frac{[H_3O^+] \times [C_2H_3O_2^-]}{[HC_2H_3O_2]} = K_{\text{ionization}}$$

Gross concentration of acetic acid = 0.2 g-mole/l

Let $x = [H_3O^+]$. Then

$$0.2 - x = [HC_2H_3O_2]$$

Substituting in the mass-action expression,

$$\frac{x \times x}{0.2 - x} = 1.8 \times 10^{-5}$$

When simplified, this yields a quadratic equation in x. Since x is small, it is possible to avoid the quadratic equation by eliminating x with respect to 0.2 in the denominator. The following expression is obtained:

$$\frac{x^2}{0.2} = 1.8 \times 10^{-5}$$

$$x = \sqrt{0.36 \times 10^{-5}} = \sqrt{3.6 \times 10^{-6}} = 1.9 \times 10^{-3}$$

Then

$$[H_3O^+] = 1.9 \times 10^{-3} \text{ g-ion/l}$$

Gross concentration $\times$ fraction ionized = ion concentration

Let y = fraction ionized

$$0.2 \times y = 1.9 \times 10^{-3}$$

$$y = \frac{1.9 \times 10^{-3}}{0.2} = 9.5 \times 10^{-3} = 0.0095$$

0.0095 = 0.95 per cent = percentage ionization of 0.2 M acetic acid solution.

Example 3. Determine (a) the gross concentration of an acetic acid solution which is 0.2 per cent ionized and (b) $[H_3O^+]$ of this solution. $K_{ionization}$ for $HC_2H_3O_2 = 1.8 \times 10^{-5}$.

$$\frac{[H_3O^+] \times [C_2H_3O_2^-]}{[HC_2H_3O_2]} = K_{ionization}$$

(a) Let x = gross concentration of acetic acid solution

$$0.2 \text{ per cent} = 0.002 = 2 \times 10^{-3}$$
$$[H_3O^+] = x(2 \times 10^{-3}) \qquad [C_2H_3O_2^-] = x(2 \times 10^{-3})$$
$$[HC_2H_3O_2] = x - x(2 \times 10^{-3})$$

Substituting in the mass-action expression,

$$\frac{x(2 \times 10^{-3}) \times x(2 \times 10^{-3})}{x - x(2 \times 10^{-3})} = 1.8 \times 10^{-5}$$

To avoid complications in solving this expression, it is permissible to eliminate $x(2 \times 10^{-3})$ in the denominator, since it is small in comparison with x.

$$x^2(2 \times 10^{-3})^2 = 1.8 \times 10^{-5}x$$
$$x = \frac{1.8 \times 10^{-5}}{4 \times 10^{-6}} = 0.45 \times 10 = 4.5$$

or gross concentration (molarity) = 4.5 M.

(b) Gross concentration $\times$ fraction ionized = ion concentration 4.5 g-moles $\times$ (2×10^{-3}) = 9×10^{-3} = 0.009 g-ion/l = $[H^3O^+]$ of this acid solution.

COMMON-ION EFFECT

If to a solution of a weak acid or a weak base a salt is added that has an ion in common with the weak acid or weak base, the ionization of the weak electrolyte is repressed. Thus if the salt ammonium acetate (highly ionized) is added to an acetic acid solution (weak acid), there is a tremendous increase in concentration of acetate ions. The high concentration of acetate ions, in turn, ties up hydronium ions, resulting in the production of more un-ionized acetic acid molecules, thereby decreasing the acidity of the solution. This can also be ascertained from the mass-action expression. If in the fraction

$$\frac{[H_3O^+] \times [C_2H_3O_2^-]}{[HC_2H_3O_2]} = K_{ionization}$$

the value of $[C_2H_3O_2^-]$ is increased, and it is required to maintain the value of $K_{ionization}$, then either $[H_3O^+]$ must decrease or $[HC_2H_3O_2]$ must increase.   The increase in $[HC_2H_3O_2]$ will be very slight.   An example will further illustrate this common-ion effect.

Example 1.   What is the $[H_3O^+]$ of a solution known to contain 0.1 g-mole of ammonium acetate in 1 l of 0.1 M acetic acid?   Assume the effective ionization of ammonium acetate is 80 per cent; $K_{ionization}$ of acetic acid = 1.8×10^{-5}.

The solution is 0.1 M in $HC_2H_3O_2$, and 0.1 M in $NH_4C_2H_3O_2$.

$$\frac{[H_3O^+] \times [C_2H_3O_2^-]}{[HC_2H_3O_2]} = K_{ionization}$$

Let $x = [H_3O^+] = [C_2H_3O_2^-]$

$$0.1 - x = [HC_2H_3O_2]$$

0.1 g-mole/l $\times$ 0.8 = 0.08 g-ion/l = $[C_2H_3O_2^-]$ from ammonium acetate
$$0.08 + x = \text{total } [C_2H_3O_2^-] \text{ in the solution}$$

Substituting in the mass-action expression,

$$\frac{x(0.08 + x)}{0.1 - x} = 1.8 \times 10^{-5}$$

This expression is a quadratic equation in x^2 and x.   Since x is small, it is permissible to neglect the x in comparison with 0.1 in the denominator and 0.08 in the numerator, or

$$\frac{x(0.08)}{0.1} = 1.8 \times 10^{-5}$$
$$x = 2.2 \times 10^{-5}$$

or

$$[H_3O^+] = 2.2 \times 10^{-5} \text{ g-ion/l} = [H_3O^+] \text{ of this solution}$$

From Example 1, page 253, it was shown that $[H_3O^+]$ in a 0.1 M acetic acid solution was 1.3×10^{-3} g-ion/l.   The addition of 0.1 M ammonium acetate to the acetic acid solution reduced the $[H_3O^+]$ to 2.2×10^{-5} g-ion/l, or $2.2 \times 10^{-5}/1.3 \times 10^{-3}$ = one-sixtieth of its former value.

This decrease in $[H_3O^+]$, or decrease in ionization of acetic acid, brought about by the high concentration of $C_2H_3O_2^-$ (common ion) furnished by $NH_4C_2H_3O_2$, is known as the *common-ion effect*.

Example 2.   (1) Calculate (*a*) the $[OH^-]$ and (*b*) percentage ionization of 0.01 M ammonia solution.   (2) Calculate (*a*) the $[OH^-]$ and (*b*) percentage ionization of 0.01 M ammonia solution containing 0.01 M NH_4Cl. $K_{ionization}$ of ammonia solution = 1.8×10^{-5}. Assume NH_4Cl to be 100 per cent ionized.

The equilibrium reaction for ammonia solution is

$$NH_3 + H_2O \rightleftharpoons NH_4^+ + OH^-$$

The mass-action expression for this equilibrium is

$$\frac{[NH_4^+] \times [OH^-]}{[NH_3]} = K_{ionization}$$

(1a) Let $x = [NH_4^+] = [OH^-]$

$$0.01 - x = [NH_3]$$

Substituting in the mass-action expression,

$$\frac{x \times x}{0.01 - x} = 1.8 \times 10^{-5}$$

Because x is small, neglect x with respect to 0.01 in denominator.

$$x^2 = 0.018 \times 10^{-5} = 18 \times 10^{-8}$$
$$x = \sqrt{18 \times 10^{-8}} = 4 \times 10^{-4}$$

or 4×10^{-4} g-ion/l = $[OH^-]$ in original 0.01 M ammonia solution.

(1b) Gross concentration $\times$ fraction ionized = ion concentration
Let y = fraction ionized

$$0.01 \times y = 4 \times 10^{-4}$$
$$y = \frac{4 \times 10^{-4}}{1 \times 10^{-2}} = 4 \times 10^{-2} = 0.04$$

$0.04 = 4$ per cent = percentage ionization of 0.01 M ammonia solution.

(2a) The solution contains 0.01 M ammonia solution and 0.01 M NH_4Cl (100 per cent ionized).

Let $z = [OH^-] = [NH_4^+]$

$$0.01 - z = [NH_3]$$

Since 0.01 M NH_4Cl is 100 per cent ionized,

$$[NH_4^+] \text{ from } NH_4Cl = 0.01 \text{ g-ion/l}$$
$$0.01 + z = \text{total } [NH_4^+] \text{ in the solution}$$

Substituting these various values in the mass-action expression,

$$\frac{(0.01 + z)z}{0.01 - z} = 1.8 \times 10^{-5}$$

Because z is small, neglect z in comparison with 0.01 in both denominator and numerator, or

$$\frac{0.01z}{0.01} = 1.8 \times 10^{-5}$$
$$z = 1.8 \times 10^{-5}$$

1.8×10^{-5} g-ion/l = [OH$^-$] in solution containing 0.01 M ammonia solution and 0.01 M NH$_4$Cl.

(2b) Gross concentration $\times$ fraction ionized = ion concentration
Let w = fraction ionized

$$0.01 \times w = 1.8 \times 10^{-5}$$
$$w = \frac{1.8 \times 10^{-5}}{1 \times 10^{-2}} = 1.8 \times 10^{-3} = 0.0018$$

0.0018 = 0.18 per cent = percentage ionization of 0.01 M ammonia solution containing 0.01 M NH$_4$Cl.

SIGNIFICANCE AND DETERMINATION OF pH VALUE

Pure water is a very weak electrolyte and, as such, ionizes to a very low degree.   The ionization of water may be represented by

$$H_2O + H_2O \rightleftharpoons H_3O^+ + OH^-$$

(At equilibrium [H$_3$O$^+$] = [OH$^-$] = 1×10^{-7} g-ion/l.)
The mass-action expression would be

$$\frac{[H_3O^+] \times [OH^-]}{[H_2O]^2} = K_{\text{equilibrium}}$$

Because of the small values of [H$_3$O$^+$] and [OH$^-$] in water, any change in either of these values will have only a slight effect on the value for [H$_2$O].   Therefore [H$_2$O] may be considered to be a constant value, and

$$[H_3O^+] \times [OH^-] = K \times [H_2O]^2 = K_{\text{ion product}}$$

Since

$$[H_3O^+] = [OH^-] = 1 \times 10^{-7} \text{ g-ion/l}$$
$$[H_3O^+] \times [OH^-] = (1 \times 10^{-7}) \times (1 \times 10^{-7}) = 1 \times 10^{-14}$$
$$= K_{\text{ion product}} \text{ for water}$$

In pure water [H$_3$O$^+$] = [OH$^-$]; it is therefore a neutral substance. Then a neutral solution would be one in which the [H$_3$O$^+$] = 1×10^{-7} g-ion/l or the [OH$^-$] = 1×10^{-7} g-ion/l.

In dealing with solutions of low acidity, the procedure is to express the acidity in terms of the *effective hydronium ion concentration*.   The term **pH value** of the solution was proposed by Sörensen to represent the effective [H$_3$O$^+$] of a dilute acid solution.   The pH value of a solution is formulated as follows:

$$pH = \log \frac{1}{[H_3O^+]} = -\log [H_3O^+]$$

or

$$[H_3O^+] = 10^{-pH}$$

Thus for pure water

$$[H_3O^+] = 1 \times 10^{-7} \text{ g-ion/l}$$

$$pH = \log \frac{1}{[H_3O^+]} = \log \frac{1}{1 \times 10^{-7}} = \log 1 - \log (1 \times 10^{-7})$$

$$\log 1 = 0 \quad \text{and} \quad -\log 10^{-7} = 7 \log 10 = 7$$

Then pH = 7, or pH of a neutral solution is 7, since in a neutral solution $[H_3O^+] = 1 \times 10^{-7}$ g-ion/l.

All aqueous solutions contain H_3O^+ and OH^- ions.

Suppose a slightly acid solution has $[H_3O^+] = 1 \times 10^{-6}$ g-ion/l. The $[OH^-]$ of this solution would be

$$[H_3O^+] \times [OH^-] = 1 \times 10^{-14} = K_{\text{ion product}} \text{ of water}$$

$$(1 \times 10^{-6}) \times [OH^-] = 1 \times 10^{-14}$$

$$[OH^-] = \frac{1 \times 10^{-14}}{1 \times 10^{-6}} = 1 \times 10^{-8}$$

or hydroxyl ion concentration would be 1×10^{-8} g-ion/l. By definition then, pH of this solution would be pH $= -\log 1 \times 10^{-6} = 6$. Likewise, if a slightly basic solution has $[OH^-] = 1 \times 10^{-4}$ g-ion/l, the $[H_3O^+]$ of this solution would be

$$[H_3O^+] \times [OH^-] = 1 \times 10^{-14}$$

$$[H_3O^+] \times (1 \times 10^{-4}) = 1 \times 10^{-14}$$

$$[H_3O^+] = \frac{1 \times 10^{-14}}{1 \times 10^{-4}} = 1 \times 10^{-10}$$

or hydronium ion concentration would be 1×10^{-10} g-ion/l, or a pH of 10.

TABLE XX. RELATION BETWEEN $[H_3O^+]$, $[OH^-]$, pH, AND pOH

| | Acidity | | | | | | | Neutral | Basicity | | | | | | |
	Strongly acidic			Weakly acidic						Weakly basic			Strongly basic		
$[H_3O^+]$	$10^{-0.5}$	10^{-1}	10^{-2}	10^{-3}	10^{-4}	10^{-5}	10^{-6}	10^{-7}	10^{-8}	10^{-9}	10^{-10}	10^{-11}	10^{-12}	10^{-13}	10^{-14}
pH	0.5	1	2	3	4	5	6	7	8	9	10	11	12	13	14
$[OH^-]$	$10^{-13.5}$	10^{-13}	10^{-12}	10^{-11}	10^{-10}	10^{-9}	10^{-8}	10^{-7}	10^{-6}	10^{-5}	10^{-4}	10^{-3}	10^{-2}	10^{-1}	10^{0}
pOH	13.5	13	12	11	10	9	8	7	6	5	4	3	2	1	0

NOTE. pOH $= \log (1/[OH^-])$, or pOH $= -\log [OH^-]$. $[OH^-] = 10^{-pOH}$.

From Table XX:

An *acid solution* is one in which $[H_3O^+]$ *is greater than* 10^{-7} g-ion/l, or pH *is less than* 7, or pOH *is greater than* 7.

A *neutral solution* is one in which $[H_3O^+] = [OH^-] = 10^{-7}$ g-ion/l, or pH = 7, or pOH = 7.

A *basic solution* is one in which $[H_3O^+]$ *is less than* 10^{-7} g-ion/l, or pH *is greater than* 7, or pOH *is less than* 7.

Example 1. What is the pH value of a solution in which $[H_3O^+] = 3 \times 10^{-3}$ g-ion/l?

$$pH = \log \frac{1}{[H_3O^+]} = \log \frac{1}{3 \times 10^{-3}} = \log \frac{10^3}{3}$$
$$= \log 10^3 - \log 3 = 3.0 - 0.48 = 2.52$$

Alternate Solution

$$[H_3O^+] = 3 \times 10^{-3} \text{ g-ion/l}$$
$$\log 3 = 0.48 \quad \text{or} \quad 3 = 10^{0.48}$$
$$[H_3O^+] = 10^{0.48} \times 10^{-3} = 10^{-2.52}$$

or

$$pH = 2.52$$

Example 2. Calculate (*a*) the $[H_3O^+]$ and (*b*) the $[OH^-]$ of a solution that has a pH value of 6.5.

(*a*)
$$[H_3O^+] = 10^{-pH}$$
$$[H_3O^+] = 10^{-6.5} = 10^{-7} \times 10^{0.5}$$
$$10^{0.5} = \text{number whose log is } 0.5 = 3$$

Then
$$[H_3O^+] = 3 \times 10^{-7} \text{ g-ion/l}$$

(*b*) $\quad [H_3O^+] \times [OH^-] = 1 \times 10^{-14}$
$$[OH^-] = \frac{1 \times 10^{-14}}{3 \times 10^{-7}} = 0.3 \times 10^{-7} = 3 \times 10^{-8}$$
$$[OH^-] = 3 \times 10^{-8} \text{ g-ion/l}$$

Example 3. What is the pH of a solution containing 0.01 *M* acetic acid and 0.01 *M* $NaC_2H_3O_2$ (100 per cent ionized)? $K_{\text{ionization}}$ of acetic acid = 1.8×10^{-5}.

$$\frac{[H_3O^+] \times [C_2H_3O_2^-]}{[HC_2H_3O_2]} = K_{\text{ionization}}$$

Since 0.01 *M* $NaC_2H_3O_2$ is 100 per cent ionized, $[C_2H_3O_2^-]$ from this source = 0.01 g-ion/l.

Let $x = [H_3O^+] = [C_2H_3O_2^-]$

$$0.01 - x = [HC_2H_3O_2]$$
$$0.01 + x = \text{total } [C_2H_3O_2^-] \text{ in solution}$$

Substituting in the mass-action expression,

$$\frac{x(0.01 - x)}{0.01 + x} = 1.8 \times 10^{-5}$$

Since x is small, neglect x with respect to 0.01 in denominator and numerator; then

$$x = 1.8 \times 10^{-5}$$
$$1.8 \times 10^{-5} \text{ g-ion/l} = [H_3O^+] \text{ of this solution}$$
$$\log 1.8 = 0.26 \qquad \text{or} \qquad 1.8 = 10^{0.26}$$
$$[H_3O^+] = 10^{0.26} \times 10^{-5} = 10^{-4.74}$$

or

$$pH = 4.74$$

Example 4. An acid solution has a molarity of 0.005 and pH of 5. What is the percentage ionization of this acid?

$$[H_3O^+] = 10^{-pH}$$
$$[H_3O^+] = 10^{-5} \text{ g-ion/l} = 1 \times 10^{-5} \text{ g-ion/l}$$

Gross concentration $\times$ fraction ionized = ion concentration
Let x = fraction ionized

$$0.005 \times x = 1 \times 10^{-5}$$
$$x = \frac{1 \times 10^{-5}}{5 \times 10^{-3}} = 0.2 \times 10^{-2} = 2 \times 10^{-3}$$

Fraction ionized = 2×10^{-3} = 0.002, or 0.2 per cent.

Problems

17-1. Calculate the $K_{\text{ionization}}$ of (a) 1 M ammonia solution that is 0.4 per cent ionized and (b) 0.1 M formic acid solution (HCOOH) that is 4.5 per cent ionized.　　　　　　　　　　　　　*Ans.* (a) 1.6×10^{-5}; (b) 2×10^{-4}.

17-2. Calculate the ionization constant of (a) 0.1 M hydrocyanic acid solution that is 0.01 per cent ionized and (b) 0.01 M ammonia solution that is 4 per cent ionized.　　　　　　　　*Ans.* (a) 1×10^{-9}; (b) 1.6×10^{-5}.

17-3. (a) A 1 M acetic acid solution ionizes 0.4 per cent; (b) a 0.001 M acetic acid solution ionizes 12 per cent. What is the ionization constant of each solution?　　　　　　　*Ans.* (a) 1.6×10^{-5}; (b) 1.4×10^{-5}.

17-4. Calculate (a) the $[H_3O^+]$ and (b) the per cent ionization of a 0.5 M acetic acid solution. The ionization constant for acetic acid is 1.8×10^{-5}.
　　　　　　Ans. (a) 3×10^{-3} g-ion/l; (b) 0.6 per cent.

17-5. Calculate (a) the $[OH^-]$ and (b) the per cent ionization of a 0.05 M ammonia solution. The ionization constant for ammonia solution is 1.8×10^{-5}.
　　　　　　Ans. (a) 9.5×10^{-4} g-ion/l; (b) 1.9 per cent.

17-6. Calculate (a) the $[H_3O^+]$ and (b) the per cent ionization of a 0.2 M HCN solution. The ionization constant for hydrocyanic acid is 7×10^{-10}.
　　　　　　Ans. (a) 1.2×10^{-5} g-ion/l; (b) 0.006 per cent.

17-7. What is the molarity of a hydrocyanic acid solution that ionizes to the extent of 0.01 per cent? The ionization constant of hydrocyanic acid is 7×10^{-10}.　　　　　　　　　　　　　　　　　　　*Ans.* 0.07 M.

17-8. What is the molarity of a nitrous acid solution that ionizes to the extent of 6.8 per cent? The ionization constant of nitrous acid is 5×10^{-4}.
　　　　　　　　　　　　　　　　　　　　　　　Ans. 0.1 M.

17-9. What is the molarity of an ammonia solution that ionizes to the extent of 0.5 per cent? The ionization constant of ammonia solution is 1.8×10^{-5}. *Ans.* 0.7 M.

17-10. Calculate the $[H_3O^+]$ in a solution that is 0.5 M in $HC_2H_3O_2$ and M in $NH_4C_2H_3O_2$. The ammonium acetate is assumed to be 80 per cent ionized. The $K_{ionization}$ of acetic acid is 1.8×10^{-5}. *Ans.* 1.1×10^{-5} g-ion/l.

17-11. Calculate the $[OH^-]$ in a solution that is 0.5 N in ammonia and 2 M in NH_4Cl. The ammonium chloride is assumed to be 80 per cent ionized. The $K_{ionization}$ of ammonia solution is 1.8×10^{-5}. *Ans.* 5.6×10^{-6} g-ion/l.

17-12. A solution is 2 N with respect to ammonia solution (0.3 per cent ionized). (a) Find the $K_{ionization}$ of ammonia solution. (b) Determine the molar concentration at which the ammonia solution is 1 per cent ionized. *Ans.* (a) 1.8×10^{-5}; (b) 0.18 M.

17-13. Calculate the $[H_3O^+]$ in a solution that contains 7.7 g of $NH_4C_2H_3O_2$ and 8 ml of 6 N $HC_2H_3O_2$ in a volume of 400 ml. Assume complete ionization of ammonium acetate. The $K_{ionization}$ for acetic acid is 1.8×10^{-5}. *Ans.* 2×10^{-5} g-ion/l.

17-14. Determine the $[H_3O^+]$ in 100 ml of acetic acid solution that is 0.1 M in $HC_2H_3O_2$ and to which sufficient $NH_4C_2H_3O_2$ has been added to increase the $[C_2H_3O_2^-]$ to 0.2 g-ion/l. The $K_{ionization}$ for acetic acid is 1.8×10^{-5}. *Ans.* 9×10^{-5} g-ion/100 ml.

17-15. Calculate the pH for each of the following solutions in which the $[H_3O^+]$ values are, respectively, (a) 5×10^{-6} g-ion/l and (b) 7.3×10^{-7} g-ion/l. *Ans.* (a) 5.3; (b) 6.1.

17-16. Calculate the pH values corresponding to each of the following $[H_3O^+]$ values: (a) 2.6×10^{-5} g-ion/l; (b) 5.9×10^{-10} g-ion/l. *Ans.* (a) 4.6; (b) 9.2.

17-17. Find (a) pH and (b) $[OH^-]$ of a solution whose $[H_3O^+]$ equals 6×10^{-4} g-ion/l. *Ans.* (a) 3.2; (b) 1.7×10^{-11} g-ion/l.

17-18. Calculate the $[H_3O^+]$, $[OH^-]$, and pH in a 0.2 N hydrochloric acid that is 90 per cent ionized. *Ans.* $[H_3O^+]$ = 0.12 g-ion/l; $[OH^-]$ = 8.3×10^{-14} g-ion/l; pH = 0.92.

17-19. Determine the $[H_3O^+]$, $[OH^-]$, and pH in a 0.5 N hydrochloric acid that is 93 per cent ionized. *Ans.* $[H_3O^+]$ = 0.047 g-ion/l; $[OH^-]$ = 2.15×10^{-13} g-ion/l; pH = 1.3.

17-20. Calculate the $[H_3O^+]$ for each solution corresponding to the following pH values: (a) 6.2; (b) 2.3. *Ans.* (a) 6×10^{-7} g-ion/l; (b) 5×10^{-3} g-ion/l.

17-21. Determine the $[H_3O^+]$ for each solution of the following pH values: (a) 5.6; (b) 9.5. *Ans.* (a) 2.5×10^{-6} g-ion/l; (b) 3×10^{-10} g-ion/l.

17-22. Calculate the $[H_3O^+]$ for each solution corresponding to each of the following pH values: (a) 7.6; (b) 4.05. *Ans.* (a) 2.5×10^{-8} g-ion/l; (b) 1×10^{-5} g-ion/l.

17-23. Calculate the pH and $[OH^-]$ in (a) 0.01 N HCl solution that is 92 per cent ionized and (b) 0.001 N NaOH solution, assuming complete ionization. *Ans.* (a) pH = 2.04; $[OH^-]$ = 1.1×10^{-12} g-ion/l; (b) pH = 11; $[OH^-]$ = 1×10^{-3} g-ion/l.

17-24. Calculate the pH of (a) 0.1 N $HC_2H_3O_2$ solution that is 1.34 per cent ionized and (b) 0.1 N ammonia solution that is ionized to the extent of 1.3 per cent. *Ans.* (a) pH = 2.87; (b) pH = 11.11.

17-25. Calculate the pH of (a) 0.05 M HCN that is ionized to the extent of 0.01 per cent and (b) 0.01 M $HC_2H_3O_2$ that is 4.15 per cent ionized.

Ans. (a) pH = 5.30; (b) pH = 3.38.

17-26. Calculate the pH and $[OH^-]$ of (a) 0.08 M $HC_2H_3O_2$ that is 1.50 per cent ionized and (b) 0.001 M HCl that is 100 per cent ionized.

Ans. (a) pH = 2.92; $[OH^-]$ = 1.5 × 10^{-12} g-ion/l; (b) pH = 3; $[OH^-]$ = 1 × 10^{-11} g-ion/l.

17-27. A saturated solution of hydrogen sulfide at 18°C is approximately 0.1 M in H_2S and ionizes in two stages:

(a) Primary ionization to an extent of 0.07 per cent

$$H_2S + H_2O \rightleftharpoons H_3O^+ + HS^-$$

(b) Secondary ionization to an extent of 0.00001 per cent

$$HS^- + H_2O \rightleftharpoons H_3O^+ + S^{-2}$$

What are the $[HS^-]$ and $[S^{-2}]$ values in this solution?

Ans. $[HS^-]$ = 7 × 10^{-5} g-ion/l; $[S^{-2}]$ = 7 × 10^{-11} g-ion/l.

17-28. Calculate the ionization constant of (a) 0.1 M solution of hydrocyanic acid that is 0.01 per cent ionized and (b) 0.03 M solution of acetic acid that is 2.45 per cent ionized.

17-29. Calculate the ionization constant of (a) 0.1 M ammonia solution that is 1.3 per cent ionized and (b) 0.001 M ammonia solution that is 12 per cent ionized.

17-30. Determine the ionization constant of (a) 1 M formic acid (HCOOH) solution that is 1.5 per cent ionized and (b) 0.01 M formic acid solution that is 13 per cent ionized.

17-31. Orthophosphoric acid solution ionizes in the following stages:

$$H_3PO_4 + H_2O \rightleftharpoons H_3O^+ + H_2PO_4^- \qquad \textit{primary ionization}$$
$$H_2PO_4^- + H_2O \rightleftharpoons H_3O^+ + HPO_4^{-2} \qquad \textit{secondary ionization}$$
$$HPO_4^{-2} + H_2O \rightleftharpoons H_3O^+ + PO_4^{-3} \qquad \textit{tertiary ionization}$$

If the orthophosphoric acid solution is 0.1 M, and the first stage ionizes 27 per cent, the second stage ionizes 0.1 per cent, and the third stage ionizes 0.0001 per cent, what is the ionization constant for each stage in the ionization of this acid solution?

17-32. The ionization constant for HCN is 7 × 10^{-10}. The degree of ionization of hydrocyanic acid is 0.01 per cent. Calculate (a) the molar concentration of the acid and (b) the $[H_3O^+]$ ion concentration.

17-33. The ionization constant for ammonia solution is 1.8 × 10^{-5}. The ammonia solution is ionized to the extent of 0.5 per cent. Determine (a) the molar concentration of the base and (b) the $[OH^-]$ ion concentration.

17-34. Calculate (a) the $[H_3O^+]$ and (b) the per cent ionization of a 0.1 M HCN solution. The ionization constant for hydrocyanic acid is 7 × 10^{-10}.

17-35. Calculate (a) the $[H_3O^+]$ and (b) the per cent ionization of 0.08 M $HC_2H_3O_2$ solution. The ionization constant for acetic acid is 1.8 × 10^{-5}.

17-36. Calculate (a) the $[OH^-]$ ion concentration and (b) the per cent ionization of a 0.2 M ammonia solution. The ionization constant of ammonia solution is 1.8 × 10^{-5}.

17-37. The $K_{\text{ionization}}$ for acetic acid is 1.8×10^{-5}. Determine (a) the concentration at which $HC_2H_3O_2$ will be 0.6 per cent ionized and (b) the $[H_3O^+]$ of this acid solution.

17-38. Calculate (a) the concentration at which an ammonia solution will be 0.8 per cent ionized and (b) the $[OH^-]$ of this solution. The ionization constant for the ammonia solution is 1.8×10^{-5}.

17-39. Calculate the $[H_3O^+]$ in 1 l of solution that is 0.1 M in $HC_2H_3O_2$ and 0.01 M in $NH_4C_2H_3O_2$. The $K_{\text{ionization}}$ for acetic acid is 1.8×10^{-5}. The ammonium acetate is completely ionized.

17-40. Calculate the $[OH^-]$ in a liter of solution that is 0.1 M in ammonia and 0.5 M in NH_4Cl. The effective ionization of ammonium chloride is assumed to be 80 per cent. The $K_{\text{ionization}}$ for ammonia solution is 1.8×10^{-5}.

17-41. Calculate the $[OH^-]$ in 100 ml of ammonia solution that is 0.2 M in NH_3 and to which sufficient NH_4Cl has been added to increase the $[NH_4^+]$ to a value of 0.5 g-ion/l. The ammonia solution is 1.2 per cent ionized. The $K_{\text{ionization}}$ for ammonia solution is 1.8×10^{-5}.

17-42. The $K_{\text{ionization}}$ for ammonia solution is 1.8×10^{-5}. Determine the $[OH^-]$ in an ammonia solution that is 0.5 M in NH_3. If this solution is made 2.5 M in NH_4Cl, what is the new $[OH^-]$? Assume the effective ionization of ammonium chloride to be 80 per cent.

17-43. Determine the acetate ion concentration required to reduce the $[H_3O^+]$ in a solution that is 0.1 M in $HC_2H_3O_2$ to 4.5×10^{-6} g-ion/l.

17-44. Find the $[NH_4^+]$ necessary to reduce to a value of 1×10^{-5} g-ion/l the $[OH^-]$ in a solution that is 0.2 M in NH_3.

17-45. What is the pH of each of the following solutions in which $[H_3O^+]$ values are (a) $1 \times 10^{-4.2}$ g-ion/l; (b) 2.2×10^{-3} g-ion/l; (c) 2.6×10^{-8} g-ion/l?

17-46. Determine the pH of each of the following solutions in which $[H_3O^+]$ values are (a) $1 \times 10^{-8.6}$ g-ion/l; (b) 4.4×10^{-4} g-ion/l; (c) $4.5 \times 10^{-7.6}$ g-ion/l.

17-47. Calculate the pH of each of the following solutions in which $[H_3O^+]$ values are (a) $1 \times 10^{-12.5}$ g-ion/l; (b) 3.6×10^{-3} g-ion/l; (c) $9.7 \times 10^{-8.5}$ g-ion/l.

17-48. Find the pH of each of the following solutions in which the $[OH^-]$ values are (a) 1×10^{-9} g-ion/l; (b) 8.6×10^{-12} g-ion/l; (c) $1.8 \times 10^{-7.7}$ g-ion/l. The $K_{\text{ion product}}$ of water $= 1 \times 10^{-14}$.

17-49. Calculate the pH of each of the following solutions in which the $[OH^-]$ values are (a) 1×10^{-12} g-ion/l; (b) 4.4×10^{-4} g-ion/l; (c) $1.5 \times 10^{-5.4}$ g-ion/l. The $K_{\text{ion product}}$ of water $= 1 \times 10^{-14}$.

17-50. Determine the pH of each of the following solutions in which the $[OH^-]$ values are (a) 1×10^{-3} g-ion/l; (b) 3.9×10^{-11} g-ion/l; (c) $8.7 \times 10^{-9.7}$ g-ion/l. The $K_{\text{ion product}}$ of water $= 1 \times 10^{-14}$.

17-51. Calculate (a) the $[OH^-]$ and (b) the pH value of a 0.001 M acetic acid solution. The ionization constant of acetic acid is 1.8×10^{-5}. The ion product of water $= 1 \times 10^{-14}$.

17-52. Find (a) $[OH^-]$ and (b) the pH value of a $0.01 M$ nitrous acid solution. The ionization constant of nitrous acid is 5×10^{-4}. The ion product of water $= 1 \times 10^{-14}$.

17-53. Determine (a) $[OH^-]$ and (b) the pH value of 0.01 M hydrocyanic acid solution. The ionization constant of hydrocyanic acid is 7×10^{-10}. The ion product of water $= 1 \times 10^{-14}$.

17-54. Determine (a) $[H_3O^+]$ and (b) the pOH value of 0.01 M ammonia solution. The ionization constant of ammonia solution is 1.8×10^{-5}. The ion product of water $= 1 \times 10^{-14}$.

17-55. What is (a) $[H_3O^+]$ and (b) $[OH^-]$ of a solution of pH value 1.6? The ion product of water $= 1 \times 10^{-14}$.

17-56. Determine (a) $[H_3O^+]$ and (b) $[OH^-]$ of a solution whose pH is 12.6. The $K_{\text{ion product}}$ of water $= 1 \times 10^{-14}$.

17-57. Find (a) $[H_3O^+]$ and (b) $[OH^-]$ of a solution whose pOH is 2.8. The $K_{\text{ion product}}$ of water $= 1 \times 10^{-14}$.

17-58. Determine (a) $[H_3O^+]$ and (b) $[OH^-]$ of a solution of pOH value 3.7. The $K_{\text{ion product}}$ of water $= 1 \times 10^{-14}$.

17-59. Determine (a) the $[OH^-]$ and (b) pH value of 1 l of a solution that is 0.1 M in $HC_2H_3O_2$ and 0.1 M in $NH_4C_2H_3O_2$ (assumed to be completely ionized). The ionization constant of acetic acid $= 1.8 \times 10^{-5}$. The ion product of water $= 1 \times 10^{-14}$.

17-60. Determine (a) the $[H_3O^+]$ and (b) pOH value of 1 l of a solution that is 0.1M in ammonia and 0.1 M in NH_4Cl (assumed to be 80 per cent ionized). The ionization constant of ammonia solution $= 1.8 \times 10^{-5}$. The ion product of water $= 1 \times 10^{-14}$.

CHAPTER XVIII

SOLUBILITY-PRODUCT PRINCIPLE

OUTLINE

Solubility.   The solubilities of slightly soluble substances are most conveniently expressed in terms of the ions that they furnish in solution.

Solubility-product constant.   Solubility of slightly soluble substances expressed as the product of the concentrations of the ions furnished by the dissolved substance.

Calculations of the SPC for $[Ba^{+2}] \times [CO_3^{-2}]$ from the solubility of $BaCO_3$ in grams per 100 ml.

The separation of the cations of Groups II and III in qualitative analysis by H_2S.

$[H_3O^+]^2 \times [S^{-2}] = 1.1 \times 10^{-23} = K$

The concentration of sulfide ion $[S^{-2}]$ is regulated by addition of a definite amount of HCl to the solution.   This HCl ionizes and furnishes a definite concentration of hydrogen ions, $[H_3O^+]$.

By suitable adjustment of the $[H_3O^+]$ the $[S^{-2}]$ is made to assume a value high enough to precipitate second-group cations rather completely as sulfides but not high enough to precipitate third-group cations at the same time; *i.e.*, $[S^{-2}] \times$ (second-group cation) > solubility product of these metallic sulfides; but $[S^{-2}] \times$ (third-group cation) < solubility product of these metallic sulfides.

The high value of $[S^{-2}]$ in alkaline solution such as used for the precipitation of Group III causes complete precipitation of Group III cations as sulfides.

Brönsted and Lowry acid-base theory.

Hydrolysis.   Hydrolysis constant.

SOLUBILITY

In qualitative chemical analysis the separations of cations into various groups and the identification tests for individual cations and anions depend on the formation or dissolving of precipitates, so-called "insoluble substances."   These precipitates are not completely insoluble; they are actually slightly soluble.   Consider the insoluble substances silver chloride, barium sulfate, and silver sulfide, respectively. The solubility of silver chloride is 1.9×10^{-3} g/l, that of barium sulfate is 2.3×10^{-3} g/l, and that of silver sulfide is 2×10^{-15} g/l.   These solubility values represent the concentrations of the various compounds in **saturated solutions** of these substances.

A saturated solution is one in which an equilibrium (physical) exists between the dissolved solute and the solid solute.   There is also an ionic equilibrium associated with the existing physical equilibrium. The two conditions of equilibrium can be represented by

$$A_nB_{m\text{crystalline}} \rightleftharpoons A_nB_{m\text{dissolved}} \rightleftharpoons nA^{+\cdots} + mB^{-\cdots}$$

It is customary in dealing with equilibrium reactions (Chap. XVII) to express concentrations in terms of moles per liter, or gram-ions per liter. Then the molar solubility of each of the foregoing substances would be:

Molecular weight AgCl = 143.3

$$\frac{1.9 \times 10^{-3} \text{ g/l}}{143.3 \text{ g/g-mole}} = 1.3 \times 10^{-5} \text{ g-mole/l of AgCl}$$

Molecular weight $BaSO_4$ = 233.4

$$\frac{2.3 \times 10^{-3} \text{ g/l}}{233.4 \text{ g/g-mole}} = 1 \times 10^{-5} \text{ g-mole/l of } BaSO_4$$

Molecular weight Ag_2S = 247.8

$$\frac{2 \times 10^{-15} \text{ g/l}}{247.8 \text{ g/g-mole}} = 8 \times 10^{-18} \text{ g-mole/l of } Ag_2S$$

Since these molar-solubility values are small, it is assumed the solute is completely (100 per cent) ionized. Then in each of the forementioned substances, the molar solubility of the slightly soluble solute represents the concentrations of ions furnished by that substance in gram-ions per liter.

SOLUBILITY-PRODUCT PRINCIPLE

In dealing with these extremely dilute solutions of slightly soluble substances, the equilibrium law is in force. Consider the equilibrium reaction for silver chloride.

$$AgCl \rightleftharpoons Ag^+ + Cl^-$$

Applying the mass-action law to this ionic equilibrium,

$$\frac{[Ag^+] \times [Cl^-]}{[AgCl]} = k_{\text{ionization}} \tag{1}$$

In a saturated solution of silver chloride, the dissolved AgCl is in equilibrium with crystalline AgCl, or

$$AgCl_{\text{crystalline}} \rightleftharpoons AgCl_{\text{dissolved}}$$

Applying the mass-action law to this physical equilibrium.

$$\frac{[AgCl_{\text{dissolved}}]}{[AgCl_{\text{crystalline}}]} = k' \tag{2}$$

The mass-action expressions (1) and (2) may be combined, with the proviso that [AgCl] and [AgCl$_{dissolved}$] mean exactly the same thing, namely, "concentration of silver chloride molecules in a saturated solution of silver chloride." Then

$$\frac{[Ag^+] \times [Cl^-]}{[AgCl]} \times \frac{[AgCl_{dissolved}]}{[AgCl_{crystalline}]} = kk'$$

or

$$\frac{[Ag^+] \times [Cl^-]}{[AgCl_{crystalline}]} = kk'$$

or

$$[Ag^+] \times [Cl^-] = kk' \times [AgCl_{crystalline}]$$

[AgCl$_{crystalline}$] is a constant, k'', and is independent of the concentration of the solution; then

$$[Ag^+] \times [Cl^-] = kk'k'' = K = \text{solubility-product constant}[1]$$

The solubility-product principle may be stated as follows: **The product of ion concentrations in a saturated solution of a slightly soluble electrolyte is a constant called the solubility-product constant (SPC).**

The solubility-product constants for substances that form precipitates encountered in chemical analysis may be found in Table II, page 292, of the Appendix.

Example 1. The solubility of barium carbonate is 1.4×10^{-3} g/100 ml. Determine the solubility-product constant of $BaCO_3$.

The ionic equilibrium reaction for barium carbonate is

$$BaCO_3 \rightleftharpoons Ba^{+2} + CO_3^{-2}$$

Molecular weight $BaCO_3 = 197.4$

$$1.4 \times 10^{-3} \text{ g/100 ml} = 1.4 \times 10^{-2} \text{ g/l}$$

$$\frac{1.4 \times 10^{-2} \text{ g/l}}{197.4 \text{ g/g-mole}} = 7.1 \times 10^{-5} \text{ g-mole/l}$$

Molar solubility $BaCO_3 = 7.1 \times 10^{-5}$ g-mole/l

As previously stated, the molar solubility of the slightly soluble solute represents the concentrations of ions furnished by that solute. Since the dissolved $BaCO_3$ is completely ionized, then 7.1×10^{-5} g-mole/l represents the concentration of ions in this solution, or $[Ba^{+2}] = 7.1 \times 10^{-5}$ g-ion/l, and $[CO_3^{-2}] = 7.1 \times 10^{-5}$ g-ion/l.

$$SPC_{BaCO_3} = [Ba^{+2}] \times [CO_3^{-2}] = (7.1 \times 10^{-5}) \times (7.1 \times 10^{-5})$$
$$= 50 \times 10^{-10} = 5.0 \times 10^{-9}$$

[1] For a more detailed derivation of solubility-product expression, the reader is referred to J. A. V. Butler, *J. Phys. Chem.*, **28**, 438 (1924).

This SPC might be called a saturation value for $BaCO_3$ since it is obtained from its solubility at a given temperature, which in turn represents an equilibrium condition or state of saturation of this slightly soluble substance. Then, if the circumstances are such that the *product of the ion concentration exceeds* 5×10^{-9}, *precipitation of* $BaCO_3$ *will take place. On the other hand, should the ion-concentration product be less than* 5×10^{-9}, *no precipitation will occur*, or a condition of unsaturation exists.

The solubility-product principle is of considerable aid in qualitative chemical analysis, particularly in dealing with controlled and selective precipitation. One is able to determine the minimum quantity of precipitant required to bring about precipitation of a given ion of known concentration, or just what values must be maintained to prevent precipitation of certain groups of ions and permit the separation of other ion groups.

Before giving further consideration to this principle, it is important to emphasize the fact that in determining the SPC, the concentrations of ions are *total* ion concentrations, and the *coefficients* of ions, as shown in the ionic equation, appear as *exponents* in the SPC expression. This can be represented by the general type of ionic equation

$$A_nB_m \rightleftharpoons nA^+ \cdots + mB^- \cdots$$

Total $A^+ \cdots$ ion concentration (g-ion/l)

$$= [A^+ \cdots] = n \times A^+ \cdots \text{ g-ion/l}$$

Total $B^- \cdots$ ion concentration (g-ion/l)

$$= [B^- \cdots] = m \times B^- \cdots \text{ g-ion/l}$$

$$\text{SPC} = [A^+ \cdots]^n \times [B^- \cdots]^m$$

The following examples illustrate these details.

Example 2. The solubility of silver chromate (Ag_2CrO_4) is 2.2×10^{-2} g/l. Determine the solubility-product constant of Ag_2CrO_4.

The ionic equilibrium reaction for silver chromate is

$$Ag_2CrO_4 \rightleftharpoons 2Ag^+ + CrO_4^{-2}$$

Molecular weight $Ag_2CrO_4 = 331.8$

$$\frac{2.2 \times 10^{-2} \text{ g/l}}{331.8 \text{ g/g-mole}} = 6.6 \times 10^{-5} \text{ g-mole/l}$$

Molar solubility of $Ag_2CrO_4 = 6.6 \times 10^{-5}$ g-mole/l

Then, 6.6×10^{-5} g-ion/l represents the concentration of each single ion in this solution.

Since the ionization of Ag_2CrO_4 produces 2 silver ions and 1 chromate ion, the *total* Ag^+ concentration $= [Ag^+] = 2 \times (6.6 \times 10^{-5})$

g-ion/l $= 1.3 \times 10^{-4}$ g-ion/l, and the *total* CrO_4^{-2} concentration $=$ $[CrO_4^{-2}] = 6.6 \times 10^{-5}$ g-ion/l.

$$SPC_{Ag_2CrO_4} = [Ag^+]^2 \times [CrO_4^{-2}] = (1.3 \times 10^{-4})^2 \times (6.6 \times 10^{-5})$$
$$= 1.1 \times 10^{-12}$$

Example 3.   The solubility of mercurous iodide (Hg_2I_2) is 1.47×10^{-7} g/l.   Calculate the solubility-product constant of this compound.

Hg_2I_2 is known as an associated molecule.   Its ionization produces 1 associated mercurous ion, Hg_2^{+2} (effective valence number $+1$), and 2 unassociated iodide ions.

The ionic equilibrium reaction for mercurous iodide is

$$Hg_2I_2 \rightleftharpoons Hg_2^{+2} + 2I^-$$
Molecular weight $Hg_2I_2 = 655$
$$\frac{1.47 \times 10^{-7} \text{ g/l}}{655 \text{ g/g-mole}} = 2.25 \times 10^{-10} \text{ g-mole/l}$$
Molar solubility of $Hg_2I_2 = 2.25 \times 10^{-10}$ g-mole/l

Assuming complete ionization of mercurous iodide,

$$[Hg_2^{+2}] = 2.25 \times 10^{-10} \text{ g-ion/l}$$
$$[I^-] = 2 \times (2.25 \times 10^{-10}) \text{ g-ion/l} = 4.5 \times 10^{-10} \text{ g-ion/l}$$
$$SPC_{Hg_2I_2} = [Hg_2^{+2}] \times [I^-]^2 = (2.25 \times 10^{-10}) \times (4.5 \times 10^{-10})^2$$
$$= 4.6 \times 10^{-29}$$

Example 4.   The solubility-product constant of lead fluoride is 3.2×10^{-8}.   Calculate the (a) $[Pb^{+2}]$ and (b) $[F^-]$ in a saturated solution of this solute.

The ionic equilibrium reaction for lead fluoride is

$$PbF_2 \rightleftharpoons Pb^{+2} + 2F^-$$
$$SPC_{PbF_2} = [Pb^{+2}] \times [F^-]^2 = 3.2 \times 10^{-8}$$

Let $x = [Pb^{+2}]$; then $2x = [F^-]$.

$$[Pb^{+2}] \times [F^-]^2 = x \times (2x)^2 = 3.2 \times 10^{-8} = 32.0 \times 10^{-9}$$
$$4x^3 = 32.0 \times 10^{-9}$$
$$x^3 = 8.0 \times 10^{-9}$$
$$x = \sqrt[3]{8.0 \times 10^{-9}} = 2.0 \times 10^{-3} \text{ g-ion/l} = [Pb^{+2}]$$
$$[F^-] = 2 \times (2.0 \times 10^{-3}) \text{ g-ion/l} = 4.0 \times 10^{-3} \text{ g-ion/l}$$

Example 5.   The SPC of ferric hydroxide is 4×10^{-38}.   Calculate (a) the solubility of ferric hydroxide in grams per liter and (b) the weight in grams of ferric ion contained in 1 ml of a saturated solution of this solute.

(a) The ionic equilibrium reaction for ferric hydroxide is

$$Fe(OH)_3 \rightleftharpoons Fe^{+3} + 3OH^-$$
$$SPC_{Fe(OH)_3} = [Fe^{+3}] \times [OH^-]^3 = 4 \times 10^{-38}$$

Let x = ion concentration (g-ion/l)

$$x \times (3x)^3 = 4 \times 10^{-38}$$
$$27x^4 = 4 \times 10^{-38}$$
$$x = \sqrt[4]{4/27 \times 10^{-38}} = \sqrt[4]{400/27 \times 10^{-40}}$$
$$= \sqrt[4]{15 \times 10^{-40}} = \sqrt[4]{15} \times 10^{-10} = 1.97 \times 10^{-10}$$

Ion concentration = 1.97×10^{-10} g-ion/l.

Since complete ionization of the solute is assumed, the ion concentration represents the molar solubility of the solute.

$$\text{Molar solubility } Fe(OH)_3 = 1.97 \times 10^{-10} \text{ g-mole/l}$$
$$\text{Molecular weight } Fe(OH)_3 = 106.9$$
$$1.97 \times 10^{-10} \text{ g-mole/l} \times 106.9 \text{ g/g-mole}$$
$$= 211 \times 10^{-10} \text{ g/l} = 2.1 \times 10^{-8} \text{ g/l}$$

(b) Ion concentration = 1.97×10^{-10} g-ion/l, or $[Fe^{+3}] = 1.97 \times 10^{-10}$ g-ion/l.

$$1 \text{ g-ion } Fe^{+3} = 55.85 \text{ g}$$
$$1.97 \times 10^{-10} \text{ g-ion/l} \times 55.85 \text{ g/g-ion}$$
$$= 110 \times 10^{-10} \text{ g/l} = 1.1 \times 10^{-8} \text{ g/l}$$

1.1×10^{-8} g/l = weight of ferric ion in grams per liter of a saturated solution of ferric hydroxide, or $\dfrac{1.1 \times 10^{-8} \text{ g/l}}{1 \times 10^3 \text{ ml/l}} = 1.1 \times 10^{-11}$ g/ml = weight of Fe^{+3} in grams per milliliter of this solution.

Example 6. Calculate the sulfide-ion concentration required to start precipitation of (a) lead sulfide and (b) bismuth sulfide from solution containing 1×10^{-5} g-ion of metallic ion per liter of solution. Solubility-product constants: $SPC_{PbS} = 4.2 \times 10^{-28}$; $SPC_{Bi_2S_3} = 1.5 \times 10^{-72}$.

(a)
$$SPC_{PbS} = [Pb^{+2}] \times [S^{-2}] = 4.2 \times 10^{-28}$$
$$[Pb^{+2}] = 1 \times 10^{-5} \text{ g-ion/l}$$

Let x = $[S^{-2}]$ required to start precipitation of PbS

$$(1 \times 10^{-5}) \times x = 4.2 \times 10^{-28}$$
$$x = \frac{4.2 \times 10^{-28}}{1 \times 10^{-5}} = 4.2 \times 10^{-23}$$

The $[S^{-2}]$ required to start precipitation of PbS is 4.2×10^{-23} g-ion/l.

(b) $$SPC_{Bi_2S_3} = [Bi^{+3}]^2 \times [S^{-2}]^3 = 1.5 \times 10^{-72}$$
$$[Bi^{+3}] = 1 \times 10^{-5} \text{ g-ion/l}$$

Let $y = [S^{-2}]$ required to start precipitation of Bi_2S_3

$$(1 \times 10^{-5})^2 \times y^3 = 1.5 \times 10^{-72}$$
$$y^3 = \frac{1.5 \times 10^{-72}}{(1 \times 10^{-5})^2} = \frac{1.5 \times 10^{-72}}{1 \times 10^{-10}} = 1.5 \times 10^{-62}$$
$$y = \sqrt[3]{1.5 \times 10^{-62}} = \sqrt[3]{15 \times 10^{-63}} = 2.5 \times 10^{-21}$$

The $[S^{-2}]$ required to start precipitation of Bi_2S_3 is 2.5×10^{-21} g-ion/l.

Example 7. The solubility-product constant of silver chromate is 1.1×10^{-12}. Determine the minimum $[CrO_4^{-2}]$ required to bring about precipitation of Ag_2CrO_4 in 2 ml of 0.5 M $AgNO_3$ solution. Assume complete ionization of silver nitrate solution.

$$1 \text{ l of } 0.5\ M\ AgNO_3 = 1\ l \times 0.5 \text{ g-mole } AgNO_3/l$$
$$2 \text{ ml} = 0.002\ l \text{ of } 0.5\ M\ AgNO_3 = 0.002\ l \times \frac{0.5 \text{ g-mole } AgNO_3}{1\ l}$$
$$= 0.001 \text{ g-mole } AgNO_3/l$$
$$0.001 \text{ g-mole } AgNO_3/l = 0.001 \text{ g-ion } Ag^+/l$$

(since complete ionization of $AgNO_3$ is assumed), or

$$[Ag^+] = 0.001 \text{ g-ion/l} = 1 \times 10^{-3} \text{ g-ion/l}$$
$$SPC_{Ag_2CrO_4} = [Ag^+]^2 \times [CrO_4^{-2}] = 1.1 \times 10^{-12}$$

Let $x = [CrO_4^{-2}]$ required to bring about precipitation of Ag_2CrO_4. Substituting in the SPC expression,

$$(1 \times 10^{-3})^2 \times x = 1.1 \times 10^{-12}$$
$$x = \frac{1.1 \times 10^{-12}}{(1 \times 10^{-3})^2} = \frac{1.1 \times 10^{-12}}{1 \times 10^{-6}} = 1.1 \times 10^{-6}$$

The minimum $[CrO_4^{-2}]$ for precipitation of $Ag_2CrO_4 = 1.1 \times 10^{-6}$ g-ion/l.

PRECIPITATION WITH HYDROGEN SULFIDE IN QUALITATIVE CHEMICAL ANALYSIS

Separation of Group II from Group III. Effect of H_3O^+ Ion Concentration. In qualitative analysis the separation of Group II cations (Hg^{+2}, Pb^{+2}, Bi^{+3}, Cu^{+2}, Cd^{+2}, As^{+3}, Sb^{+3}, Sn^{+4}) in a *hydrochloric acid medium* with hydrogen sulfide from those of Group III (Al^{+3}, Cr^{+3}, Zn^{+2}, Fe^{+3}, Mn^{+2}, Co^{+2}, Ni^{+2}) affords an excellent example of selective precipitation. The division into these groups is, however, not so sharply defined as indicated. If an excessive quantity of HCl is present in a solution containing the cations of both groups, the sulfides of Cd^{+2}, Pb^{+2}, and Sn^{+4} are incompletely precipitated by H_2S, and considerable amounts of these cations escape precipitation. On the other hand, if the HCl present in the solution when Group II is precipitated by H_2S is less than a certain definite amount, the sulfides of Zn^{+2}, Co^{+2}, and Ni^{+2} are partially precipitated with Group II.

Many of the sulfides of Group II are quite soluble in solutions of high concentrations of hydrochloric acid. For example,

$$CdCl_2 + H_2S \rightleftharpoons CdS + 2HCl$$

It is apparent from this reversible reaction, should $CdCl_2$ solution contain a high concentration of hydrochloric acid to begin with, that when this solution is saturated with hydrogen sulfide, a condition will prevail in which no CdS will be precipitated, i.e., the SPC of CdS will not be exceeded. In order to precipitate CdS, the S^{-2} concentration must be so regulated that, for a given Cd^{+2} concentration, the SPC for CdS will be exceeded. The following examples are presented as applications of this principle.

Hydrogen sulfide is only slightly soluble in water and a saturated solution of it at 18°C is approximately 0.1 M. It is a very weak dibasic acid, and its low ionization proceeds in two stages represented as

$$H_2S + H_2O \rightleftharpoons H_3O^+ + HS^- \qquad \textit{primary ionization}$$
$$HS^- + H_2O \rightleftharpoons H_3O^+ + S^{-2} \qquad \textit{secondary ionization}$$

The mass-action expressions for each of these ionization reactions are

$$\frac{[H_3O^+] \times [HS^-]}{[H_2S]} = 9 \times 10^{-8} = K_{\text{ionization (primary)}} \qquad (1)$$

$$\frac{[H_3O^+] \times [S^{-2}]}{[HS^-]} = 1.2 \times 10^{-15} = K_{\text{ionization (secondary)}} \qquad (2)$$

Multiplying Equation (1) by (2), the expression for total ionization of H_2S saturated solution is

$$\frac{[H_3O^+] \times [HS^-]}{[H_2S]} \times \frac{[H_3O^+] \times [S^{-2}]}{[HS^-]} = (9 \times 10^{-8}) \times (1.2 \times 10^{-15})$$

$$\frac{[H_3O^+]^2 \times [S^{-2}]}{[H_2S]} = 1.1 \times 10^{-22}$$

Since

$$[H_2S] = 0.1 \text{ g-mole/l}$$
$$[H_3O^+]^2 \times [S^{-2}] = 0.1 \times (1.1 \times 10^{-22})$$
$$= 1.1 \times 10^{-23} = K_{H_2S}$$

This constant for a saturated solution of H_2S for all intents and purposes can be considered as the SPC of H_2S and enables one to control the sulfide-ion concentration by regulating the H_3O^+ concentration. In reality, this controlling of the S^{-2} concentration is an example of the common-ion effect. H_2S is a weak electrolyte, and the addition of HCl, a strong electrolyte with a common ion, to a saturated solution of H_2S will repress the ionization of the H_2S. In other words, the large increase in H_3O^+ concentration will cause a decrease in the S^{-2} concentration in order to maintain constancy of the ion product for H_2S.

Example 1. Find the S^{-2} concentration (gram-ion/l) in a solution of 0.3 M HCl that has been saturated with H_2S. Assume the HCl to be 90 per cent ionized.

$$0.3\ M = 0.3\ \text{g-mole/l}$$
$$0.3\ \text{g-mole/l} \times 0.9 = 0.27\ \text{g-ion/l} = [H_3O^+]\ \text{from HCl}$$

Neglecting the small amount of $[H_3O^+]$ from H_2S solution,

$$[H_3O^+]^2 \times [S^{-2}] = 1.1 \times 10^{-23}$$

Let $x = [S^{-2}]$ in g-ion/l

$$(0.27)^2 \times x = 1.1 \times 10^{-23}$$
$$x = \frac{1.1 \times 10^{-23}}{(0.27)^2} = 1.5 \times 10^{-22}$$

$[S^{-2}] = 1.5 \times 10^{-22}$ g-ion/l.

Example 2. (a) If a solution contains 0.001 g-ion/l of Pb^{+2}, what S^{-2} gram-ion concentration will be required to start precipitation of PbS? (b) if the foregoing solution is saturated with H_2S, what value of $[H_3O^+]$ would be required to prevent precipitation of PbS?

$$SPC_{PbS} = 4.2 \times 10^{-28} \qquad K_{H_2S} = 1.1 \times 10^{-23}$$
(a) $\qquad [Pb^{+2}] = 0.001\ \text{g-ion/l} = 1 \times 10^{-3}\ \text{g-ion/l}$
$$[Pb^{+2}] \times [S^{-2}] = 4.2 \times 10^{-28}$$

Let $x = [S^{-2}]$ gram-ion concentration required to start precipitation of PbS

$$(1 \times 10^{-3}) \times x = 4.2 \times 10^{-28}$$
$$x = \frac{4.2 \times 10^{-28}}{1 \times 10^{-3}} = 4.2 \times 10^{-25}$$

$[S^{-2}]$ gram-ion concentration $= 4.2 \times 10^{-25}$ g-ion/l.

(b) $\qquad [H_3O^+]^2 \times [S^{-2}] = 1.1 \times 10^{-23}$
$$[S^{-2}] = 4.2 \times 10^{-25}\ \text{g-ion/l}$$

Let $y = [H_3O^+]$ of saturated H_2S solution

$$y^2 \times 4.2 \times 10^{-25} = 1.1 \times 10^{-23}$$
$$y = \sqrt{\frac{1.1 \times 10^{-23}}{4.2 \times 10^{-25}}} = \sqrt{0.262 \times 10^2} = \sqrt{26.2} = 5.1$$

Any value of $[H_3O^+]$ greater than 5.1 g-ion/l would prevent precipitation of PbS. (Why?)

Example 3. A solution is 0.1 M in Cd^{+2} and 0.3 M in HCl. This solution is saturated with H_2S. The SPC for CdS is 3.6×10^{-29}. The HCl is assumed to be 90 per cent ionized. How much Cd^{+2} will remain in solution?

$$0.3 \ M \ HCl = 0.3 \ \text{g-mole/l}$$
$$0.3 \ \text{g-mole/l} \times 0.9 = 0.27 \ \text{g-ion/l} = [H_3O^+]$$
$$[H_3O^+]^2 \times [S^{-2}] = 1.1 \times 10^{-23} = K_{H_2S}$$

Let $x = [S^{-2}]$ in this solution

$$(0.27)^2 \times [S^{-2}] = 1.1 \times 10^{-23}$$
$$[S^{-2}] = \frac{1.1 \times 10^{-23}}{(0.27)^2} = 1.5 \times 10^{-22} \ \text{g-ion/l}$$
$$[Cd^{+2}] \times [S^{-2}] = 3.6 \times 10^{-29}$$
$$[Cd^{+2}] \times (1.5 \times 10^{-22}) = 3.6 \times 10^{-29}$$
$$[Cd^{+2}] = \frac{3.6 \times 10^{-29}}{1.5 \times 10^{-22}} = 2.4 \times 10^{-7} \ \text{g-ion/l}$$

2.4×10^{-7} g-ion/l of Cd^{+2} will remain in solution.

Example 4. An acid solution that contains 0.01 g-ion/l of (a) Pb^{+2} and (b) Mn^{+2} is saturated with hydrogen sulfide. What is the range of $[H_3O^+]$ for selective precipitation of PbS in the presence of Mn^{+2}?

$$SPC_{PbS} = 4.2 \times 10^{-28} \qquad SPC_{MnS} = 1.4 \times 10^{-15}$$

(a) $\qquad [Pb^{+2}] \times [S^{-2}] = 4.2 \times 10^{-28} \qquad [Pb^{+2}] = 0.01 \ \text{g-ion/l}$

Let $x = [S^{-2}]$

$$(0.01)x = 4.2 \times 10^{-28}$$
$$x = \frac{4.2 \times 10^{-28}}{1 \times 10^{-2}} = 4.2 \times 10^{-26} \ \text{g-ion/l}$$

$[S^{-2}] = 4.2 \times 10^{-26}$ g-ion/l = concentration of S^{-2} at which precipitation of PbS will begin.

$$[H_3O^+]^2 \times [S^{-2}] = 1.1 \times 10^{-23}$$

Let $y = [H_3O^+]$

$$y^2(4.2 \times 10^{-26}) = 1.1 \times 10^{-23}$$

$$y = \sqrt{\frac{1.1 \times 10^{-23}}{4.2 \times 10^{-26}}} = \sqrt{0.262 \times 10^3} = \sqrt{262} = 16 \text{ g-ion/l}$$

$[H_3O^+] = 16$ g-ion/l $= H_3O^+$ concentration at which $[S^{-2}] = 4.2 \times 10^{-26}$.

(b) $[Mn^{+2}] \times [S^{-2}] = 1.4 \times 10^{-15}$ $[Mn^{+2}] = 0.01$ g-ion/l

Let $y = [S^{-2}]$

$$(0.01)y = 1.4 \times 10^{-15}$$

$$y = \frac{1.4 \times 10^{-15}}{1 \times 10^{-2}} = 1.4 \times 10^{-13} \text{ g-ion/l}$$

$[S^{-2}] = 1.4 \times 10^{-13}$ g-ion/l $=$ concentration of S^{-2} at which precipitation of MnS will begin.

$$[H_3O^+]^2 \times [S^{-2}] = 1.1 \times 10^{-23}$$

Let $z = [H_3O^+]$

$$z^2(1.4 \times 10^{-13}) = 1.1 \times 10^{-23}$$

$$z = \sqrt{\frac{1.1 \times 10^{-23}}{1.4 \times 10^{-13}}} = \sqrt{0.78 \times 10^{-10}} = 8.8 \times 10^{-6} \text{ g-ion/l}$$

The $[H_3O^+]$ range from 16 g-ion/l to 8.8×10^{-6} g-ion/l permits the precipitation of PbS in the presence of Mn^{+2}.

The precipitation of metallic sulfides with ammonium sulfide $[(NH_4)_2S]$ affords another application of the solubility-product principle. The usual procedure is to make the solution containing the cations ammoniacal and then pass H_2S into the solution which forms $(NH_4)_2S$. The ionization of $(NH_4)_2S$ is very much greater than that of a saturated solution of H_2S and as a consequence a higher concentration of S^{-2} prevails, which causes precipitation of various sulfides. In fact, those sulfides which are incompletely precipitated in an acid medium are readily precipitated in the basic solution.

Example 5. If the $[S^{-2}]$ in a solution of ammonium sulfide is 0.05 g-ion/l, what quantity of (a) Pb^{+2} and (b) Zn^{+2} would remain unprecipitated in 1 ml of solution?

$$SPC_{PbS} = 4.2 \times 10^{-28} \qquad SPC_{ZnS} = 4.5 \times 10^{-24}$$

(a) $[Pb^{+2}] \times [S^{-2}] = 4.2 \times 10^{-28}$

$$[S^{-2}] = 0.05 \text{ g-ion/l}$$

Let $x = [Pb^{+2}]$

$$x \times 0.05 = 4.2 \times 10^{-28}$$
$$x = \frac{4.2 \times 10^{-28}}{5 \times 10^{-2}} = 0.84 \times 10^{-26} = 8.4 \times 10^{-27}$$

$[Pb^{+2}] = 8.4 \times 10^{-27}$ g-ion/l or 8.4×10^{-30} g-ion/ml $= [Pb^{+2}]$ that would remain unprecipitated in 1 ml of the solution.

(b) $$[Zn^{+2}] \times [S^{-2}] = 4.5 \times 10^{-24}$$
$$[S^{-2}] = 0.05 \text{ g-ion/l}$$

Let $y = [Zn^{+2}]$

$$y \times 0.05 = 4.5 \times 10^{-24}$$
$$y = \frac{4.5 \times 10^{-24}}{5 \times 10^{-2}} = 0.9 \times 10^{-22} = 9 \times 10^{-23}$$

$[Zn^{+2}] = 9 \times 10^{-23}$ g-ion/l or 9×10^{-26} g-ion/ml $= [Zn^{+2}]$ that would remain unprecipitated in 1 ml of solution.

It should be noted that these values of $[Pb^{+2}]$ and $[Zn^{+2}]$ are extremely small and that therefore practically complete precipitation of PbS and ZnS in the solution is ensured when $(NH_4)_2S$ is the precipitant.

Example 6. Show, by calculations, that when a solution containing 0.001 g-ion of Mg^{+2} per liter of solution is made 0.1 M in ammonia solution and 0.1 M in NH_4Cl (assume 100 per cent ionization), magnesium hydroxide will not be precipitated.

$$SPC_{Mg(OH)_2} = 5.5 \times 10^{-12} \qquad K_{\text{ionization ammonia solution}} = 1.8 \times 10^{-5}$$
$$SPC_{Mg(OH)_2} = [Mg^{+2}] \times [OH^-]^2 = 5.5 \times 10^{-12}$$

(a) Let $x = [OH^-] =$ the $[OH^-]$ just necessary to start precipitation of $Mg(OH)_2$.

$$[Mg^{+2}] = 0.001 \text{ g-ion/l} = 1 \times 10^{-3} \text{ g-ion/l}$$
$$(1 \times 10^{-3}) \times x^2 = 5.5 \times 10^{-12}$$
$$x^2 = \frac{5.5 \times 10^{-12}}{1 \times 10^{-3}} = 5.5 \times 10^{-9}$$
$$x = \sqrt{5.5 \times 10^{-9}} = \sqrt{55 \times 10^{-10}} = 7.3 \times 10^{-5}$$

7.3×10^{-5} g-ion/l $= [OH^-]$ just necessary to start precipitation of $Mg(OH)_2$ in this solution.

(b) Let $y = [OH^-]$ in this solution. 0.1 M NH_4Cl furnishes 0.1 g-ion/l of NH_4^+.

$$0.1 + y = \text{total } [NH_4^+] \text{ in the solution}$$
$$0.1 - y = [NH_3]$$
$$\frac{[NH_4^+] \times [OH^-]}{[NH_3]} = K_{\text{ionization}}$$
$$\frac{(0.1 + y)y}{0.1 - y} = 1.8 \times 10^{-5}$$

Neglecting y because it is small in comparison to 0.1 in denominator and numerator,

$$y = 1.8 \times 10^{-5}$$
$$1.8 \times 10^{-5} \text{ g-ion/l} = [OH^-] \text{ in this solution}$$

1.8×10^{-5} g-ion/l is a value of $[OH^-]$ less than 7.3×10^{-5} g-ion/l; consequently $Mg(OH)_2$ will not be precipitated in this solution. In order to precipitate $Mg(OH)_2$, the $[OH^-]$ must have a value greater than 7.3×10^{-5} g-ion/l, the saturation value of $[OH^-]$ in this specific solution.

Example 7. A solution contains 0.02 g-ion of Ba^{+2} and Ca^{+2} per liter of solution. (a) What is the range of $[SO_4^{-2}]$ that will precipitate Ba^{+2} as $BaSO_4$ without precipitating Ca^{+2} as $CaSO_4$? (b) What is the concentration of Ba^{+2} when $CaSO_4$ will begin to precipitate?

$$SPC_{BaSO_4} = 1 \times 10^{-10} \qquad SPC_{CaSO_4} = 6.1 \times 10^{-5}$$
$$SPC_{BaSO_4} = [Ba^{+2}] \times [SO_4^{-2}] = 1 \times 10^{-10}$$
$$[Ba^{+2}] = 0.02 \text{ g-ion/l} = 2 \times 10^{-2} \text{ g-ion/l}$$

(a) Let $x = [SO_4^{-2}]$ necessary to start precipitation of Ba^{+2} as $BaSO_4$

$$(2 \times 10^{-2})x = 1 \times 10^{-10}$$
$$x = \frac{1 \times 10^{-10}}{2 \times 10^{-2}} = 0.5 \times 10^{-8} = 5 \times 10^{-9}$$

5×10^{-9} g-ion/l $= [SO_4^{-2}]$ necessary to start precipitation of Ba^{+2} as $BaSO_4$.

$$SPC_{CaSO_4} = [Ca^{+2}] \times [SO_4^{-2}] = 6.1 \times 10^{-5}$$
$$[Ca^{+2}] = 0.02 \text{ g-ion/l} = 2 \times 10^{-2} \text{ g-ion/l}$$

Let $y = [SO_4^{-2}]$ necessary to start precipitation of Ca^{+2} as $CaSO_4$

$$(2 \times 10^{-2})y = 6.1 \times 10^{-5}$$
$$y = \frac{6.1 \times 10^{-5}}{2 \times 10^{-2}} = 3 \times 10^{-3}$$

3×10^{-3} g-ion/l $= [SO_4^{-2}]$ necessary to start precipitation of Ca^{+2} as $CaSO_4$.

The range of $[SO_4^{-2}]$ for precipitation of Ba^{+2} as $BaSO_4$ in the presence of Ca^{+2} lies between 5×10^{-9} g-ion/l and 3×10^{-3} g-ion/l. Then $[SO_4^{-2}] = 3 \times 10^{-3}$ g-ion/l, the $[SO_4^{-2}]$ necessary to start precipitation of Ca^{+2} as $CaSO_4$.

(b) Let $z = [Ba^{+2}]$ that will remain in solution when $CaSO_4$ begins to precipitate.

$$SPC_{BaSO_4} = [Ba^{+2}] \times [SO_4^{-2}] = 1 \times 10^{-10}$$
$$z(3 \times 10^{-3}) = 1 \times 10^{-10}$$
$$z = \frac{1 \times 10^{-10}}{3 \times 10^{-3}} = 3.3 \times 10^{-8}$$

3.3×10^{-8} g-ion/l of Ba^{+2} will remain in solution when $CaSO_4$ begins to precipitate. This is a negligible amount of Ba^{+2}; therefore Ba^{+2} will be completely precipitated before any $CaSO_4$ could form.

ACID-BASE THEORY

According to the Brönsted and Lowry theory of acids and bases, an acid will donate a proton to a base, and a base will accept a proton from an acid. Thus, when hydrogen chloride is dissolved in water to form hydrochloric acid, the following reactions occur:

First stage: When HCl gives up its proton, the Cl^- remaining must be a base, since it can accept a proton. The Cl^- is called the conjugate base of the acid HCl. Thus

$$\underset{A_1}{HCl} \rightleftharpoons \underset{proton}{H^+} + \underset{B_1}{Cl^-}$$

Second stage: The proton will next be coordinated to water, or be accepted by water acting as a base to form the hydronium ion (H_3O^+), which is called the conjugate acid of the base H_2O. Thus

$$\underset{proton}{H^+} + \underset{B_2}{H_2O} \rightleftharpoons \underset{A_2}{H_3O^+}$$

Combining these two stage reactions,

$$\underset{A_1}{HCl} + \underset{B_2}{H_2O} \rightleftharpoons \underset{A_2}{H_3O^+} + \underset{B_1}{Cl^-}$$

where A_1 is the acid whose conjugate base is B_1, and B_2 is the base whose conjugate acid is A_2. Then in an aqueous solution of an acid there are two conjugate pairs.

The strength of an acid can be defined by this theory as follows: A strong acid is one which readily releases a proton and whose conjugate base is weak. A weak acid is one which does not readily release a proton and whose conjugate base is strong.

In the foregoing example, in the formation of hydrochloric acid solution, the two bases, B_1 or Cl^- and B_2 or H_2O, are competing for the proton. The H_2O (B_2) wins out over the Cl^- (B_1) in competition for the proton, or the Cl^- is a weak conjugate base. In other words, hydrochloric acid solution is a strong acid because it readily releases a proton and it has a weak conjugate base, Cl^-. In the case of acetic acid solution, it is a weak acid because it does not readily release the proton, and it has a strong conjugate base, $C_2H_3O_2^-$.

When ammonia dissolves in water, the following reaction prevails:

$$H_2O \rightleftharpoons H^+ + OH^- \qquad \textit{first stage}$$
$$ A_1 \qquad \text{proton} \qquad B_1$$

$$NH_3 + H^+ \rightleftharpoons NH_4^+ \qquad \textit{second stage}$$
$$B_2 \qquad \text{proton} \qquad A_2$$

$$H_2O + NH_3 \rightleftharpoons NH_4^+ + OH^- \qquad \textit{final reaction}$$
$$A_1 \qquad B_2 \qquad A_2 \qquad B_1$$

In the competition for the proton the strong conjugate base, OH^-, wins out over the weak base, NH_3, and the proton is held more strongly by OH^- than by NH_3; thus ammonia is considered to be a weak base, and its conjugate acid, NH_4^+, is strong.

It is possible then to include under the general term *acid*, those molecules, cations, or anions that give up a proton. Thus examples of some acids are HCl, H_2SO_4, HCO_3^-, HSO_4^-, HPO_4^{-2}, NH_4^+, H_3O^+, and so on. Conversely, *bases* are those molecules, cations, or anions that will accept a proton. Examples of some bases are OH^-, NO_3^-, Cl^-, $C_2H_3O_2^-$, NH_3, H_2O, HCO_3^-, CO_3^{-2}, $H_2PO_4^-$, and so on.

It will be noted that HCO_3^-, bicarbonate ion, is listed in both acid and base groups; that is to say, the HCO_3^- can release a proton to a strong base, thereby acting as an acid; it can accept a proton from a strong acid to form H_2CO_3, thereby acting as a base. This is shown by the equations

$$HCO_3^- + OH^- \rightleftharpoons H_2O + CO_3^{-2}$$
$$A_1 \qquad B_2 \qquad A_2 \qquad B_1$$
$$\text{acid} \qquad \text{strong base}$$

$$H_3O^+ + HCO_3^- \rightleftharpoons H_2CO_3 + H_2O$$
$$A_1 \qquad B_2 \qquad A_2 \qquad B_1$$
$$\text{strong acid} \quad \text{base}$$

Thus an ion (or molecule) which can act as either acid or base will have its acidic tendency encouraged by the presence of a strong base, and its basic tendency encouraged by the presence of a strong acid. Substances capable of acting as either acid or base are called **amphoteric** substances.

HYDROLYSIS

It has been shown that acid-base reactions are typified by the general equation

$$A_1 + B_2 \rightleftharpoons A_2 + B_1$$

where B_1 is the conjugate base of acid A_1 and A_2 is the conjugate acid of base B_2.

Many substances when dissolved in water give rise to a basic reaction, and some give an acidic reaction. These are, in reality, acid-base reactions. Thus, sodium carbonate [a salt of a very weak acid, $Na^+(H_2O)$, and a strong base, CO_3^{-2}] dissolved in water gives a basic reaction for the following reasons:

$$2H_2O \rightleftharpoons H_3O^+ + OH^-$$
$$CO_3^{-2} + H_3O^+ \rightleftharpoons HCO_3^- + H_2O$$

or

$$\underset{A_1}{H_2O} + \underset{B_2}{CO_3^{-2}} \rightleftharpoons \underset{A_2}{HCO_3^-} + \underset{B_1}{OH^-}$$

The CO_3^{-2} is a strong base. It will readily combine with H_3O^+ in solution to form HCO_3^- (weak conjugate acid), thus leaving a high concentration of hydroxyl ions (OH^-) in solution, thereby causing a basic reaction. The $Na(H_2O)^+$ has a negligible effect in this reaction, being hardly an acid at all.

When ammonium chloride (a salt of a fairly strong acid, NH_4^+, and a very weak base, Cl^-) dissolves in water, an acidic reaction is obtained for the following reasons:

$$\underset{A_1}{NH_4^+} + \underset{B_2}{H_2O} \rightleftharpoons \underset{A_2}{H_3O^+} + \underset{B_1}{NH_3}$$

The ammonium chloride furnishes a high concentration of NH_4^+ (quite strongly acidic). The NH_4^+ will give a proton to water forming a fairly high concentration of hydronium ion (H_3O^+), which gives the solution of ammonium chloride an acidic reaction. The Cl^- has negligible effect in this reaction. These acid-base reactions, in which substances upon dissolving react with the solvent water, are called hydrolysis. It can be said that

1. Salts of weak acids (strong basic anion) and strong bases (weak acidic cation), upon dissolving in water, hydrolyze to give basic reaction.

2. Salts of strong acids (weak basic anion) and weak bases (strong acidic cation), upon dissolving in water, hydrolyze to give acidic reactions.

3. Salts of strong acids (weak basic anion) and strong bases (weak acidic cation), upon dissolving in water, hydrolyze to a very slight

extent, if at all. The solutions give a neutral reaction. Sodium chloride solution would be an example of this type of reaction.

4. In the case of salts of weak acids (strong basic anion) and weak bases (strong acidic cation), upon dissolving in water, the strong basic anion and the strong acidic cation react with water to practically the same degree, and although hydrolysis is large, the resulting solution gives a neutral reaction.

Certain other hydrolysis reactions involve the formation of volatile compounds and also insoluble substances.   Thus

$$\left.\begin{array}{l} PI_3 + 3H_2O \rightarrow H_3PO_3 + 3HI\uparrow \\ Al_2S_3 + 6H_2O \rightarrow 2Al(OH)_3\downarrow + 3H_2S\uparrow \\ Mg_3N_2 + 6H_2O \rightarrow 3Mg(OH)_2\downarrow + 2NH_3\uparrow \end{array}\right\} \quad \textit{irreversible}$$

$$\left.\begin{array}{l} BiCl_3 + H_2O \rightleftharpoons BiOCl\downarrow + 2HCl \\ FeCl_3 + 3H_2O \rightleftharpoons Fe(OH)_3\downarrow + 3HCl \\ Fe(C_2H_3O_2)_3 + 2H_2O \rightleftharpoons Fe(OH)_2C_2H_3O_2\downarrow + 2HC_2H_3O_2 \end{array}\right\} \quad \textit{reversible}$$

From the foregoing discussion on hydrolysis it becomes apparent that when hydrolysis gives a basic reaction, as in the case of sodium acetate (strongly basic anion), hydronium ions are continually being pulled away by the strong $C_2H_3O_2^-$, to form un-ionized $HC_2H_3O_2$, thereby leaving OH^- ions to accumulate in the solution. This has the net effect of shifting the equilibrium reactions both of acetic acid and of water.

In the previous chapter, the ionization constant of acetic acid ($K_{\text{ionization}} = 1.8 \times 10^{-5}$) and the ion product of water ($K_{\text{ion product}}$ H_2O $= 1 \times 10^{-14}$), respectively, were given consideration.

The hydrolysis of sodium acetate is a reaction in which the Na^+ does not have any effect on the reaction. The essential equilibrium reaction then is

$$C_2H_3O_2^- + H_2O \rightleftharpoons HC_2H_3O_2 + OH^-$$

According to the law of mass action,

$$\frac{[HC_2H_3O_2] \times [OH^-]}{[C_2H_3O_2^-]} = K_{\text{hydrolysis constant}} \quad (1)$$

Note that $[H_2O]$ is omitted from this expression, since this concentration is practically constant, owing to the small ionization of water. It is therefore included in the $K_{\text{hydrolysis constant}}$.

$$\frac{[H_3O^+] \times [C_2H_3O_2^-]}{[HC_2H_3O_2]} = K_{\text{ionization}} \quad (2)$$

$$\frac{[H_3O^+]}{K_{\text{ionization}}} = \frac{[HC_2H_3O_2]}{[C_2H_3O_2^-]} \quad (3)$$

Substituting in expression (1),

$$\frac{[H_3O^+] \times [OH^-]}{K_{ionization}} = K_{hydrolysis} \quad (4)$$

Since

$$[H_3O^+] \times [OH^-] = K_{ion\ product\ H_2O} \quad (5)$$

$$\frac{K_{ion\ product\ H_2O}}{K_{ionization}} = K_{hydrolysis} \quad (6)$$

then

$$\frac{[HC_2H_3O_2] \times [OH^-]}{[C_2H_3O_2^-]} = \frac{K_{ion\ product\ H_2O}}{K_{ionization}} = K_{hydrolysis} \quad (7)$$

Example 1. Determine the $[OH^-]$ and the $[HC_2H_3O_2]$ as a result of the hydrolysis of a 0.01 M sodium acetate solution, assuming complete ionization of $NaC_2H_3O_2$. $K_{ionization}$ of $HC_2H_3O_2 = 1.8 \times 10^{-5}$; $K_{ion\ product\ H_2O} = 1 \times 10^{-14}$.

From the foregoing development,

$$\frac{[HC_2H_3O_2] \times [OH^-]}{[C_2H_3O_2^-]} = \frac{K_{H_2O}}{K_{ionization}} = \frac{1 \times 10^{-14}}{1.8 \times 10^{-5}} = 5.5 \times 10^{-10}$$
$$= K_{hydrolysis\ NaC_2H_3O_2} \quad (1)$$

Let $x = [OH^-] = [HC_2H_3O_2]$, since 1 OH^- is formed for each 1 $HC_2H_3O_2$.

$$0.01 - x = [C_2H_3O_2^-]$$

Substituting in expression (1),

$$\frac{x \times x}{0.01 - x} = 5.5 \times 10^{-10}$$

At equilibrium $[C_2H_3O_2^-]$ is practically equal to 0.01 g-ion/l, the concentration of $NaC_2H_3O_2$, and the x in comparison to 0.01 in the denominator may be neglected.

$$\frac{x^2}{0.01} = 5.5 \times 10^{-10}$$
$$x = 2.3 \times 10^{-6}\ \text{g-mole/l} = [OH^-]\ \text{and}\ [HC_2H_3O_2]$$

Example 2. Calculate (a) the hydrolysis constant for NH_4Cl and (b) the $[OH^-]$ in 0.1 M NH_4Cl solution. $K_{ionization}$ ammonia solution = 1.75×10^{-5}; $K_{H_2O} = 1 \times 10^{-14}$.

Equilibrium is acquired in this solution when $K_{ionization}$ of ammonia solution and $K_{H_2O\ ion\ product}$ are satisfied.

$$\frac{[NH_4^+] \times [OH^-]}{[NH_3]} = 1.75 \times 10^{-5}$$
$$[H_3O^+] \times [OH^-] = 1 \times 10^{-14}$$

The equilibrium reaction for hydrolysis of NH_4Cl is

$$NH_4^+ + H_2O \rightleftharpoons H_3O^+ + NH_3$$

Note the Cl^- has no effect in this reaction since it is a very weak base.

$$\frac{[H_3O^+] \times [NH_3]}{[NH_4^+]} = K_{\text{hydrolysis}} \tag{1}$$

The $[H_2O]$ does not vary because of its small ionization and is therefore included in $K_{\text{hydrolysis}}$.

$$\frac{[NH_4^+] \times [OH^-]}{[NH_3]} = K_{\text{ionization}} \tag{2}$$

$$\frac{[OH^-]}{K_{\text{ionization}}} = \frac{[NH_3]}{[NH_4^+]} \tag{3}$$

Substituting in expression (1),

$$\frac{[H_3O^+] \times [OH^-]}{K_{\text{ionization}}} = K_{\text{hydrolysis}} \tag{4}$$

$$[H_3O^+] \times [OH^-] = K_{\text{H}_2\text{O ion product}} \tag{5}$$

$$\frac{K_{\text{H}_2\text{O ion product}}}{K_{\text{ionization}}} = K_{\text{hydrolysis}} \tag{6}$$

Then

$$\frac{[H_3O^+] \times [NH_3]}{[NH_4^+]} = \frac{K_{\text{H}_2\text{O ion product}}}{K_{\text{ionization}}} = K_{\text{hydrolysis}} \tag{7}$$

(a) $\dfrac{[H_3O^+] \times [NH_3]}{[NH_4^+]} = \dfrac{1 \times 10^{-14}}{1.75 \times 10^{-5}} = 5.7 \times 10^{-10}$

$$= K_{\text{hydrolysis}} \text{ of } NH_4Cl \tag{8}$$

Let $x = [H_3O^+] = [NH_3]$, since 1 g-mole NH_3 is formed for 1 g-ion H_3O^+.

$$0.1 - x = [NH_4^+]$$

Substituting in expression (8),

$$\frac{x \times x}{0.1 - x} = 5.7 \times 10^{-10}$$

Neglecting x with respect to 0.1 in the denominator, owing to the fact that NH_4^+ is practically equal to the original concentration of NH_4Cl, 0.1 g-ion/l,

$$\frac{x^2}{0.1} = 5.7 \times 10^{-10}$$

$$x = 7.5 \times 10^{-6} = [H_3O^+]$$

(b) $\qquad [H_3O^+] \times [OH^-] = 1 \times 10^{-14}$

Let $y = [OH^-]$

$$(7.5 \times 10^{-6})y = 1 \times 10^{-14}$$

$$y = \frac{1 \times 10^{-14}}{7.5 \times 10^{-6}} = 1.3 \times 10^{-9}$$

or $[OH^-] = 1.3 \times 10^{-9}$ g-ion/l.

Problems

Unless otherwise specified, the relatively insoluble substances dealt with in the following problems are assumed to be completely ionized.

18-1. The solubility of (a) FeS is 2.37×10^{-10} mole/l and (b) PbI$_2$, is 1.3×10^{-3} mole/l. Determine the solubility-product constant of each substance.
Ans. (a) 5.6×10^{-20}; (b) 8.7×10^{-9}.

18-2. The solubility of (a) SrCO$_3$ is 3×10^{-5} mole/l and (b) Zn(OH)$_2$ is 2.25×10^{-6} mole/l. Determine the solubility-product constant of each substance.
Ans. (a) $9 0 \times 10^{-10}$; (b) 4.5×10^{-17}.

18-3. The solubility of (a) SrSO$_4$ is 5.3×10^{-4} mole/l and (b) Ag$_2$MnO$_4$ is 2×10^{-4} mole/l. Calculate the solubility-product constant of each substance.
Ans. (a) 2.8×10^{-7}; (b) 3.2×10^{-11}.

18-4. The solubility of (a) MgCO$_3$ is 4.3×10^{-1} g/l and (b) Cd(OH)$_2$ is 2.1×10^{-3} g/l. Calculate the solubility-product constant of each substance.
Ans. (a) 2.6×10^{-5}; (b) 1.2×10^{-14}.

18-5. The solubility of (a) BaSO$_4$ is 2.5×10^{-3} g/l and (b) Sn(OH)$_2$ is 3.5×10^{-7} g/l. Calculate the solubility-product constant of each substance.
Ans. (a) 1.1×10^{-10}; (b) 5×10^{-26}.

18-6. The solubility of (a) BaCrO$_4$ is 3.6×10^{-3} g/l and (b) Hg$_2$Br$_2$ is 1.32×10^{-5} g/l. Determine the solubility-product constant of each substance.
Ans. (a) 2.0×10^{-10}; (b) 5.2×10^{-23}.

18-7. The solubility of (a) Ag$_3$PO$_4$ is 6.5×10^{-3} g/l and (b) MgNH$_4$PO$_4$ is 9.2×10^{-3} g/l. Calculate the solubility-product constant of each substance.
Ans. (a) 1.6×10^{-18}; (b) 2.5×10^{-13}.

18-8. The solubility of CaSO$_4$ is 2.00 g/l. Assume the ionization of CaSO$_4$ to be 95 per cent; calculate the solubility-product constant of this substance.
Ans. 1.9×10^{-4}.

18-9. The solubility-product constant of lead sulfate is 1.8×10^{-8}. Calculate the solubility of PbSO$_4$ in grams per liter. *Ans.* 4×10^{-2} g/l.

18-10. The solubility-product constant of calcium oxalate is 2.6×10^{-9}. Calculate the solubility of CaC$_2$O$_4$ in grams per liter. *Ans.* 6×10^{-3} g/l.

18-11. The solubility-product constant of silver bromide is 3.3×10^{-13}. Determine the solubility of AgBr in grams per liter. *Ans.* 1×10^{-4} g/l.

18-12. The solubility-product constant of mercurous iodide is 4.5×10^{-29}. Determine the solubility of Hg$_2$I$_2$ in grams per liter. *Ans.* 1.5×10^{-7} g/l.

18-13. The solubility-product constant of lead iodide is 8.7×10^{-9}. Determine the solubility of PbI$_2$ in grams per liter. *Ans.* 5.9×10^{-1} g/l.

18-14. Find the solubility of ferric hydroxide in grams per liter. The solubility-product constant of Fe(OH)$_3$ is 4×10^{-38} *Ans.* 2×10^{-8} g/l.

18-15. Determine the minimum CrO$_4^{-2}$ concentration in gram-ions per liter required to precipitate the cations of each of the following relatively insoluble chromates: (a) BaCrO$_4$; (b) Ag$_2$CrO$_4$; (c) PbCrO$_4$. The total cation concentration in each solution is 0.5 g-ion/l, respectively. SPC_{BaCrO_4} $= 2 \times 10^{-10}$; $SPC_{Ag_2CrO_4} = 1.1 \times 10^{-12}$; $SPC_{PbCrO_4} = 1.8 \times 10^{-14}$.

Ans. (a) 4×10^{-10} g-ion/l; (b) 4.4×10^{-12} g-ion/l; (c) 3.6×10^{-14} g-ion/l.

18-16. Find the minimum PO_4^{-3} concentration, in gram-ions per liter, required to precipitate the cations of each of the following relatively insoluble phosphates: (a) Ag_3PO_4; (b) $Ca_3(PO_4)_2$; (c) $Pb_3(PO_4)_2$. The total cation concentration in each solution is 10 mg-ion/ml, respectively. $SPC_{Ag_3PO_4} = 1.6 \times 10^{-18}$; $SPC_{Ca_3(PO_4)_2} = 1 \times 10^{-25}$; $SPC_{Pb_3(PO_4)_2} = 3 \times 10^{-44}$.

Ans. (a) 4×10^{-11} g-ion/l; (b) 1×10^{-14} g-ion/l; (c) 5×10^{-24} g-ion/l.

18-17. Find the minimum I^- concentration, in gram-ions per liter, required to precipitate the cations of each of the following relatively insoluble iodides: (a) AgI; (b) PbI_2; (c) Hg_2I_2. The total cation concentration in each solution is 100 mg/l, respectively. $SPC_{AgI} = 8.5 \times 10^{-17}$; $SPC_{PbI_2} = 8.7 \times 10^{-9}$; $SPC_{Hg_2I_2} = 4.5 \times 10^{-29}$.

Ans. (a) 9×10^{-14} g-ion/l; (b) 4.2×10^{-3} g-ion/l; (c) 4×10^{-13} g-ion/l.

18-18. What is the minimum OH^- concentration, in gram-ions per liter, required to precipitate the cations of each of the following relatively insoluble hydroxides: (a) $Mg(OH)_2$; (b) $Fe(OH)_3$? The total cation concentration in each solution is 10 mg/ml, respectively. $SPC_{Mg(OH)_2} = 5.5 \times 10^{-12}$; $SPC_{Fe(OH)_3} = 4 \times 10^{-38}$.

Ans. (a) 3.7×10^{-6} g-ion/l; (b) 6×10^{-13} g-ion/l.

18-19. Find the range of $[SO_4^{-2}]$ for the selective precipitation of $SrSO_4$ in the presence of Ca^{+2}. The cation concentration in the solution is 0.3 g-ion/l. $SPC_{SrSO_4} = 2.8 \times 10^{-7}$; $SPC_{CaSO_4} = 6 \times 10^{-5}$.

Ans. 9×10^{-7} g-ion/l to 2×10^{-4} g-ion/l.

18-20. Find the range of $[S^{-2}]$ for the selective precipitation of (a) CuS in the presence of Pb^{+2} and (b) HgS in the presence of Pb^{+2}. The cation concentration in the solution is 0.2 mg-ion/ml. $SPC_{CuS} = 4 \times 10^{-38}$; $SPC_{PbS} = 3.4 \times 10^{-28}$; $SPC_{HgS} = 3 \times 10^{-54}$.

Ans. (a) 2×10^{-37} g-ion/l to 1.7×10^{-27} g-ion/l; (b) 1.5×10^{-53} g-ion/l to 1.7×10^{-27} g-ion/l.

18-21. Find the range of $[S^{-2}]$ for the selective precipitation of (a) Ag_2S in the presence of Pb^{+2} and (b) CuS in the presence of Bi^{+3}. The cation concentration in the solution is 0.1 mg-ion/ml. $SPC_{Ag_2S} = 1 \times 10^{-51}$; $SPC_{PbS} = 3.4 \times 10^{-28}$; $SPC_{Bi_2S_3} = 1.6 \times 10^{-72}$; $SPC_{CuS} = 4 \times 10^{-38}$.

Ans. (a) 1×10^{-49} g-ion/l to 3.4×10^{-27} g-ion/l; (b) 4×10^{-37} g-ion/l to 5.4×10^{-24} g-ion/l.

18-22. A solution containing 0.558 g of Fe^{+2} and 1.124 g of Cd^{+2} per liter is 0.27 M in HCl (100 per cent ionized). Hydrogen sulfide is passed into this solution. (a) Determine the range of $[S^{-2}]$ for selective precipitation of CdS and FeS. (b) Which sulfide will be precipitated in this solution when saturated with H_2S? $SPC_{CdS} = 3.6 \times 10^{-29}$; $SPC_{FeS} = 3.7 \times 10^{-19}$; $SPC_{H_2S} = 1.1 \times 10^{-23}$.

Ans. (a) 3.6×10^{-27} g-ion/l to 3.7×10^{-17} g-ion/l; (b) only CdS will precipitate. $[S^{-2}]$ in solution is 1.5×10^{-22} g-ion/l.

18-23. A solution containing 0.01 mg-ion/ml each of Zn^{+2} and Co^{+2} is 1.2 N in HCl (assume 100 per cent ionized). Hydrogen sulfide is passed into this solution. (a) Determine the range of $[S^{-2}]$ for selective precipitation of ZnS and CoS. (b) Determine which sulfide will or will not be precipitated when this solution is saturated with H_2S. $SPC_{ZnS} = 4.5 \times 10^{-24}$; SPC_{CoS}

$= 2 \times 10^{-27}$; $SPC_{H_2S} = 1.1 \times 10^{-23}$.

Ans. (a) 2×10^{-25} g-ion/l to 4.5×10^{-22} g-ion/l; (b) only CoS will precipitate. [S^{-2}] in solution is 7.6×10^{-24} g-ion/l.

18-24. What quantity of Mn^{+2} in milligrams per milliliter escapes precipitation in a solution in which [S^{-2}] is 5 mg-ion/l? $SPC_{MnS} = 1.4 \times 10^{-15}$.

Ans. 1.5×10^{-11} mg/ml.

18-25. By calculations, show that the quantity in milligrams per milliliter of Cd^{+2} and Ni^{+2} escaping precipitation in a solution in which [S^{-2}] is 0.125 mg-ion /ml is negligible. $SPC_{CdS} = 3.6 \times 10^{-29}$; $SPC_{NiS} = 1 \times 10^{-26}$.

Ans. 3.3×10^{-26} mg/ml of Cd^{+2} escapes precipitation, and 4.7×10^{-24} mg/ml of Ni^{+2} escapes precipitation.

18-26. The solubility of (a) AgBr is 1.1×10^{-4} mole/l and (b) CaF$_2$ is 2.1×10^{-4} mole/l. Calculate the solubility-product constant of each substance.

18-27. The solubility of (a) AgI is 9×10^{-9} mole/l and (b) Hg$_2$Cl$_2$ is 6.5×10^{-7} mole/l. Determine the solubility-product constant of each substance.

18-28. The solubility of (a) CaC$_2$O$_4$ is 2.6×10^{-9} mole/l and (b) PbBr$_2$ is 6.3×10^{-6} mole/l. Determine the solubility-product constant of each solute.

18-29. In a saturated solution (a) of BaCrO$_4$, the [Ba^{+2}] is 1.4×10^{-5} g-ion/l; (b) of Hg$_2$I$_2$, the [Hg$_2^{+2}$] is 2.2×10^{-10} g-ion/l. Find the solubility-product constant of each solute.

18-30. In a saturated solution (a) of PbSO$_4$, the [Pb^{+2}] is 1.3×10^{-4} g-ion/l; (b) of Ag$_3$PO$_4$, the [Ag$^+$] is 4.8×10^{-5} g-ion/l. Calculate the solubility-product constant of each solute.

18-31. In a saturated solution (a) of Ag$_2$S, the [Ag$^+$] is 1.26×10^{-17} g-ion/l; (b) of PbI$_2$, the [Pb^{+2}] is 1.3×10^{-3} g-ion/l. Calculate the solubility-product constant of each solute.

18-32. The solubility of (a) PbBr$_2$ is 4.28 g/l and (b) Pb$_3$(PO$_4$)$_2$ is 6×10^{-7} g/l. Determine the solubility-product constant of each solute.

18-33. The solubility of (a) Al(OH)$_3$ is 2.3×10^{-7} g/l and (b) Ca$_3$(PO$_4$)$_2$ is 1.2×10^{-3} g/l. Determine the solubility-product constant of each solute.

18-34. The solubility of (a) Pb(OH)$_2$ is 9.9×10^{-4} g/l and (b) Ag$_2$C$_2$O$_4$ is 4.2×10^{-2} g/l. Calculate the solubility-product constant of each solute.

18-35. The solubility-product constant of (a) FeS is 3.7×10^{-19} and (b) Fe(OH)$_3$ is 4×10^{-38}. Determine the [Fe^{+3}] in each of these saturated solutions. Which one of these two substances is the more soluble?

18-36. The solubility-product constant of (a) PbS is 3.4×10^{-28} and (b) Pb(OH)$_2$ is 2.8×10^{-16}. Determine the [Pb^{+2}] in each of these saturated solutions. Which one of these two substances is the more soluble?

18-37. The solubility-product constants of (a) AgCl is 1.56×10^{-10} and (b) Ag$_2$C$_2$O$_4$ is 1.1×10^{-11}. By calculation, show which of these two silver salts furnishes the smaller [Ag$^+$] value.

18-38. The solubility-product constant of (a) PbCrO$_4$ is 1.8×10^{-14} and (b) PbI$_2$ is 8.7×10^{-9}. By calculation show which of these two lead salts furnishes the smaller [Pb^{+2}] value.

18-39. The solubility-product constant of (a) Ag$_2$S is 1×10^{-51} and (b) PbS is 3.4×10^{-28}. Calculate the minimum [S^{-2}] required to start precipitation of each of these sulfides.

18-40. The solubility-product constant of (a) HgI$_2$ is 3.2×10^{-29} and (b) Hg$_2$I$_2$ is 4.5×10^{-29}. Calculate the minimum [I$^-$] required to bring about precipitation of each of these iodides.

18-41. The solubility-product constant of (a) $Fe(OH)_2$ is 1.6×10^{-14} and (b) $Fe(OH)_3$ is 4×10^{-38}. Calculate the minimum $[OH^-]$ required to bring about precipitation of each of these hydroxides.

18-42. A solution contains 200 mg of ferric chloride in 100 ml. Assume the ionization of the ferric chloride in this solution to be 60 per cent. The solubility product $[Fe^{+3}] \times [OH^-]^3 = 4 \times 10^{-38}$. Calculate the minimum amount of $[OH^-]$ necessary to start precipitation of $Fe(OH)_3$.

18-43. A solution contains 200 mg of aluminum chloride in 100 ml. Assume the ionization of the aluminum chloride in this solution to be 60 per cent. The solubility product $[Al^{+3}] \times [OH^-]^3 = 1.9 \times 10^{-33}$. Calculate the minimum amount of $[OH^-]$ necessary to start precipitation of $Al(OH)_3$.

18-44. Determine the $[Pb^{+2}]$ in a solution that is 0.3 M in HCl (90 per cent ionized) and saturated with H_2S. SPC_{H_2S} is 1.1×10^{-23}; SPC_{PbS} is 3.4×10^{-28}.

18-45. Calculate the $[Cd^{+2}]$ in a solution that is 0.3 M in H_3O^+ and is saturated with H_2S. SPC_{H_2S} is 1.1×10^{-23}; SPC_{CdS} is 3.6×10^{-29}.

18-46. Calculate the $[H_3O^+]$ that will prevent the precipitation of NiS by H_2S in a solution that contains 0.1 mg-ion Ni^{+2}/ml. SPC_{H_2S} is 1.1×10^{-23}; SPC_{NiS} is 1.0×10^{-26}.

18-47. Determine the $[H_3O^+]$ that will prevent the precipitation of MnS by H_2S in a solution that contains 0.1 mg-ion Mn^{+2}/ml. SPC_{H_2S} is 1.1×10^{-23}; SPC_{MnS} is 1.4×10^{-15}.

18-48. Determine the $[H_3O^+]$ that will prevent the precipitation of ZnS by H_2S in a solution that contains 0.2 g-ion Zn^{+2}/l. SPC_{H_2S} is 1.1×10^{-23}; SPC_{ZnS} is 4.5×10^{-24}.

18-49. Find the range of $[H_3O^+]$ that will be required for the selective precipitation of PbS in the presence of Ni^{+2}. The cation concentrations of this solution are 0.1 g-ion/l. $SPC_{H_2S} = 1.1 \times 10^{-23}$; $SPC_{PbS} = 3.4 \times 10^{-28}$; $SPC_{NiS} = 1 \times 10^{-26}$.

18-50. Find the range of $[H_3O^+]$ that will be required for the selective precipitation of CdS in the presence of Fe^{+2}. The cation concentrations in this solution are 0.1 g-ion/l. $SPC_{H_2S} = 1.1 \times 10^{-23}$; $SPC_{CdS} = 3.6 \times 10^{-29}$; $SPC_{FeS} = 3.7 \times 10^{-19}$.

18-51. If the $[S^{-2}]$ in an ammonium sulfide solution is 0.5 mg-ion/ml, show by calculations that there is practically complete precipitation as sulfides of the Pb^{+2}, Mn^{+2}, and Zn^{+2} in 5 ml of this solution. $SPC_{PbS} = 3.4 \times 10^{-28}$; $SPC_{MnS} = 1.4 \times 10^{-15}$; $SPC_{ZnS} = 4.5 \times 10^{-24}$

18-52. Find the range of $[CrO_4^{-2}]$ for the selective precipitation of $BaCrO_4$ in the presence of Sr^{+2}. The concentration of the cations is 0.2 g-ion/l. The solubility of $BaCrO_4$ is 1.4×10^{-5} g-mole/l, and that of $SrCrO_4$ is 6×10^{-3} g-mole/l.

18-53. The solubility of barium chromate is 3.6×10^{-3} g/l at 20°C. Given a solution that contains 200 mg of barium acetate to which is added 0.5 ml of 0.2 N K_2CrO_4, the volume measuring 100 ml. The potassium chromate is ionized to the extent of 80 per cent. Calculate (a) the solubility-product constant of $BaCrO_4$ and (b) the weight of barium chromate that remains in solution.

18-54. The solubility of strontium chromate is 1.2 g/l at 20°C. Given a solution that contains 200 mg of strontium acetate to which is added 0.5 ml of 0.2 N K_2CrO_4, the volume measuring 100 ml. The potassium chromate is ionized to the extent of 80 per cent. Calculate (a) the solubility-product constant of $SrCrO_4$ and (b) the weight of strontium chromate that will remain in solution.

18-55. A solution is known to contain 10 ml of 0.5 N $MgCl_2$ in 50 ml. Assume the ionization of $MgCl_2$ as 70 per cent. Calculate the minimum $[OH^-]$ that will start precipitation of $Mg(OH)_2$. $SPC_{Mg(OH)_2}$ is 5.5×10^{-12}.

18-56. A solution contains 200 mg of magnesium chloride in 50 ml. Assume the ionization of $MgCl_2$ as 70 per cent. Determine the minimum $[OH^-]$ that will start precipitation of $Mg(OH)_2$. $SPC_{Mg(OH)_2}$ is 5.5×10^{-12}.

18-57. A solution, acidified with hydrochloric acid and containing 200 mg of lead chloride in 100 ml, is saturated with hydrogen sulfide, at room temperature and atmospheric pressure. Under these conditions, it was found that 0.0001 g of $PbCl_2$ escaped precipitation with H_2S. The hydrochloric acid is 12 N. Assume the ionization of this hydrochloric acid solution to be 90 per cent. Calculate the number of milliliters of hydrochloric acid of the foregoing normality that must have been present in the solution. The $SPC_{H_2S} = 1.1 \times 10^{-23}$; $SPC_{PbS} = 3.4 \times 10^{-28}$.

18-58. Calculate the number of milligrams of Cu^{+2} and Zn^{+2} that will escape precipitation when 5 ml of a solution that is 0.3 M in HCl (90 per cent ionized) and containing 0.0001 g-ion/l of each cation is saturated with H_2S. $SPC_{H_2S} = 1.1 \times 10^{-23}$; $SPC_{CuS} = 4 \times 10^{-38}$; $SPC_{ZnS} = 4.5 \times 10^{-24}$.

18-59. The $K_{ionization}$ for HCN is 7×10^{-10}, and K_{H_2O} is 1×10^{-14}. Determine (a) the $K_{hydrolysis}$ for 0.1 M KCN solution and (b) the $[OH^-]$ in this solution.

18-60. The $K_{ionization}$ for HNO_2 is 5×10^{-4}, and K_{H_2O} is 1×10^{-14}. Determine (a) the $K_{hydrolysis}$ for 0.1 M KNO_2 solution and (b) the $[OH^-]$ in this solution.

18-61. Determine the percentage of hydrolysis of (a) 0.001 M $NaNO_2$ and (b) M $NaNO_2$ solutions. The $K_{ionization}$ for HNO_2 is 5×10^{-4}, and K_{H_2O} is 1×10^{-14}.

18-62. Calculate the percentage of hydrolysis of (a) M KCN and (b) 0.01 MKCN solutions. The $K_{ionization}$ for HCN is 7×10^{-10}, and K_{H_2O} is 1×10^{-14}.

APPENDIX

TABLE I. DENSITY OF GASES

Gas	Formula	Grams per liter at 0°C, 760 mm	Gas	Formula	Grams per liter at 0°C, 760 mm
Air		1.2929	Hydrogen	H_2	0.08987
Acetylene	C_2H_2	1.173	Hydrogen sulfide	H_2S	1.539
Ammonia	NH_3	0.7710	Krypton	Kr	3.708
Argon	A	1.7824	Methane	CH_4	0.7168
Bromine	Br_2	7.1388	Neon	Ne	0.9002
Butane, iso-	C_4H_{10}	2.673	Nitrogen	N_2	1.2506
Carbon dioxide	CO_2	1.9769	Nitric oxide	NO	1.3402
Carbon monoxide	CO	1.2504	Nitrous oxide	N_2O	1.9778
Chlorine	Cl_2	3.214	Oxygen	O_2	1.4290
Ethane	C_2H_6	1.3566	Phosphine	PH_3	1.5294
Ethylene	C_2H_4	1.2604	Propane	C_3H_8	2.020
Fluorine	F_2	1.695	Silicon tetrafluoride	SiF_4	4.684
Helium	He	0.1785			
Hydrogen fluoride	H_2F_2	0.894	Sulfur dioxide	SO_2	2.9269
Hydrogen bromide	HBr	3.6445	Steam at 100°C		0.581
Hydrogen chloride	HCl	1.6392	Xenon	Xe	5.851

TABLE II. SOLUBILITY-PRODUCT CONSTANTS

Compound	Molecular weight	Solubility-product constant (room temperature)
AgCl	143.3	1.56×10^{-10}
AgBr	187.8	3.3×10^{-13}
AgI	234.8	8.5×10^{-17}
Ag$_3$AsO$_4$	462.6	1×10^{-23}
Ag$_2$CrO$_4$	331.8	1.1×10^{-12}
Ag$_3$PO$_4$	418.6	1.6×10^{-18}
BaCO$_3$	197.4	8.1×10^{-9}
BaC$_2$O$_4$	225.4	1×10^{-7}
BaCrO$_4$	253.4	2×10^{-10}
BaSO$_4$	233.4	1.1×10^{-10}
CaCO$_3$	100.1	8.7×10^{-9}
CaSO$_4$	156.1	6.1×10^{-5}
Ca$_3$(PO$_4$)$_2$	310.3	1×10^{-25}
CaC$_2$O$_4$	123.1	2.6×10^{-9}
Hg$_2$Cl$_2$	472.1	1.1×10^{-18}
Hg$_2$Br$_2$	561.0	5.2×10^{-23}
Hg$_2$I$_2$	655.0	4.5×10^{-29}
MgCO$_3$	84.3	2.6×10^{-5}
MgNH$_4$PO$_4$	137.4	2.5×10^{-13}
PbCl$_2$	278.1	2.4×10^{-4}
PbBr$_2$	367.1	6.3×10^{-6}
PbI$_2$	461.1	8.7×10^{-9}
PbCO$_3$	267.2	1.5×10^{-13}
PbCrO$_4$	323.2	1.8×10^{-14}
PbSO$_4$	303.3	1.8×10^{-8}
Pb$_3$(PO$_4$)$_2$	811.7	3×10^{-44}
SrCO$_3$	147.6	9×10^{-10}
SrC$_2$O$_4$	175.7	5.6×10^{-8}
SrCrO$_4$	203.6	3.6×10^{-5}
SrSO$_4$	183.7	2.8×10^{-7}
Al(OH)$_3$	78	1.9×10^{-33}
Cd(OH)$_2$	146.4	1.2×10^{-14}
Co(OH)$_2$	93.0	2×10^{-16}
Cr(OH)$_3$	103.0	6.7×10^{-31}
Fe(OH)$_3$	106.9	4×10^{-38}
Mg(OH)$_2$	58.3	5.5×10^{-12}
Mn(OH)$_2$	89.0	4.5×10^{-14}
Ni(OH)$_2$	92.7	1.6×10^{-14}
Pb(OH)$_2$	241.2	2.8×10^{-16}
Sn(OH)$_2$	152.7	5×10^{-26}
Zn(OH)$_2$	99.4	4.5×10^{-17}
Ag$_2$S	247.8	1×10^{-51}
Bi$_2$S$_3$	514.2	1.6×10^{-72}
CdS	144.5	3.6×10^{-29}
CoS	91.0	2×10^{-27}
CuS	95.6	4×10^{-38}
FeS	87.0	3.7×10^{-19}
HgS	232.7	3×10^{-54}
MnS	87.0	1.4×10^{-15}
NiS	90.8	1×10^{-26}
PbS	239.3	3.4×10^{-28}
SnS	150.8	8×10^{-29}
ZnS	97.4	4.5×10^{-24}
H$_2$S	34.1	1.1×10^{-23}

TABLE III. IONIZATION CONSTANTS

Acid	→ Base	+ Proton	Ionization constant
HCN	→ CN^-	+ p	7×10^{-10}
$HC_2H_3O_2$	→ $C_2H_3O_2^-$	+ p	1.8×10^{-5}
HNO_2	→ NO_2^-	+ p	5×10^{-4}
HCOOH	→ $HCOO^-$	+ p	2×10^{-4}
HSO_4^-	→ SO_4^{--}	+ p	3×10^{-2}
H_2SO_3	→ HSO_3^-	+ p	1.7×10^{-2}
HSO_3^-	→ SO_3^{--}	+ p	1×10^{-7}
H_2CO_3	→ HCO_3^-	+ p	3×10^{-7}
HCO_3^-	→ CO_3^{--}	+ p	6×10^{-11}
H_2S	→ HS^-	+ p	9.1×10^{-8}
HS^-	→ S^{--}	+ p	1.2×10^{-15}
$H_2C_2O_4$	→ $HC_2O_4^-$	+ p	5.9×10^{-2}
$HC_2O_4^-$	→ $C_2O_4^{--}$	+ p	6.4×10^{-5}
H_3BO_3	→ $H_2BO_3^-$	+ p	5.8×10^{-10}
H_3AsO_4	→ $H_2AsO_4^-$	+ p	5×10^{-3}
$H_2AsO_4^-$	→ $HAsO_4^{--}$	+ p	1×10^{-7}
$HAsO_4^{--}$	→ AsO_4^{---}	+ p	1×10^{-13}
H_3PO_4	→ $H_2PO_4^-$	+ p	7.5×10^{-3}
$H_2PO_4^-$	→ HPO_4^{--}	+ p	2×10^{-7}
HPO_4^{--}	→ PO_4^{---}	+ p	4×10^{-13}
$NH_3 + H_2O$	→ $NH_4^+ + OH^-$		1.8×10^{-5}

$$\frac{[H_3O^+]^2 \times [S^{--}]}{[H_2S]} = 1.1 \times 10^{-22}$$

$$[H_3O^+]^2 \times [S^{--}] = 1.1 \times 10^{-23}$$

$$[H_3O^+] \times [OH^-] = 1 \times 10^{-14}$$

TABLE IV. PERCENTAGE OF EFFECTIVE IONIZATION OF ELECTROLYTES
AT 18°C*

Electrolyte	Formula	Percentage ionization
Acids (0.1 N):		
Hydriodic acid	HI	92.8
Hydrobromic acid	HBr	92.5
Hydrochloric acid	HCl	92.0
Nitric acid	HNO_3	92.0
Sulfuric acid	H_2SO_4 ($H_2SO_4 \rightarrow HSO_4^- + p$)	90.0
	($HSO_4^- \rightarrow SO_4^{--} + p$)	60.0
Acetic acid	$HC_2H_3O_2$	1.3
Carbonic acid	H_2CO_3 ($H_2CO_3 \rightarrow HCO_3^- + p$)	0.12
Hydrosulfuric acid	H_2S ($H_2S \rightarrow HS^- + p$)	0.05
Hydrocyanic acid	HCN	0.01
Bases (0.1 N):		
Sodium hydroxide	NaOH	91.0
Potassium hydroxide	KOH	91.0
Lithium hydroxide	LiOH	87.0
Barium hydroxide	$Ba(OH)_2$	77.0
Calcium hydroxide (0.015 N)	$Ca(OH)_2$	90.0
Ammonia solution	$NH_3 + H_2O \rightarrow NH_4^+ + OH^-$	1.3
Salts (0.1 N):		
Potassium bromide	KBr	86.0
Potassium iodide	KI	88.0
Potassium chloride	KCl	86.0
Potassium nitrate	KNO_3	83.0
Potassium sulfate	K_2SO_4	72.0
Potassium acetate	$KC_2H_3O_2$	83.0
Potassium carbonate	K_2CO_3	71.0
Sodium nitrate	$NaNO_3$	83.0
Sodium acetate	$NaC_2H_3O_2$	79.0
Sodium sulfate	Na_2SO_4	70.0
Sodium chloride	NaCl	84.0
Ammonium chloride	NH_4Cl	84.0
Barium chloride	$BaCl_2$	40.0
Zinc sulfate	$ZnSO_4$	40.0
Copper sulfate	$CuSO_4$	40.0
Zinc chloride	$ZnCl_2$	74.0
Mercuric chloride	$HgCl_2$	1.0

* Strong electrolytes, *i.e.*, most salts, strong acids, and strong bases, are practically completely ionized in dilute aqueous solution. The table, as presented here, gives the degree of apparent or effective ionization of 0.1 N solutions of several electrolytes.

TABLE V. ELECTROCHEMICAL SERIES
(Standard Electrode Potentials)

Reducer $\leftrightarrows$ Oxidizer + $\ominus$	Volts
$Li^0 \rightarrow Li^+ + \ominus$	-3.02
$Cs^0 \rightarrow Cs^+ + \ominus$	-3.02
$Rb^0 \rightarrow Rb^+ + \ominus$	-2.99
$K^0 \rightarrow K^+ + \ominus$	-2.922
$Ba^0 \rightarrow Ba^{++} + 2\ominus$	-2.90
$Sr^0 \rightarrow Sr^{++} + 2\ominus$	-2.89
$Ca^0 \rightarrow Ca^{++} + 2\ominus$	-2.87
$Na^0 \rightarrow Na^+ + \ominus$	-2.712
$Mg^0 \rightarrow Mg^{++} + 2\ominus$	-2.34
$Al^0 \rightarrow Al^{+++} + 3\ominus$	-1.67
$Mn^0 \rightarrow Mn^{++} + 2\ominus$	-1.05
$Zn^0 \rightarrow Zn^{++} + 2\ominus$	-0.762
$Cr^0 \rightarrow Cr^{+++} + 3\ominus$	-0.71
$H_2C_2O_4 \rightarrow 2CO_2 + 2H^+ + 2\ominus$	-0.49
$Fe^0 \rightarrow Fe^{++} + 2\ominus$	-0.440
$Cd^0 \rightarrow Cd^{++} + 2\ominus$	-0.402
$Co^0 \rightarrow Co^{++} + 2\ominus$	-0.277
$Ni^0 \rightarrow Ni^{++} + 2\ominus$	-0.250
$Sn^0 \rightarrow Sn^{++} + 2\ominus$	-0.136
$Pb^0 \rightarrow Pb^{++} + 2\ominus$	-0.126
$H_2^0 \rightarrow 2H^+ + 2\ominus$	0.000
$Sb^0 \rightarrow Sb^{+++} + 3\ominus$	$+0.10$
$H_2S \rightarrow S^0 + 2H^+ + 2\ominus$	$+0.141$
$Sn^{++} \rightarrow Sn^{+4} + 2\ominus$	$+0.15$
$Cu^+ \rightarrow Cu^{++} + \ominus$	$+0.167$
$H_2SO_3 + H_2O \rightarrow SO_4^{--} + 4H^+ + 2\ominus$	$+0.20$
$Sb^0 + H_2O \rightarrow SbO^+ + 2H^+ + 3\ominus$	$+0.212$
$As^0 + 2H_2O \rightarrow HAsO_2 + 3H^+ + 3\ominus$	$+0.248$
$Bi^0 + H_2O \rightarrow BiO^+ + 2H^+ + 3\ominus$	$+0.32$
$2HCN \rightarrow (CN)_2 + 2H^+ + \ominus$	$+0.33$
$Cu^0 \rightarrow Cu^{++} + 2\ominus$	$+0.345$
$2I^- \rightarrow I_2^0 + 2\ominus$	$+0.535$
$HAsO_2 + 2H_2O \rightarrow H_3AsO_4 + 2H^+ + 2\ominus$	$+0.559$
$Fe^{++} \rightarrow Fe^{+++} + \ominus$	$+0.771$
$2Hg^0 \rightarrow Hg_2^{++} + 2\ominus$	$+0.799$
$Ag^0 \rightarrow Ag^+ + \ominus$	$+0.800$
$N_2O_4 + 2H_2O \rightarrow 2NO_3^- + 4H^+ + 2\ominus$	$+0.81$
$Hg_2^{++} \rightarrow 2Hg^{++} + 2\ominus$	$+0.91$
$NO + 2H_2O \rightarrow NO_3^- + 4H^+ + 3\ominus$	$+0.96$
$2Br^- \rightarrow Br_2^0 + 2\ominus$	$+1.065$
$Mn^{++} + 2H_2O \rightarrow MnO_2 + 4H^+ + 2\ominus$	$+1.28$
$2Cl^- \rightarrow Cl_2^0 + 2\ominus$	$+1.358$
$2Cr^{+++} + 7H_2O \rightarrow Cr_2O_7^{--} + 14H^+ + 6\ominus$	$+1.36$
$Pb^{++} + 2H_2O \rightarrow PbO_2 + 4H^+ + 2\ominus$	$+1.456$
$Mn^{++} + 4H_2O \rightarrow MnO_4^- + 8H^+ + 5\ominus$	$+1.52$
$MnO_2 + 2H_2O \rightarrow MnO_4^- + 4H^+ + 3\ominus$	$+1.67$
$Hg^0 \rightarrow Hg^{++} + 2\ominus$	$+1.70$
$2H_2O \rightarrow H_2O_2 + 2H^+ + 2\ominus$	$+1.77$

TABLE VI. TABLE OF LOGARITHMS

Natural numbers	0	1	2	3	4	5	6	7	8	9	Proportional parts								
											1	2	3	4	5	6	7	8	9
10	0000	0043	0086	0128	0170	0212	0253	0294	0334	0374	4	8	12	17	21	25	29	33	37
11	0414	0453	0492	0531	0569	0607	0645	0682	0719	0755	4	8	11	15	19	23	26	30	34
12	0792	0828	0864	0899	0934	0969	1004	1038	1072	1106	3	7	10	14	17	21	24	28	31
13	1139	1173	1206	1239	1271	1303	1335	1367	1399	1430	3	6	10	13	16	19	23	26	29
14	1461	1492	1523	1553	1584	1614	1644	1673	1703	1732	3	6	9	12	15	18	21	24	27
15	1761	1790	1818	1847	1875	1903	1931	1959	1987	2014	3	6	8	11	14	17	20	22	25
16	2041	2068	2095	2122	2148	2175	2201	2227	2253	2279	3	5	8	11	13	16	18	21	24
17	2304	2330	2355	2380	2405	2430	2455	2480	2504	2529	2	5	7	10	12	15	17	20	22
18	2553	2577	2601	2625	2648	2672	2695	2718	2742	2765	2	5	7	9	12	14	16	19	21
19	2788	2810	2833	2856	2878	2900	2923	2945	2967	2989	2	4	7	9	11	13	16	18	20
20	3010	3032	3054	3075	3096	3118	3139	3160	3181	3201	2	4	6	8	11	13	15	17	19
21	3222	3243	3263	3284	3304	3324	3345	3365	3385	3404	2	4	6	8	10	12	14	16	18
22	3424	3444	3464	3483	3502	3522	3541	3560	3579	3598	2	4	6	8	10	12	14	15	17
23	3617	3636	3655	3674	3692	3711	3729	3747	3766	3784	2	4	6	7	9	11	13	15	17
24	3802	3820	3838	3856	3874	3892	3909	3927	3945	3962	2	4	5	7	9	11	12	14	16
25	3979	3997	4014	4031	4048	4065	4082	4099	4116	4133	2	3	5	7	9	10	12	14	15
26	4150	4166	4183	4200	4216	4232	4249	4265	4281	4298	2	3	5	7	8	10	11	13	15
27	4314	4330	4346	4362	4378	4393	4409	4425	4440	4456	2	3	5	6	8	9	11	13	14
28	4472	4487	4502	4518	4533	4548	4564	4579	4594	4609	2	3	5	6	8	9	11	12	14
29	4624	4639	4654	4669	4683	4698	4713	4728	4742	4757	1	3	4	6	7	9	10	12	13
30	4771	4786	4800	4814	4829	4843	4857	4871	4886	4900	1	3	4	6	7	9	10	11	13
31	4914	4928	4942	4955	4969	4983	4997	5011	5024	5038	1	3	4	6	7	8	10	11	12
32	5051	5065	5079	5092	5105	5119	5132	5145	5159	5172	1	3	4	5	7	8	9	11	12
33	5185	5198	5211	5224	5237	5250	5263	5276	5289	5302	1	3	4	5	6	8	9	10	12
34	5315	5328	5340	5353	5366	5378	5391	5403	5416	5428	1	3	4	5	6	8	9	10	11
35	5441	5453	5465	5478	5490	5502	5514	5527	5539	5551	1	2	4	5	6	7	9	10	11
36	5563	5575	5587	5599	5611	5623	5635	5647	5658	5670	1	2	4	5	6	7	8	10	11
37	5682	5694	5705	5717	5729	5740	5752	5763	5775	5786	1	2	3	5	6	7	8	9	10
38	5798	5809	5821	5832	5843	5855	5866	5877	5888	5899	1	2	3	5	6	7	8	9	10
39	5911	5922	5933	5944	5955	5966	5977	5988	5999	6010	1	2	3	4	5	7	8	9	10
40	6021	6031	6042	6053	6064	6075	6085	6096	6107	6117	1	2	3	4	5	6	8	9	10
41	6128	6138	6149	6160	6170	6180	6191	6201	6212	6222	1	2	3	4	5	6	7	8	9
42	6232	6243	6253	6263	6274	6284	6294	6304	6314	6325	1	2	3	4	5	6	7	8	9
43	6335	5345	6355	6365	6375	6385	6395	6405	6415	6425	1	2	3	4	5	6	7	8	9
44	6435	6444	6454	6464	6474	6484	6493	6503	6513	6522	1	2	3	4	5	6	7	8	9
45	6532	6542	6551	6561	6571	6580	6590	6599	6609	6618	1	2	3	4	5	6	7	8	9
46	6628	6637	6646	6656	6665	6675	6684	6693	6702	6712	1	2	3	4	5	6	7	7	8
47	6721	6730	6739	6749	6758	6767	6776	6785	6794	6803	1	2	3	4	5	5	6	7	8
48	6812	6821	6830	6839	6848	6857	6866	6875	6884	6893	1	2	3	4	4	5	6	7	8
49	6902	6911	6920	6928	6937	6946	6955	6964	6972	6981	1	2	3	4	4	5	6	7	8
50	6990	6998	7007	7016	7024	7033	7042	7050	7059	7067	1	2	3	3	4	5	6	7	8
51	7076	7084	7093	7101	7110	7118	7126	7135	7143	7152	1	2	3	3	4	5	6	7	8
52	7160	7168	7177	7185	7193	7202	7210	7218	7226	7235	1	2	2	3	4	5	6	7	7
53	7243	7251	7259	7267	7275	7284	7292	7300	7308	7316	1	2	2	3	4	5	6	6	7
54	7324	7332	7340	7348	7356	7364	7372	7380	7388	7396	1	2	2	3	4	5	6	6	7

TABLE OF LOGARITHMS. (*Continued*)

Natural numbers	0	1	2	3	4	5	6	7	8	9	Proportional parts								
											1	2	3	4	5	6	7	8	9
55	7404	7412	7419	7427	7435	7443	7451	7459	7466	7474	1	2	2	3	4	5	5	6	7
56	7482	7490	7497	7505	7513	7520	7528	7536	7543	7551	1	2	2	3	4	5	5	6	7
57	7559	7566	7574	7582	7589	7597	7604	7612	7619	7627	1	2	2	3	4	5	5	6	7
58	7634	7642	7649	7657	7664	7672	7679	7686	7694	7701	1	1	2	3	4	4	5	6	7
59	7709	7716	7723	7731	7738	7745	7752	7760	7767	7774	1	1	2	3	4	4	5	6	7
60	7782	7789	7796	7803	7810	7818	7825	7832	7839	7846	1	1	2	3	4	4	5	6	6
61	7853	7860	7868	7875	7882	7889	7896	7903	7910	7917	1	1	2	3	4	4	5	6	6
62	7924	7931	7938	7945	7952	7959	7966	7973	7980	7987	1	1	2	3	3	4	5	6	6
63	7993	8000	8007	8014	8021	8028	8035	8041	8048	8055	1	1	2	3	3	4	5	5	6
64	8062	8069	8075	8082	8089	8096	8102	8109	8116	8122	1	1	2	3	3	4	5	5	6
65	8129	8136	8142	8149	8156	8162	8169	8176	8182	8189	1	1	2	3	3	4	5	5	6
66	8195	8202	8209	8215	8222	8228	8235	8241	8248	8254	1	1	2	3	3	4	5	5	6
67	8261	8267	8274	8280	8287	8293	8299	8306	8312	8319	1	1	2	3	3	4	5	5	6
68	8325	8331	8338	8344	8351	8357	8363	8370	8376	8382	1	1	2	3	3	4	4	5	6
69	8388	8395	8401	8407	8414	8420	8426	8432	8439	8445	1	1	2	2	3	4	4	5	6
70	8451	8457	8463	8470	8476	8482	8488	8494	8500	8506	1	1	2	2	3	4	4	5	6
71	8513	8519	8525	8531	8537	8543	8549	8555	8561	8567	1	1	2	2	3	4	4	5	5
72	8573	8579	8585	8591	8597	8603	8609	8615	8621	8627	1	1	2	2	3	4	4	5	5
73	8633	8639	8645	8651	8657	8663	8669	8675	8681	8686	1	1	2	2	3	4	4	5	5
74	8692	8698	8704	8710	8716	8722	8727	8733	8739	8745	1	1	2	2	3	4	4	5	5
75	8751	8756	8762	8768	8774	8779	8785	8791	8797	8802	1	1	2	2	3	3	4	5	5
76	8808	8814	8820	8825	8831	8837	8842	8848	8854	8859	1	1	2	2	3	3	4	5	5
77	8865	8871	8876	8882	8887	8893	8899	8904	8910	8915	1	1	2	2	3	3	4	4	5
78	8921	8927	8932	8938	8943	8949	8954	8960	8965	8971	1	1	2	2	3	3	4	4	5
79	8976	8982	8987	8993	8998	9004	9009	9015	9020	9026	1	1	2	2	3	3	4	4	5
80	9031	9036	9042	9047	9053	9058	9063	9069	9074	9079	1	1	2	2	3	3	4	4	5
81	9085	9090	9096	9101	9106	9112	9117	9122	9128	9133	1	1	2	2	3	3	4	4	5
82	9138	9143	9149	9154	9159	9165	9170	9175	9180	9186	1	1	2	2	3	3	4	4	5
83	9191	9196	9201	9206	9212	9217	9222	9227	9232	9238	1	1	2	2	3	3	4	4	5
84	9243	9248	9253	9258	9263	9269	9274	9279	9284	9289	1	1	2	2	3	3	4	4	5
85	9294	9299	9304	9309	9315	9320	9325	9330	9335	9340	1	1	2	2	3	3	4	4	5
86	9345	9350	9355	9360	9365	9370	9375	9380	9385	9390	1	1	2	2	3	3	4	4	5
87	9395	9400	9405	9410	9415	9420	9425	9430	9435	9440	0	1	1	2	2	3	3	4	4
88	9445	9450	9455	9460	9465	9469	9474	9479	9484	9489	0	1	1	2	2	3	3	4	4
89	9494	9499	9504	9509	9513	9518	9523	9528	9533	9538	0	1	1	2	2	3	3	4	4
90	9542	9547	9552	9557	9562	9566	9571	9576	9581	9586	0	1	1	2	2	3	3	4	4
91	9590	9595	9600	9605	9609	9614	9619	9624	9628	9633	0	1	1	2	2	3	3	4	4
92	9638	9643	9647	9652	9657	9661	9666	9671	9675	9680	0	1	1	2	2	3	3	4	4
93	9685	9689	9694	9699	9703	9708	9713	9717	9722	9727	0	1	1	2	2	3	3	4	4
94	9731	9736	9741	9745	9750	9754	9759	9763	9768	9773	0	1	1	2	2	3	3	4	4
95	9777	9782	9786	9791	9795	9800	9805	9809	9814	9818	0	1	1	2	2	3	3	4	4
96	9823	9827	9832	9836	9841	9845	9850	9854	9859	9863	0	1	1	2	2	3	3	4	4
97	9868	9872	9877	9881	9886	9890	9894	9899	9903	9908	0	1	1	2	2	3	3	4	4
98	9912	9917	9921	9926	9930	9934	9939	9943	9948	9952	0	1	1	2	2	3	3	4	4
99	9956	9961	9965	9969	9974	9978	9983	9987	9991	9996	0	1	1	2	2	2	3	3	4

TABLE VII. PERIODIC

Group / Series	I$_A$	II$_A$	III$_B$	IV$_B$	V$_B$	VI$_B$	VII$_B$	VIII
1	1 H (1.008) *1*							
2 *2*	3 Li (6.94) *1*	4 Be (9.013) *2*						
3 *2, 8*	11 Na (22.997) *1*	12 Mg (24.32) *2*						
4 *2, 8*	19 K (39.1) *8, 1*	20 Ca (40.08) *8, 2*	21 Sc (44.96) *9, 2*	22 Ti (47.90) *10, 2*	23 V (50.95) *11, 2*	24 Cr (52.01) *13, 1*	25 Mn (54.93) *13, 2*	26 Fe (55.85) *14, 2*
5 *2, 8, 18*	37 Rb (85.48) *8, 1*	38 Sr (87.63) *8, 2*	39 Y (88.92) *9, 2*	40 Zr (91.22) *10, 2*	41 Nb (92.91) *12, 1*	42 Mo (95.95) *13, 1*	43 Tc (99) *14, 1*	44 Ru (101.7) *15, 1*
6 *2, 8, 18*	55 Cs (132.91) *18, 8, 1*	56 Ba (137.36) *18, 8, 2*	57–71 Rare-earth elements	72 Hf (178.6) *32, 10, 2*	73 Ta (180.88) *32, 11, 2*	74 W (183.92) *32, 12, 2*	75 Re (186.31) *32, 13, 2*	76 Os (190.2) *32, 14, 2*
7 *2, 8, 18, 32*	87 Fr (223) *18, 8, 1*	88 Ra (226.05) *18, 8, 2*	89 Ac (227) *18, 9, 2*	90 Th (232.12) *18, 10, 2*	91 Pa (231) *18, 11, 2*	92 U (238.07) *18, 12, 2*		
Lanthanum series (rare earths) (57–71)	57 La (138.92) *18, 9, 2*	58 Ce (140.13) *19, 9, 2*	59 Pr (140.92) *20, 9, 2*	60 Nd (144.27) *21, 9, 2*	61 Pm (145) *22, 9, 2*	62 Sm (150.43) *23, 9, 2*		
Actinium series (89–98)	89 Ac (227)	90 Th (232.12)	91 Pa (231)	92 U (238.07)	93 Np (237)	94 Pu (242)		

*Upper number = atomic number. Lower number in parentheses = atomic weight. Number in italics underneath the atomic weight.

CHART OF THE ELEMENTS*

VIII			I$_B$	II$_B$	III$_A$	IV$_A$	V$_A$	VI$_A$	VII$_A$	0
										2 He (4.003) 2
					←————————Nonmetals————————→					
					5 B (10.82) *3*	6 C (12.01) *4*	7 N (14.008) *5*	8 O (16.00) *6*	9 F (19.00) *7*	10 Ne (20.183) *8*
					13 Al (26.98) *3*	14 Si (28.09) *4*	15 P (30.975) *5*	16 S (32.066) *6*	17 Cl (35.457) *7*	18 A (39.944) *8*
27 Co (58.94) *15, 2*	28 Ni (58.69) *16, 2*	29 Cu (63.54) *18, 1*	30 Zn (65.38) *18, 2*	31 Ga (69.72) *18, 3*	32 Ge (72.60) *18, 4*	33 As (74.91) *18, 5*	34 Se (78.96) *18, 6*	35 Br (79.916) *18, 7*	36 Kr (83.8) *18, 8*
45 Rh (102.91) *16, 1*	46 Pd (106.7) *18*	47 Ag (107.880) *18, 1*	48 Cd (112.41) *18, 2*	49 In (114.76) *18, 3*	50 Sn (118.70) *18, 4*	51 Sb (121.76) *18, 5*	52 Te (127.61) *18, 6*	53 I (126.91) *18, 7*	54 Xe (131.3) *18, 8*
77 Ir (193.1) *32, 17*	78 Pt (195.23) *32, 17, 1*	79 Au (197.2) *32, 18, 1*	80 Hg (200.61) *32, 18, 2*	81 Tl (204.39) *32, 18, 3*	82 Pb (207.21) *32, 18, 4*	83 Bi (209.0) *32, 18, 5*	84 Po (210) *32, 18, 6*	85 At (211) *32, 18, 7*	86 Rn (222) *32, 18, 8*

63 Eu (152.0) *24, 9, 2*	64 Gd (156.9) *25, 9, 2*	65 Tb (159.2) *26, 9, 2*	66 Dy (162.46) *27, 9, 2*	67 Ho (164.94) *28, 9, 2*	68 Er (167.20) *29, 9, 2*	69 Tm (169.4) *30, 9, 2*	70 Yb (173.04) *31, 9, 2*	71 Lu (174.99) *32, 9, 2*	
95 Am (243)	96 Cm (243)	97 Bk (245)	98 Cf (246)						

of electrons in filled shells in italics in first column on the left. Remaining number of electron*

INDEX

$$\frac{[H_3O^+] \times [OH^-]}{H_2O} = K_{equip}$$

$$\frac{36.4}{55.4} \times \frac{10.2}{1.2} \times$$